CORE-PLUS MATHEMATICS PROJECT

Course **3**
Part B

Contemporary Mathematics in Context

A Unified Approach

CORE-PLUS MATHEMATICS PROJECT

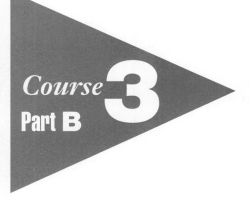

Course Part B 3

Contemporary Mathematics in Context

A Unified Approach

Arthur F. Coxford
James T. Fey
Christian R. Hirsch
Harold L. Schoen
Gail Burrill
Eric W. Hart
Ann E. Watkins
with
Mary Jo Messenger
Beth E. Ritsema
Rebecca K. Walker

Glencoe McGraw-Hill

New York, New York   Columbus, Ohio   Chicago, Illinois   Peoria, Illinois   Woodland Hills, California

Glencoe/McGraw-Hill

A Division of The McGraw·Hill Companies

This project was supported, in part, by the National Science Foundation.
The opinions expressed are those of the authors and not necessarily those of the Foundation.

Send all inquires to:
Glencoe/McGraw-Hill
8787 Orion Place
Columbus, OH 43240-4027

ISBN 0-07-827547-4 (Part A)　　　　　　　　Contemporary Mathematics in Context
ISBN 0-07-827548-2 (Part B)　　　　　　　　Course 3 Part B Teacher's Guide

1 2 3 4 5 6 7 8 9 10 004/004 10 09 08 07 06 05 04 03 02

About the Core-Plus Mathematics Project

The **Core-Plus Mathematics Project (CPMP)** is a multi-year project funded by the National Science Foundation to develop student and teacher materials for a complete high school mathematics curriculum. Courses 1–3 comprise a core curriculum appropriate for *all* students. The fourth-year course continues the preparation of students for college mathematics.

Development Team

Project Directors

Christian R. Hirsch
Western Michigan University

Arthur F. Coxford
University of Michigan

James T. Fey
University of Maryland

Harold L. Schoen
University of Iowa

Senior Curriculum Developers

Gail Burrill
University of Wisconsin-Madison

Eric W. Hart
Western Michigan University

Ann E. Watkins
California State University, Northridge

Professional Development Coordinator

Beth E. Ritsema
Western Michigan University

Evaluation Coordinator

Steven W. Ziebarth
Western Michigan University

Advisory Board

Diane Briars
Pittsburgh Public Schools

Jeremy Kilpatrick
University of Georgia

Kenneth Ruthven
University of Cambridge

David A. Smith
Duke University

Edna Vasquez
Detroit Renaissance High School

Curriculum Development Consultants

Alverna Champion
Grand Valley State University

Cherie Cornick
Wayne County Alliance for Mathematics and Science

Edgar Edwards
(Formerly) Virginia State Department of Education

Richard Scheaffer
University of Florida

Martha Siegel
Towson University

Edward Silver
University of Michigan

Lee Stiff
North Carolina State University

Technical Coordinator

Wendy Weaver
Western Michigan University

Collaborating Teachers

Emma Ames
Oakland Mills High School, Maryland

Cheryl Bach Hedden
Sitka High School, Alaska

Mary Jo Messenger
Howard County Public Schools, Maryland

Valerie Mills
Ann Arbor Public Schools, Michigan

Jacqueline Stewart
Okemos High School, Michigan

Michael Verkaik
Holland Christian High School, Michigan

Marcia Weinhold
Kalamazoo Area Mathematics and Science Center, Michigan

Graduate Assistants

Judy Flowers
University of Michigan

Gina Garza-King
Western Michigan University

Robin Marcus
University of Maryland

Chris Rasmussen
University of Maryland

Bettie Truitt
University of Iowa

Roberto Villarubi
University of Maryland

Rebecca Walker
Western Michigan University

Production and Support Staff

James Laser

Kelly MacLean

Michelle Magers

Cheryl Peters

Jennifer Rosenboom

Anna Seif

Kathryn Wright

Teresa Ziebarth
Western Michigan University

Software Developers

Jim Flanders
Colorado Springs, Colorado

Eric Kamischke
Interlochen, Michigan

Core-Plus Mathematics Project Field-Test Sites

Special thanks are extended to these teachers and their students who participated in the testing and evaluation of Course 3.

Ann Arbor Huron High School
Ann Arbor, Michigan
  Ginger Gajar
  Brenda Garr

Ann Arbor Pioneer High School
Ann Arbor, Michigan
  Jim Brink
  Tammy Schirmer

Arthur Hill High School
Saginaw, Michigan
  Virginia Abbott

Battle Creek Central High School
Battle Creek, Michigan
  Teresa Ballard
  Steven Ohs

Bedford High School
Temperance, Michigan
  Ellen Bacon
  David J. DeGrace

Bloomfield Hills Andover High School
Bloomfield Hills, Michigan
  Jane Briskey
  Homer Hassenzahl
  Cathy King
  Linda Robinson
  Mike Shelly
  Roger Siwajek

Brookwood High School
Snellville, Georgia
  Ginny Hanley
  Marie Knox

Caledonia High School
Caledonia, Michigan
  Deborah Bates
  Jenny Diekevers
  Kim Drefcenski
  Larry Timmer
  Gerard Wagner

Centaurus High School
Lafayette, Colorado
  Gail Reichert

Clio High School
Clio, Michigan
  Bruce Hanson
  Lee Sheridan

Davison High School
Davison, Michigan
  Evelyn Ailing
  John Bale
  Dan Tomczak

Dexter High School
Dexter, Michigan
  Kris Chatas

Ellet High School
Akron, Ohio
  Marcia Csipke
  Jim Fillmore

Firestone High School
Akron, Ohio
  Barbara Crucs

Flint Northern High School
Flint, Michigan
  Al Wojtowicz

Goodrich High School
Goodrich, Michigan
  John Doerr
  Barbara Ravas
  Bonnie Stojek

Grand Blanc High School
Grand Blanc, Michigan
  Charles Carmody
  Maria Uhler-Chargo

Grass Lake Junior/Senior High School
Grass Lake, Michigan
  Brad Coffey
  Larry Poertner

Gull Lake High School
Richland, Michigan
   Dorothy Louden

Kalamazoo Central High School
Kalamazoo, Michigan
   Gloria Foster
   Amy Schwentor

Kelloggsville Public Schools
Wyoming, Michigan
   Nancy Hoorn
   Steve Ramsey
   John Ritzler

Midland Valley High School
Langley, South Carolina
   Ron Bell
   Janice Lee

North Lamar High School
Paris, Texas
   Tommy Eads
   Barbara Eatherly

Okemos High School
Okemos, Michigan
   Lisa Magee
   Jacqueline Stewart

Portage Northern High School
Portage, Michigan
   Pete Jarrad
   Scott Moore
   Jerry Swoboda

Prairie High School
Cedar Rapids, Iowa
   Dave LaGrange
   Judy Slezak

San Pasqual High School
Escondido, California
   Damon Blackman
   Ron Peet

Sitka High School
Sitka, Alaska
   Mikolas Bekeris
   Cheryl Bach Hedden
   Dan Langbauer
   Tom Smircich

Sturgis High School
Sturgis, Michigan
   Kathy Parkhurst
   Jo Ann Roe

Sweetwater High School
National City, California
   Bill Bokesch

Tecumseh High School
Tecumseh, Michigan
   Jennifer Keffer
   Elizabeth Lentz
   Carl Novak

Traverse City High School
Traverse City, Michigan
   Diana Lyon-Schumacher
   Ken May
   Diane Moore

Vallivue High School
Caldwell, Idaho
   Scott Coulter
   Kathy Harris

Ypsilanti High School
Ypsilanti, Michigan
   Keith Kellman
   Mark McClure
   Valerie Mills

Overview of Course 3
Part A

Unit 1 ▶ Multiple-Variable Models

Multiple-Variable Models develops student ability to construct and reason with linked quantitative variables and relations involving several variables and several constraints.
Topics include formulas, including the Law of Sines and the Law of Cosines, relating several variables by a single equation; systems of equations with several dependent variables or constraints; patterns of change in one or more variables in response to changes in others; solution of systems of equations and inequalities; and linear programming.

Lesson 1 *Linked Variables*
Lesson 2 *Algebra, Geometry, and Trigonometry*
Lesson 3 *Linked Equations*
Lesson 4 *Linear Programming*
Lesson 5 *Looking Back*

Unit 2 ▶ Modeling Public Opinion

Modeling Public Opinion develops student understanding of how public opinion can be measured. The situations analyzed include elections (in which there are more than two choices) and sample surveys, including political polling.
Topics include preferential voting, vote-analysis methods, Arrow's theorem, fairness in social decision making; surveys, sampling, sampling distributions, relationship between a sample and a population, confidence intervals, margin of error; and critical analysis of elections and surveys.

Lesson 1 *Voting Models*
Lesson 2 *Surveys and Samples*
Lesson 3 *Sampling Distributions: From Population to Sample*
Lesson 4 *Confidence Intervals: From Sample to Population*
Lesson 5 *Looking Back*

Unit 3 ▶ Symbol Sense and Algebraic Reasoning

Symbol Sense and Algebraic Reasoning develops student ability to represent and draw inferences about algebraic relations and functions using symbolic expressions and manipulations.
Topics include formalization of function concept, notation, domain, and range; use of polynominal, exponential, and rational expressions to model relations among quantitative variables; field properties of real numbers and their application to expression of algebraic relations in equivalent forms and to solution of equations and inequalities by methods including factoring and the quadratic formula; and algebraic proof.

Lesson 1 *Algebra and Functions*
Lesson 2 *Algebraic Operations: Part 1*
Lesson 3 *Algebraic Operations: Part 2*
Lesson 4 *Reasoning to Solve Equations and Inequalities*
Lesson 5 *Proof through Algebraic Reasoning*
Lesson 6 *Looking Back*

Unit 4 ▶ Shapes and Geometric Reasoning

Shapes and Geometric Reasoning introduces students to formal reasoning and deduction in geometric settings.
Topics include inductive and deductive reasoning, counterexamples, the role of assumptions in proof; conclusions concerning supplementary and vertical angles and the angles formed by parallel lines and transversals; conditions insuring similarity and congruence of triangles and their application to quadrilaterals and other shapes; and necessary and sufficient conditions for parallelograms.

Lesson 1 *Reasoned Arguments*
Lesson 2 *Reasoning about Similar and Congruent Triangles*
Lesson 3 *Parallelograms: Necessary and Sufficient Conditions*
Lesson 4 *Looking Back*

Overview of Course 3
Part B

Unit 5 ▶ Patterns in Variation

Patterns in Variation extends student understanding of the measurement of variation, develops student ability to use the normal distribution as a model of variation, and introduces students to the probability and statistical inference involved in the control charts used in industry for statistical process control.

Topics include standard deviation and its properties, normal distribution and its relation to standard deviation, statistical process control, control charts, control limits, mutually exclusive events, and the Addition Rule of Probability.

Lesson 1   *Measuring Variation with the Standard Deviation*
Lesson 2   *The Normal Distribution*
Lesson 3   *Statistical Process Control*
Lesson 4   *Looking Back*

Unit 6 ▶ Families of Functions

Families of Functions reviews and extends student ability to recognize different function patterns in numerical and graphical data and to interpret and construct appropriate symbolic representations modeling those data patterns.

Topics include review of linear, polynominal, exponential, rational, and trigonometric functions (including effects of parameters on numeric and graphic patterns), and construction of function rules for function tables and graphs that are transformations of basic types (translation, reflection, stretch).

Lesson 1   *Function Models Revisited*
Lesson 2   *Customizing Models 1: Reflections and Vertical Transformations*
Lesson 3   *Customizing Models 2: Horizontal Transformations*
Lesson 4   *Looking Back*

Unit 7 ▶ Discrete Models of Change

Discrete Models of Change extends student ability to represent, analyze, and solve problems in situations involving sequential and recursive change.

Topics include iteration and recursion as tools to model and analyze sequential change in real-world contexts; arithmetic, geometric, and other sequences; arithmetic and geometric series; finite differences; linear and nonlinear recurrence relations; and function iteration, including graphical iteration and fixed points.

Lesson 1   *Modeling Sequential Change Using Recursion*
Lesson 2   *A Discrete View of Function Models*
Lesson 3   *Iterating Functions*
Lesson 4   *Looking Back*

Capstone ▶ Making the Best of It: Optimal Forms and Strategies

Making the Best of It: Optimal Forms and Strategies is a thematic, two-week, project-oriented activity that enables students to pull together and apply the important mathematical concepts and methods developed throughout the course.

Contents

Part B

Unit 5 ▶ Patterns in Variation

Unit 6 ▶ Families of Functions

Correlation of Course 3 to NCTM Standards

The *Contemporary Mathematics in Context* curriculum and the instructional and assessment practices it promotes address the focal points of the National Council of Teachers of Mathematics' *Principles and Standards for School Mathematics*. By design, the **process standards** on Problem Solving, Reasoning and Proof, Communication, Connections, and Representation are an integral part of each lesson of every unit in the curriculum.

The chart below correlates Course 3 units with the **content standards** for grades 9–12 in terms of focus (✓) and connections (+).

Correlation of Course 3 to NCTM Standards					
Course 3 Units / **NCTM Grades 9–12 Content Standards**	Number and Operations	Algebra	Geometry	Measurement	Data Analysis and Probability
Multiple-Variable Models	✓	✓	✓	+	
Modeling Public Opinion	+			+	✓
Symbol Sense and Algebraic Reasoning	✓	✓	+	+	+
Shapes and Geometric Reasoning	✓	+	✓	+	+
Patterns in Variation	+	+		+	✓
Families of Functions	+	✓	✓	+	+
Discrete Models of Change	+	✓	+	+	+
Capstone—Making the Best of It: Optimal Forms and Strategies	+	✓	✓	+	✓

Curriculum Overview

▶ Introduction

Contemporary Mathematics in Context Course 3 continues a four-year integrated mathematics program developed by the **Core-Plus Mathematics Project (CPMP)**. The curriculum builds upon the theme of mathematics as sense-making. Through investigations of real-life contexts, students develop a rich understanding of important mathematics that makes sense to them and, in turn, enables them to make sense out of new situations and problems. The curriculum materials have the following mathematical and instructional features.

■ Unified Content

Each year the curriculum advances students' understanding of mathematics along interwoven strands of algebra and functions, statistics and probability, geometry and trigonometry, and discrete mathematics. These strands are unified by fundamental themes, by common topics, and by mathematical habits of mind such as visual thinking, recursive thinking, and searching for and explaining patterns.

■ Mathematical Modeling

The curriculum emphasizes mathematical modeling, including the processes of data collection, representation, interpretation, prediction, and simulation.

■ Access and Challenge

The curriculum is designed to make more mathematics accessible to more students, while at the same time challenging the most able students. Differences in students' performance and interest can be accommodated by the depth and level of abstraction to which core topics are pursued, by the nature and degree of difficulty of applications, and by providing opportunities for student choice of homework tasks and projects.

■ Technology

Numerical, graphics, and programming/link capabilities such as those found on many graphing calculators are assumed and appropriately used throughout the curriculum. This use of technology permits the curriculum and instruction to emphasize multiple representations (verbal, numerical, graphical, and symbolic) and to focus on goals in which mathematical thinking and problem solving are central.

■ Active Learning

Instructional materials promote active learning and teaching centered around collaborative small-group investigations of problem situations, followed by teacher-led whole class summarizing activities that lead to analysis, abstraction, and further application of underlying mathematical ideas. Students are actively engaged in exploring, conjecturing, verifying, generalizing, applying, proving, evaluating, and communicating mathematical ideas.

■ Multi-dimensional Assessment

Comprehensive assessment of student understanding and progress through both curriculum-embedded assessment opportunities and supplementary assessment tasks supports instruction and enables monitoring and evaluation of each student's performance in terms of mathematical processes, content, and dispositions.

This curriculum promises to make mathematics accessible and more meaningful to more students. Developing mathematics along multiple strands nurtures the differing strengths and talents of students and simultaneously helps them to develop diverse mathematical insights. Developing mathematics from a modeling perspective permits students to experience mathematics as a means of making sense of data and problems that arise in diverse contexts within and across cultures. Engaging students in collaborating on tasks in small groups develops their ability to both deal with, and find commonality in, diversity of ideas. Using calculators as a means for learning and doing mathematics enables students to develop versatile ways of dealing with realistic situations and reduces the manipulative skill filter which has prevented large numbers of students from continuing their study of significant mathematics. In addition, calculator graphics offer powerful new ways of visualizing mathematics across each of the strands.

▶Unified Mathematics

Contemporary Mathematics in Context is a unified curriculum that replaces the traditional Algebra-Geometry-Advanced Algebra/Trigonometry-Precalculus sequence. Each course features "strands" of algebra and functions, statistics and probability, geometry and trigonometry, and discrete mathematics. Each of these strands is developed within focused units, connected by fundamental ideas such as symmetry, matrices, functions, and data analysis and curve-fitting. The strands also are connected across units by mathematical habits of mind such as visual thinking, recursive thinking, searching for and explaining patterns, making and checking conjectures, reasoning with multiple representations, inventing mathematics, and providing convincing arguments and proofs. The strands are unified further by the fundamental themes of data, representation, shape, and change. Important mathematical ideas are frequently revisited through this attention to connections within and across strands, enabling students to develop a robust connected understanding of mathematics.

Algebra and Functions

The algebra and functions strand develops student ability to recognize, represent, and solve problems involving relations among quantitative variables. Central to the development is the use of functions as mathematical models. The key algebraic models in the curriculum are linear, exponential, power, polynomial, logarithmic, rational, and trigonometric functions. Each algebraic model is investigated in at least four linked representations—verbal, graphic, numeric, and symbolic—with the aid of technology. Attention is also given to modeling systems of equations, both linear and nonlinear, and to symbolic reasoning and manipulation.

Statistics and Probability

The primary role of the statistics and probability strand is to develop student ability to analyze data intelligently, to recognize and measure variation, and to understand the patterns that underlie probabilistic situations. The ultimate goal is for students to understand how inferences can be made about a population by looking at a sample from that population. Graphical methods of data analysis, simulations, sampling, and experience with the collection and interpretation of real data are featured.

Geometry and Trigonometry

The primary goal of the geometry and trigonometry strand is to develop visual thinking and student ability to construct, reason with, interpret, and apply mathematical models of patterns in the visual world and physical contexts. The focus is on describing patterns with regard to shape, size, and location; representing visual patterns with drawings, coordinates, or vectors; predicting changes and invariants in shape; and organizing geometric facts and relationships through deductive reasoning.

Discrete Mathematics

The discrete mathematics strand develops student ability to model and solve problems involving enumeration, sequential change, decision-making in finite settings, and relationships among a finite number of elements. Topics include matrices, vertex-edge graphs, recursion, voting methods, and systematic counting methods (combinatorics). Key themes are discrete mathematical modeling, existence (*Is there a solution?*), optimization (*What is the best solution?*), and algorithmic problem solving (*Can you efficiently construct a solution?*).

▶Organization of Course 3

The curriculum for Course 3 consists of seven units and a culminating capstone experience. Each of the units is comprised of four to six multi-day lessons in which major ideas are developed through investigations of rich applied problems. Units vary in length from approximately four to six weeks. The final element of Course 3, the capstone, is a thematic two-week project-oriented activity that enables students to pull together and apply the important modeling concepts and methods developed in the entire course.

In developing Course 3, the Core-Plus Mathematics Project chose mathematical content which the developers believed was the most important mathematics all eleventh-grade students should have the opportunity to learn. In particular, the content of the last units in the text is not viewed as optional as is often the case with traditional textbooks. As with Courses 1 and 2, the text for Course 3 is available in a two-volume edition. A school block-scheduling classes will find flexibility for designing course content with two volumes that is not normally available with single volume textbooks.

The organization of the student text differs in several other ways from traditional textbooks. There are no boxed-off definitions, "worked-out" examples, or content summaries. Students learn mathematics by doing mathematics. Concept images are developed as students complete investigations; later concept definitions appear. Mathematical ideas are developed and then shared by groups of students at strategically placed Checkpoints in the lessons. This discussion leads to a class summary of shared understandings.

▶Instructional Model

The manner in which students encounter mathematical ideas can contribute significantly to the quality of their learning and the depth of their understanding. Lessons in *Contemporary Mathematics in Context* are therefore designed around a specific cycle of instructional activities intended primarily for small-group work in the classroom and for individual work outside of the classroom.

In Class The four-phase cycle of classroom activities—*Launch, Explore, Share and Summarize*, and *Apply*—is designed to actively engage students in investigating and making sense of problem situations, in constructing important mathematical concepts and methods, in generalizing and proving mathematical relationships, and in communicating their thinking and the results of their efforts. The summary below describes these phases of classroom instruction.

In-Class Instruction

LAUNCH full-class discussion

Think About This Situation

The lesson begins with a teacher-led discussion of a problem situation and of related questions to **think about**. This discussion sets the context for the student work to follow and helps to generate student interest; it also provides an opportunity for the teacher to assess student knowledge and to clarify directions for the group activities. *Teacher is director and moderator.*

EXPLORE small-group investigation

INVESTIGATION 1

Classroom activity then shifts to having students **investigate** focused problems and questions related to the launching situation by gathering data, looking for patterns, constructing models and meanings, and making and verifying conjectures. As students collaborate in small groups, the teacher circulates from group to group providing guidance and support, clarifying or asking questions, giving hints, providing encouragement, and drawing group members into the discussion to help groups work more cooperatively. The unit materials and related questions posed by students drive the learning. *Teacher is facilitator.*

SHARE AND SUMMARIZE full-class discussion

Checkpoint

A teacher-led full-class discussion (referred to as a Checkpoint) of concepts and methods developed by different small groups then provides an opportunity to **share** progress and thinking. This discussion leads to a class **summary** of important ideas or to further exploration of a topic if competing perspectives remain. Varying points of view and differing conclusions that can be justified should be encouraged. *Teacher is moderator.*

APPLY individual task

On Your Own

Finally, students are given a task to complete on their own to **access** their initial understanding of concepts and methods. The teacher circulates in the room assessing levels of understanding. *Teacher is intellectual coach.*

Out of Class In addition to the classroom investigations, *Contemporary Mathematics in Context* provides sets of MORE tasks, which are designed to engage students in *Modeling* with, *Organizing*, *Reflecting* on, and *Extending* their mathematical knowledge. MORE tasks are provided for each lesson in the CPMP materials and are central to the learning goals of each lesson. These tasks are intended primarily for individual work outside of class. Selection of MORE tasks should be based on student performance and the availability of time and technology. Also, students should exercise some choice of tasks to pursue, and at times they should be given the opportunity to pose their own problems and questions to investigate. The chart below describes the types of tasks in a typical MORE set.

MORE: Out-of-Class Activities	
Modeling	*Modeling* tasks are related to or provide new contexts to which students can apply the ideas and methods that they have developed in the lesson.
Organizing	*Organizing* tasks offer opportunities for integrating the formal mathematics underlying the mathematical models developed in the lesson and for making connections with other strands.
Reflecting	*Reflecting* tasks encourage thinking about thinking, about mathematical meanings, and about processes, and promote self-monitoring and evaluation of understanding.
Extending	*Extending* tasks permit further, deeper, or more formal study of the topics under investigation.

Summarizing Activities In the *Contemporary Mathematics in Context* curriculum, students learn mathematics by doing mathematics. However, it is important that students prepare and maintain summaries of important concepts and methods that are developed. To assist in this matter, the "On Your Own" task in the final lesson of each unit asks students to prepare, in outline form, a summary of the important ideas developed in the unit. Templates to guide preparation of these unit summaries can be found in the *Teaching Resources*. In addition, students should create a Math Toolkit that organizes important class-generated ideas and selected Checkpoint responses as they complete investigations. "Constructing a Math Toolkit" prompts are provided in this *Teacher's Guide* to assist in identifying key concepts and methods as they are developed by students. (See the *Teaching Resources* for blackline masters to assist students in organizing their Math Toolkits.)

▶Curriculum-Embedded Assessment

Assessing what students know and are able to do is an integral part of *Contemporary Mathematics in Context* and there are opportunities for assessment in each phase of the instructional cycle. Initially, as students pursue the investigations that make up the curriculum, the teacher is able to informally assess student understanding of mathematical processes, content, and their disposition toward mathematics. Then at the end of each investigation, the Checkpoint and class discussion provide an opportunity for teachers to assess the levels of understanding that various groups of students have reached as they share and summarize their findings. Finally, the "On Your Own" problems and the tasks in the MORE sets provide further opportunities to assess the level of understanding of each individual student.

A more detailed description of the CPMP assessment program is given on pages xxi–xxv of this text and in *Implementing the Core-Plus Mathematics Curriculum*.

Implementing the Curriculum

▶ Planning for Instruction

The *Contemporary Mathematics in Context* curriculum is not only changing the mathematics all students have the opportunity to learn, but also changing how that learning occurs and is assessed. Active learning is most effective when accompanied with active teaching. Just as the student text is designed to actively engage students in doing mathematics, the teacher's resource materials are designed to support teachers in planning for instruction; in observing, listening, questioning, facilitating student work, and orchestrating classroom discussion; and in managing the classroom.

The *Teacher's Guide* provides suggestions, based on the experiences of field-test teachers, for implementing this exciting new curriculum in your classroom. You probably will find new ideas that can at first be overwhelming. The developers highly recommend that teachers who are teaching *Contemporary Mathematics in Context* for the first time do so at least in pairs who share a common planning period.

Each of the items listed below is included in the *Teacher's Guide* for each unit.

- Unit Overview
- Objectives, suggested timeline, and materials needed
- Instructional notes and suggestions
- Suggested assignments for each MORE set
- Solutions for Investigations and MORE tasks
- Unit summary and a look ahead ("Looking Back, Looking Ahead")

The *Teaching Resources* include blackline masters for creating transparencies and handouts. *Assessment Resources* include quizzes for individual lessons, end-of-unit exams, take-home assessment tasks, projects, and semester exam tasks. Special calculator software has been developed to support students' investigations and modeling applications in each of the four strands. The software for the TI-82, TI-83, and TI-92 graphing calculators is available on disk for downloading from Macintosh and DOS- or Windows-based (PC) computers.

Each unit of *Contemporary Mathematics in Context* includes either content which may be new to many teachers or new approaches to familiar content. Thus, a first step toward planning the teaching of a unit is to review the scope and sequence of the unit. This review provides an overall feel for the goals of the unit and how it holds together. The *Scope and Sequence* guide shows how the specific mathematical topics fit in the complete four-year curriculum. Working through the student investigations, if possible with a colleague, provides help in thinking about and understanding mathematical ideas that may be unfamiliar.

In the *Teacher's Guide* you will find teaching notes for each lesson, including instructional suggestions and sample student responses to investigations and MORE sets. Thinking about the range of possible responses and solutions to problems in a lesson proves to be very helpful in facilitating student work.

Although not stated, it is assumed that students have access to graphing calculators at all times for in-class work and ideally for out-of-class work as well. Downloading and becoming familiar with the specially-designed calculator software will require advanced planning, as will acquiring physical materials.

The developers recommend that the homework (MORE) assignment *not* be held off until the end of the lesson or the investigation just preceding the MORE set. Some teachers choose to post the MORE assignment at the beginning of a lesson along, with the due date—usually a day or two following planned completion of the lesson. Other teachers prefer to assign particular MORE tasks at appropriate points during the course of the multiday lesson and then assign the remaining tasks toward the end of the lesson. Note that all recommended assignments include provision for student choice of some tasks. This is but one of many ways in which this curriculum is designed to accommodate and support differences in students' interests and performance levels.

It is strongly recommended that student solutions to Organizing tasks be discussed in class. These tasks help students organize and formalize the mathematics developed in context and connect it to other mathematics they have studied. Structuring the underlying mathematics and building connections are best accomplished by comparing and discussing student work and synthesizing key ideas within the classroom.

▶Orchestrating Lessons

The *Contemporary Mathematics in Context* materials are designed to engage students in a four-phase cycle of classroom activities. The activities often require both students and teachers to assume roles quite different than those in more traditional mathematics classrooms. Sophomores or juniors beginning Course 3 should be quite familiar with their roles in the classroom. Although realistic problem solving and investigative work by students are the heart of the curriculum, how teachers orchestrate the launching of an activity and the sharing and summarizing of results is critical to successful implementation. Teachers who have not taught Courses 1 or 2 should collaborate with colleagues who can assist them in gaining expertise in their new role.

Students enter the classroom with differing backgrounds, experience, and knowledge. These differences can be viewed as assets. Engaging the class in a free-flowing give-and-take discussion of how students think about the launch situations serves to connect lessons with the informal understandings of data, shape, change, and chance that students bring to the classroom. Try to maximize the participation of students in these discussions by emphasizing that their ideas and possible approaches are valued and important and that definitive answers are not necessarily expected at this time.

Once launched, a lesson may involve students working together collaboratively in small groups for a period of days punctuated occasionally by brief, whole-class discussion of questions students have raised. In this setting, the lesson becomes driven primarily by the instructional materials themselves. Rather than orchestrating class discussion, the teacher shifts to circulating among the groups and observing, listening, and interacting with students by asking guiding or probing questions. These small-group investigations lead to (re)invention of important mathematics that makes sense to students. Sharing and agreeing as a class on the mathematical ideas that groups are developing is the purpose of the Checkpoints in the instructional materials.

Class discussions at Checkpoints are orchestrated somewhat differently than during the launch of a lesson. At this stage, mathematical ideas and methods still may be under development and may vary for individual groups. So class discussion should involve groups comparing their methods and results, analyzing their work, and arriving at conclusions agreed upon by the class.

The investigations deepen students' understanding of mathematical ideas and extend their mathematical language in contexts. Technical terminology and symbolism are introduced as needed. This sometimes occurs in student materials immediately following a Checkpoint and before the corresponding "On Your Own" task. These connections should be introduced by the teacher as a natural way of closing the class discussion summarizing the Checkpoint.

Managing Classroom Activities

▶ Active Learning and Collaborative Work

The *Contemporary Mathematics in Context* curriculum materials are designed to promote active, collaborative learning and group work for two important reasons. First, a collaborative environment fosters students' ability to make sense of mathematics and develop deep mathematical understandings. Collaborative learning is an effective method for engaging all the students in the learning process, particularly students who have been underrepresented in mathematics classes. Second, practice in collaborative learning in the classroom is practice for real life: students develop and exercise the same skills in the classroom that they need in their lives at home, in the community, and in the workplace.

Value of Individuals

Perhaps the most fundamental belief underlying the use of collaborative learning is that every student is viewed as a valuable resource and contributor. In other words, every student participates in group work and is given the opportunity and time to voice ideas and opinions. Implementing this concept is not easy. It does not happen automatically. In order to set a tone that will promote respect for individuals and their contributions, classroom rules should be established and agreed upon by the learning community. Students should be included in the process of formulating the rules. The teacher should initiate a discussion of group rules and then post them in the classroom. The teacher should model all of the rules correctly to show that "we" begins with "me." Those who do not adhere to the rules must accept the consequences in accordance with classroom or school disciplinary procedures.

Importance of Social Connections

Even in classrooms in which the rules for showing respect have been clearly established, experience has shown that students still cannot talk with one another about mathematics (or social studies, or literature, or any other subject) if they do not first have positive social connections.

One way to develop this kind of common base is through team-building activities. These short activities may be used at the beginning of the year to help students get acquainted with the whole class and may be used during the year whenever new groups are formed to help groupmates know one another better. Team-building activities help students learn new and positive things about classmates with whom they may have attended classes for years, but have not known in depth. The time taken for these quick team-builders pays off later in helping students feel comfortable enough to work with the members of their group.

Need for Teaching Social Skills

Experience has also shown that social skills are critical to the successful functioning of any small group. Because there is no guarantee that students of any particular age will have the social skills necessary for effective group work, it is often necessary to teach these skills to build a collaborative learning environment.

These social skills are specific skills, not general goals. Examples of specific social skills that the teacher can teach in the classroom include responding to ideas respectfully, keeping track of time, disagreeing in an agreeable way, involving everyone, and following directions. Though goals such as cooperating and listening are important, they are too general to teach.

One method of teaching social skills is to begin by selecting a specific skill and then having the class brainstorm to develop a script for practicing that skill. Next, the students practice that skill during their group work. Finally, in what is called the processing, the students discuss within their groups how well they performed the assigned social skill. Effective teaching of social skills requires practicing and processing; merely describing a specific social skill is not enough. Actual practice and processing are necessary for students to really learn the skill and to increase the use of appropriate behaviors during group work and other times during class.

One of the premises of collaborative learning is that by developing the appropriate skills through practice, anyone in the class can learn to work in a group with anyone else. Learning to work in groups is a continuous process, however, and the process can be helped by decisions that the teacher makes. *Implementing the Core-Plus Mathematics Curriculum* provides information and support to help teachers make decisions about group size, composition, method of selection, student reaction to working in groups, and the duration of groups. (It also provides advice on dealing effectively with student absences.)

The culture created within the classroom is crucial to the success of this curriculum. It is important to inculcate in students a sense of inquiry and responsibility for their own learning. Without this commitment, active, collaborative learning by students cannot be effective. In order for students to work collaboratively, they must be able to understand the value of working together. Some students seem satisfied with the rationale that it is important in the business world. Others may need to understand that the struggle of verbalizing their thinking, listening to others' thinking, questioning themselves and other group members, and coming to an agreement increases their understanding and retention of the mathematics while contributing to the formation of important thinking skills or habits of mind.

Issues of helping students to work collaboratively will become less pressing as both you and your students experience this type of learning. You may find it helpful to refer to *Implementing the Core-Plus Mathematics Curriculum* and discuss effective cooperative groups with colleagues a few weeks into the semester.

▶ Assessment

Throughout the *Contemporary Mathematics in Context* curriculum, the term "assessment" is meant to include all instances of gathering information about students' levels of understanding and their disposition toward mathematics for purposes of making decisions about instruction. You may want to consult the extended section on assessment in *Implementing the Core-Plus Mathematics Curriculum.*

The dimensions of student performance that are assessed in this curriculum (see chart below) are consistent with the assessment recommendations of the National Council of Teachers of Mathematics in the *Assessment Standards for School Mathematics* (NCTM, 1995). They are much broader than those of a typical testing program.

Assessment Dimensions

Process	Content	Attitude
Problem Solving	Concepts	Beliefs
Reasoning	Applications	Perseverance
Communication	Representational Strategies	Confidence
Connections	Procedures	Enthusiasm

Sources of Assessment Information

Several kinds of assessment are available to teachers using *Contemporary Mathematics in Context*. Some of these sources reside within the curriculum itself; some of them are student-generated; and some are supplementary materials designed specifically for assessment. Understanding the nature of these sources is a prerequisite for selecting assessment tools, establishing guidelines on how to score assessments, making judgments about what students know and are able to do, and assigning grades.

Curriculum Sources

Two features of the curriculum, questioning and observation by the teacher, provide fundamental and particularly useful ways of gathering assessment information. The student text uses questions to facilitate student understanding of new concepts, of how these concepts fit with earlier ideas and with one another, and of how they can be applied in problem situations. Whether students are working individually or in groups, the teacher is given a window to watch how the students think about and apply mathematics as they attempt to answer the questions posed by the curriculum materials. In fact, by observing how students respond to the curriculum-embedded questions, the teacher can assess student performance across all process, content, and attitude dimensions described in the chart on page xxi.

Specific features in the student material that focus on different ways students respond to questions are the Checkpoint, "On Your Own," and MORE (*Modeling*, *Organizing*, *Reflecting*, and *Extending*) sets. Checkpoint features are intended to bring students together, usually after they have been working in small groups, so they may share and discuss the progress each group has made during a sequence of related activities. Each Checkpoint is intended to be a whole-class discussion, so it should provide an opportunity for teachers to assess, informally, the levels of understanding that the various groups of students have reached.

Following each Checkpoint, the "On Your Own" tasks are meant to be completed by students working individually. Student responses to these tasks provide an opportunity for teachers to assess the level of understanding of each student.

The tasks in the MORE sets serve many purposes, including post-investigation assessment. Each type of task in a MORE set has a different instructional purpose. Modeling tasks help students demonstrate how well they understand and can apply the concepts and procedures developed in an investigation. Organizing tasks demonstrate how well students understand connections between the content of an investigation and other mathematical and real-world ideas. In-class discussions based on Organizing tasks are a crucial step in assisting students' development of a full understanding of the mathematical content and connections. Reflecting tasks provide insights into students' beliefs, attitudes, and judgments of their own competence. Extending tasks show how well students are able to extend the present content beyond the level addressed in an investigation. The performance of students or groups of students in each of these types of tasks provides the teacher with further information to help assess applicability, connectedness, and depth of the students' evolving understanding of mathematics.

Finally, an opportunity for group self-assessment is provided in the last element of each unit, the "Looking Back" lesson. These tasks help students pull together and demonstrate what they have learned in the unit and at the same time provide helpful review and confidence-building for students.

Student-Generated Sources

Other possible sources of assessment information are writings and materials produced by students in the form of student mathematics toolkits and journals.

Mathematics Toolkits Students should create a Math Toolkit that organizes important class-generated ideas and selected Checkpoint responses as they complete investigations. Constructing a Math Toolkit prompts are provided in the *Teacher's Guide* to assist in identifying key concepts and methods as they are developed by students. (See the *Teaching Resources* for blackline masters to assist students in organizing their Math Toolkits.)

Journals Student journals are notebooks in which students are encouraged to write (briefly, but frequently) their personal reflections concerning the class, the mathematics they are learning, and their progress. These journals are an excellent way for the teacher to gain insights into how individual students are feeling about the class, what they do and do not understand, and what some of their particular learning difficulties are. For many students, the journal is a non-threatening way to communicate with the teacher about matters that may be too difficult or too time-consuming to talk about directly. Journals also encourage students to assess their own understanding of, and feelings about, the mathematics they are studying. The teacher should collect, read, and respond to each journal at least once a month.

The *Contemporary Mathematics in Context* assessment program provides many items that can be placed in students' portfolios, including reports of individual and group projects, Math Toolkit or journal entries, teacher-completed observation checklists, end-of-unit assessments especially the take-home tasks and projects. See *Implementing the Core-Plus Mathematics Curriculum* for additional portfolio information.

Assessment Resources

The *Contemporary Mathematics in Context* teacher resource materials include for each unit a third source of assessment information—*Assessment Resources*. Included in the *Assessment Resources* are end-of-lesson quizzes and end-of-unit assessments in the form of an in-class unit exam, take-home assessment tasks, and projects. Calculators are required in most cases and are intended to be available to students. Teacher discretion should be used regarding student access to their textbook and Math Toolkit for assessments. In general, if the goals to be assessed are problem solving and reasoning, while memory of facts and procedural skill are of less interest, resources should be allowed. However, if automaticity of procedures or unaided recall are being assessed, it is appropriate to prohibit resource materials. Since many rich opportunities for assessing students are embedded in the curriculum itself, you may choose not to use all the lesson quizzes for each unit.

End-of-Lesson Quizzes Two forms of a quiz covering the main ideas of each lesson are provided. These quizzes, which are the most traditional of all the assessment methods and instruments included with the *Contemporary Mathematics in Context* materials, are comprised of fairly straightforward problems meant to determine if students have developed understanding of the important concepts and procedures of each lesson.

In-Class Exams Two forms of in-class exams are provided for each unit and are intended to be completed in a 50-minute class period. The two forms of each exam are not necessarily equivalent, although they assess essentially the same mathematical ideas. Teachers should preview the two versions carefully, and feel free to revise or delete items and add new ones, if necessary, using the *Assessment and Maintenance Worksheet Builder* CD-Rom.

Take-Home Assessments Take-home assessment tasks are included for each unit. The students or the teacher should choose one or, at most, two of these tasks. These assessments, some of which are best done by students working in pairs or small groups, provide students with the opportunity to organize the information from the completed unit, to extend the ideas of the unit into other areas of interest to them, to work with another student or group of students, and to avoid the time pressure often generated by in-class exams.

Projects Assessment traditionally has been based on evaluating work that students have completed in a very short time period and under restricted conditions. Some assessment, however, should involve work done over a longer time period and with the aid of resources. Thus, assessment projects are included in unit assessments. These projects, which are intended to be completed by small groups of students, provide an opportunity for students to conduct an investigation that extends and applies the main ideas from the unit and to write a summary of their findings.

Midterm and Final Assessment A bank of assessment tasks, from which to construct an exam that fits your particular class needs and emphases, is also provided.

Scoring Assessments

High expectations of the quality of students' written work will encourage students to reach their potential. Assigning scores to open-ended assessments and to observations of students' performance requires more subjective judgment by the teacher than does grading short-answer or multiple-choice tests. It is therefore not possible to provide a complete set of explicit guidelines for scoring open-ended assessment items and written or oral reports. However, some general guidelines may be helpful. When scoring student work on open-ended assessment tasks, the goal is to reward in a fair and consistent way the kinds of thinking and understanding that the task is meant to measure. To score open-ended assessment tasks, teachers should have a general rubric, or scoring scheme, with several response levels in mind; a specific rubric; and anchor items. (See *Implementing the Core-Plus Mathematics Curriculum* for more details.) The general rubric is the foundation for scoring across a wide range of types of open-ended tasks. The following general rubric can be used for most assessment tasks provided with *Contemporary Mathematics in Context.*

General Scoring Rubric

4 points	Contains complete response with clear, coherent, and unambiguous explanation; includes clear and simple diagram, if appropriate; communicates effectively to identified audience; shows understanding of question's mathematical ideas and processes; identifies all important elements of question; includes examples and counterexamples; gives strong supporting arguments
3 points	Contains good solid response with some, but not all, of the characteristics above; explains less completely; may include minor error of execution but not of understanding
2 points	Contains complete response, but explanation is muddled; presents incomplete arguments; includes diagrams that are inappropriate or unclear, or fails to provide a diagram when it would be appropriate; indicates some understanding of mathematical ideas, but in an unclear way; shows clear evidence of understanding some important ideas while also making one or more fundamental, specific errors
1 point	Omits parts of question and response; has major errors; uses inappropriate strategies
0 points	No response; frivolous or irrelevant response

Assigning Grades

Because the *Contemporary Mathematics in Context* approach and materials provide a wide variety of assessment information, the teacher will be in a good position to assign a fair grade for student work. With such a wide choice for assessment, a word of caution is appropriate: *it is easy to overassess students, and care must be taken to avoid doing so*. A quiz need not be given after every lesson nor an in-class exam after every unit. The developers believe it is best to vary assessment methods from lesson to lesson, and from unit to unit. If information on what students understand and are able to do is available from their homework and in-class work, it may not be necessary to take the time for a formal quiz after each lesson. Similarly, information from project work may replace an in-class exam.

Deciding exactly how to weigh the various kinds of assessment information is a decision that the teacher will need to make and communicate clearly to the students.

Maintaining Skills

The developers have identified a set of paper-and-pencil technical competencies that all students should acquire. To provide additional practice with these core competencies, a special maintenance feature is included in blackline master form in the *Teaching Resources* or on the *Assessment and Maintenance Worksheet Builder* CD-Rom. Beginning with Unit 4 of Course 1, "Graph Models," and then continuing with each unit thereafter, a supplementary set of maintenance tasks provides periodic review and additional practice of basic skills. These skills will be continually revisited to ensure mastery by each student at some point in the curriculum.

Use of the maintenance material following the start of Lesson 2 of each unit will allow students time to work simultaneously on skills during the latter part of a unit without interrupting the flow of the unit. You may wish to allow a few minutes at the end of selected class periods to revisit these skills with various groups of students who need assistance while other groups choose an Extending task to complete.

The maintenance material prepared for each unit spans technical competencies across each of the strands. In each case, the first presented task is a contextual problem, but the remaining tasks are not contextualized. Students should *not* use a calculator for these tasks unless so directed.

Reference and Practice Books (RAP Books)

A *Reference and Practice* book is available to accompany Course 3 of the program. The Course 3 RAP book provides students with summaries of concepts and skills from Course 2; practice sets to review and maintain concepts and skills; and exercise sets that provide test-taking practice for standardized tests. This handbook also contains tips for taking standardized tests. These supplements are intended for student reference and use outside of regularly scheduled class times. Suggested assignments are listed in the Planning Guide for each unit.

▶Additional Resources

The Core-Plus Mathematics Project (CPMP) maintains a Web site at www.wmich.edu/cpmp as a resource for schools. You may find the "Frequently Asked Questions" helpful as you think about your uniform district replies to community questions.

In addition, CPMP moderates a listserv that allows teachers to have discussions about mathematical content and implementation of *Contemporary Mathmatics in Context*. For additional information and to subscribe to the listserv, email cpmp@wmich.edu.

Unit 5 ▶ Patterns in Variation

UNIT OVERVIEW Following the ideas of American W. Edwards Deming, considered by many to be the father of Japanese industry's use of quality control, statistical methods are used increasingly in American industry to improve the quality of products. Companies that are committed to the improvement of their products require that the methods be understood by everyone, from employees on the shop floor to those in the executive suite. Called quality control, statistical process control, quality improvement, and other names, the techniques used are highly mathematical. In this unit, students will study the mathematics behind these methods. The topics include standard deviation, normal distribution, the multiplication rule of probability, and the addition rule of probability. These are topics that some students may study in high school, but frequently outside of the important context of their use by industry.

Patterns in Variation provides students with experience in thinking about and working with the variation in data gathered from measurements. The first two lessons involve students in thinking about the shape of distributions, relating the shape to the mean and standard deviation, and thinking about the standard deviation as a unit of measure that can be used to describe location in a normal distribution. Students may be surprised to discover the variety of situations in which approximately normal distributions occur.

The mean and the standard deviation are the most useful measures of center and spread for distributions that are roughly symmetrical and have no outliers. The mean, standard deviation, and normal distribution are natural partners. Students will explore the relationships among the three in the first two lessons.

The third lesson introduces students to control charts, which display samples of measurements taken over time. When the measurements come from a distribution that is approximately normal, it is possible to establish a set of criteria for defining when a process goes "out of control." These criteria are based on probabilistic arguments and are the foundation for the quality control tests that are used in industry. In particular, students study tests taken from the influential *Western Electric Statistical Quality Control Handbook*.

Patterns in Variation

Unit **5**

Unit 5

345

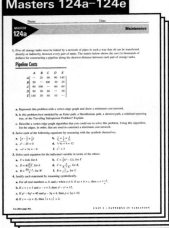

Unit 5 Objectives

■ To understand the standard deviation as a measure of variability in a distribution

■ To understand the normal distribution as a model of variability

■ To understand and be able to use the number of standard deviations from the mean as a measure of the position of a value in a normal distribution

■ To understand the construction, interpretation, and theory of control charts

■ To understand and apply the Addition Rule for mutually exclusive events

See Teaching Masters 124a–124e for Maintenance tasks that students can work on after Lesson 1.

Unit 5 Planning Guide

Lesson Objectives	MORE Assignments	Suggested Pacing	Materials
Lesson 1 *Measuring Variation with the Standard Deviation* • To compute the standard deviation from a set of data and to estimate the standard deviation from a histogram • To interpret the standard deviation of a given set of data • To recognize that the standard deviation is sensitive to extreme values • To understand the effect of a transformation on the standard deviation	**after page 350** Students can begin Modeling Task 3 or 4; Organizing Task 1; Reflecting Task 1, 2, or 3; or any Extending task from p. 355. **page 355** **Modeling:** 1 and choice of one* **Organizing:** 1, 3, and 4 **Reflecting:** 2 and choice of one* **Extending:** Choose one*	5 days	• Graph paper • Rulers with inch and millimeter markings (one per student) • Teaching Resources 125–130 • Assessment Resources 193–198 • *Optional*: RAP Book Exercise Set 14
Lesson 2 *The Normal Distribution* • To recognize that in a normal distribution, 68% of the data are within one standard deviation of the mean, 95% are within two standard deviations, and 99.7% are within three standard deviations of the mean • To describe charateristics of a normal distribution, such as its symmetry and the relationship between the mean and median • To understand that the number of standard deviations from the mean is a measure of location • To use a table of the normal distribution	**after page 367** Students can begin Organizing Task 1 from p. 375. **after page 371** Students can begin Reflecting Task 1, 2, or 4 or Extending Task 1 from p. 375. **page 375** **Modeling:** 2 and choice of one* **Organizing:** 2 and choice of one* **Reflecting:** 1 and 3 **Extending:** 1 and choice of one*	5 days	• Graph paper • Teaching Resources 124a–124e, 131a–140 • Assessment Resources 199–204 • *Optional*: RAP Book Practice Set 7
Lesson 3 *Statistical Process Control* • To recognize when the mean and standard deviation change on a plot over time • To use control charts and the tests for out-of-control behavior • To understand why it is best to watch a process for awhile before trying to adjust it • To compute the probability of a false alarm on a set of readings, that is, the probability that a test will give an out-of-control signal for a process that is under control • To understand the Addition Rule for mutually exclusive events	**after page 393** Students can begin any task from p. 396 except Reflecting Task 3. **page 396** **Modeling:** 3 and choice of one* **Organizing:** 1 and 3 **Reflecting:** 3 and 4 **Extending:** Choose one* **after page 405** Students can begin Modeling Task 1 or 2; Organizing Task 1, 2, or 3; or Reflecting Task 1, 2, 3, or 4 from p. 411. **page 411** **Modeling:** 1, 2, and 3 **Organizing:** 1 and choice of one* **Reflecting:** 5 and choice of one* **Extending:** 4	8 days	• Graph paper • Teaching Resources 141–152 • Assessment Resources 205–210 • *Optional*: RAP Book Exercise Set 15
Lesson 4 *Looking Back* • To review the major objectives of the unit		2-3 days (includes testing)	• Graph paper • Teaching Resources 153–154 • Unit Summary Master • Assessment Resources 211–228 • *Optional*: RAP Book Practice Set 8

*When choice is indicated, it is important to leave the choice to the student.
Note: It is best if Organizing tasks are discussed as a whole class after they have been assigned as homework.

Measuring Variation with the Standard Deviation

Manufacturing involves processes that vary. When Boeing builds a jet airplane, steps in the production process include design, buying raw materials and some parts, manufacturing other parts, assembling the parts, and testing the result. If different machines are used to make the same type of part, the sizes of the produced parts could be slightly different. Even parts made by the same machine will vary slightly in their dimensions.

Think About This Situation

Variation is inherent in the manufacturing of products, ranging from computer chips to jumbo jets.

a Name some specific problems that could occur with an airplane if the manufacturing process produces parts that vary too much in size.

b How could a company detect and minimize variation in the manufacturing of products?

c What ways do you know for measuring variability?

d How does a box plot help you visualize variability? How does a histogram help? How does a stem-and-leaf plot help?

In this unit, you will investigate how some basic statistical methods can improve the production process and the quality of a service or product. Using statistical signals to improve quality is called **statistical process control**, **quality control**, or **quality improvement**. These methods can be effectively applied to any area in which there is variation in the process—essentially every area of human endeavor!

Measuring Variation with the Standard Deviation

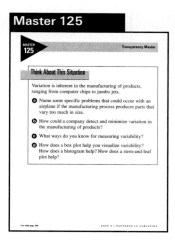

Unit 5

LESSON OVERVIEW Students have learned that it is important to describe a set of data with a measure of variability, as well as with a measure of center. In this lesson, students review measuring variability around the median using the interquartile range (IQR) and around the mean using the mean absolute deviation (MAD). The initial introduction to these mathematical concepts is found in the unit "Patterns in Data" from Course 1. Students then compute the standard deviation for a set of measurements and compare this to the MAD. The effects on the standard deviation of a linear transformation of data and the effects of outliers are explored in Investigation 2.

Lesson Objectives

- To compute the standard deviation from a set of data and to estimate the standard deviation from a histogram
- To interpret the standard deviation of a given set of data
- To recognize that the standard deviation is sensitive to extreme values
- To understand the effect of a transformation on the standard deviation

LAUNCH   full-class discussion

Think About This Situation

See Teaching Master 125.

For the reviews in Parts c and d, you might have students physically line up according to date of birth, count from each end to the middle to find the median, and quartiles. Students can make a "living histogram" with each student lining up behind his or her month of birth.

ⓐ Students may suggest problems that would cause an airplane to crash. Encourage them to think of other, less serious problems that could also occur, such as leaky faucets, air conditioning problems, or seats that do not recline correctly.

ⓑ This item will help you assess the informal knowledge that students bring to the idea of quality control. Some students may have family members who work in industry and can describe to your class the quality control methods used by their companies.

ⓒ Students should recall using the range and the interquartile range (IQR) and the mean absolute deviation (MAD). You may need to ask questions to help students recall the meaning and the process of calculating these measures.

See additional Teaching Notes on page T419C.

Master 126

Master 127

EXPLORE small-group investigation

INVESTIGATION 1 ▶ Calculating and Interpreting the Standard Deviation

This investigation begins with activities that assist students in recalling previously used measures of variation. The goal of the investigation is to have students understand that the standard deviation measures how much values vary from their mean. As you circulate among the groups, you might ask students to interpret their numerical answers. The standard deviation can be thought of as a typical distance from the mean, so a distribution with a small standard deviation tends to have values that are close to the mean. A distribution with a large standard deviation tends to have values that are far from the mean.

1. **See Teaching Master 126.**
   a. Variability would exist in measuring the perimeter, in measuring the braid against the ruler, in the rulers themselves, in how tightly the braid was stretched as it was being cut, and even in the width of the scissors used to cut the braid.
   b. Measurements will vary. They are supposed to vary, so be sure students don't compare measurements at this stage.
   c. **See Teaching Master 127.**
   Class measurements will depend on the individual measurements from Part b. Students may be surprised at how much variation there is in their measurements. Some of the variation may be due to out-and-out mistakes, such as misuse of the ruler, but most variation will be due to the judgments and estimates students made in the measurement process.

   Discuss the strategies students used to find the perimeter. If students decided to take advantage of the symmetry, they saved time by measuring only part of the perimeter, but their estimates will probably have larger error built in because with fewer measurements, there is less of a "cancelling effect" by over- and undermeasuring.

2. a. These summary statistics will depend on the measurements from your class.
   b. The IQR gives the range of the middle half of the data. If the IQR is large, the plotted measurements will be spread out. If it is small, they will be clustered more closely.
   c. Answers will vary, depending on the data collected.

INVESTIGATION 1 Computing and Interpreting the Standard Deviation

In earlier courses, you learned about three measures that describe the variation in a set of data: the range, the interquartile range (IQR), and the mean absolute deviation (MAD). Another measure used to describe the variation in a set of data is the *standard deviation*. In this lesson, you will learn how to compute the standard deviation, and you will explore some of its uses and properties.

1. Suppose your class is working on a project making school award certificates. You have decided to outline the edge of a design on the certificates with a continuous piece of thin gold braid.

Certificate of Distinction

This certificate is awarded to

_____

to recognize achievement in

_____

on this day, _____.

   a. What variability would exist in the process of preparing the strips of braid?

   b. Without comparing measurements to those of other students, find the perimeter (in millimeters) of the outline on the sample certificate above. Record your perimeter measurement.

   c. As a class, make a line plot of the perimeters recorded by the members of your class. Describe the distribution.

2. Recall that the interquartile range (IQR) of a distribution is a measure of how much the middle half of the values vary. It is a measure of variation often associated with the median.

   a. Find the median, the quartiles (Q_1 and Q_3), and the IQR of the class set of perimeter measurements. Mark these on your line plot.

   b. What does the interquartile range tell you about how much the measurements vary?

   c. You may recall that an *outlier* is a data value x such that $x > Q_3 + 1.5(IQR)$ or $x < Q_1 - 1.5(IQR)$. Are there any outliers according to this 1.5(IQR) rule? If so, describe their location on your line plot.

3. In your previous work, when the mean was used to describe the center of a distribution, you used the mean absolute deviation (MAD) as a measure of variation. It is the average distance of the data values from the mean.

   a. Compute the MAD for the perimeter measurements from your group only. Use the formula

   $$\text{MAD} = \frac{\sum |x - \bar{x}|}{n}$$

   where the values of x are your measurements, $\bar{x}$ is the mean of your measurements, and n is the number of values.

   b. What does the MAD tell you about the variation in the measurements of the perimeter?

   c. Why is absolute value used in the formula for the MAD?

4. The **standard deviation** is another measure of how much the values vary about the mean. It is found by first computing the average of the *squares* of the differences between each data point and the mean, and then finding the square root of that average.

   a. In your group, discuss how you would compute the standard deviation of the perimeter measurements made by your group. How might you organize your work?

   b. Individually, compute the standard deviation. Compare your answers and resolve any differences.

   c. Compare the MAD of the measurements of your group to the standard deviation of the measurements of your group. Are they the same or different? Is the same conclusion true for other groups' measurements?

   d. Compare the process for computing the standard deviation to the process for computing the mean absolute deviation. In what ways are they alike? In what ways are they different?

   e. Write a symbolic rule for computing the standard deviation (SD) of a set of n data values.

5. Now exchange perimeter measurements with another group.

   a. Compute the standard deviation of the measurements of that group.

   b. Is the other group's standard deviation larger or smaller than your group's standard deviation? How might you explain this in terms of the data?

6. Think about the process of finding the standard deviation.

   a. What is accomplished by squaring the differences from the mean?

   b. What is accomplished by dividing by n?

   c. Why do you need to take the square root?

   d. What unit of measurement should be attached to the standard deviation of the measurements of the perimeters? Why?

   e. What formulas have you seen that involve a sum of squared differences?

3. **a.** The value will depend on the group's measurements.
   b. The MAD gives the average distance of the values from the mean.
   c. Without the absolute value, the sum of the deviations would be zero. It is always true that $\sum (x - \bar{x}) = 0$.

   NOTE: Students have seen and discussed this concept or a similar concept on several occasions: when they first investigated the MAD (Course 1), when they measured the differences between rankings needed for computing a rank correlation coefficient (Course 2), and when they measured the errors from the best-fit line (Course 2). In each case, the sum of the differences is zero.

   ---

4. **a.** First, compute the mean. One way to organize the rest of the work is to complete a table like the following:

x	$x - \bar{x}$	$(x - \bar{x})^2$
Sum	0	

   After finding the sum $\sum (x - \bar{x})^2$, divide it by n and take the square root.
   b. Results will depend on the measurements.
   c. The MAD will be different from the standard deviation unless all measurements were equal or all points were the same distance from the mean, such as {6, 6, 8, 8}. Usually, the MAD is less than or equal to the standard deviation.
   d. They are alike in that they are both types of average distances from the mean. In both cases, a measurement of distance from the mean is computed for each data value, summed, and divided by the number of data values. They are different in the way the distance from the mean is used in the computation. The absolute value of the difference between the data point and the mean is used for the MAD. The square of the difference between the data point and the mean is used for the standard deviation. Since the deviations are squared when computing the standard deviation, the last step is to take the square root. This has the effect of keeping the same units for the standard deviation as for the data. For example, when the perimeters are in millimeters, the standard deviation will also be in millimeters.

See additional Teaching Notes on page T419C.

Unit 5

7. **a.** Answers will depend on perimeter measurements.
   b. In some cases it will be larger, and in some cases it will be smaller. There is no general rule.

8. **a.** Responses will vary, depending on the measurements from the group.
   b. **See Teaching Master 128**.
   c. The larger the mean, the greater the hand spans in the group. The greater the standard deviation, the greater the variation in the hand spans of the group members. If some groups have a large standard deviation and some groups have little difference in their hand spans, students should be able to identify those groups by the statistics. Students should find that it is difficult to identify groups whose statistics are similar.
   d. Answers will vary for each group. For some groups, the standard deviation of the group may be larger than the standard deviation of the class; for other groups, it may be smaller. There is no general rule indicating whether the standard deviation of a sample is larger or smaller than the standard deviation of a population.

9. **a.** The Chicago Bulls basketball team will have the greater mean height. All of the players on the team are tall, and some are very tall. The people in Chicago named Smith will probably have a mean height close to the national average height, and this is less than the mean height of a professional basketball team. The people named Smith would have the larger standard deviation. The basketball players are all tall, but there are both tall and short people named Smith.
   b. If we consider only members of the 1997–98 Chicago Bulls, the mean height of the men is 79.2" with standard deviation 3.5". The distribution might look something like this:

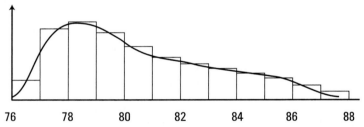

If we consider only adults named Smith, the mean height of the men is probably 68.8" with standard deviation 2.65" and of the females is probably 63.6" with standard deviation 2.5". (See student page 376.) The combined distribution might look something like the sample below.

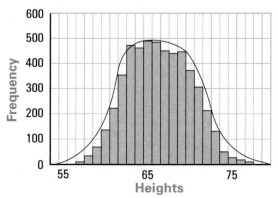

7. Graphing calculators and statistical computer software will calculate the standard deviation of data that have been entered into a list.

   a. Use your calculator or software to find the mean and the standard deviation (usually denoted σ on the menu) of the perimeter measurements for your entire class. Compare these numbers to your line plot from Activity 1 Part c. Does the mean appear to be the balance point of the distribution? Does the standard deviation appear to represent a distance from the mean that is typical for the data values?

   b. Is the standard deviation of the class larger or smaller than the standard deviation of your group? What characteristic of the data made that the case? Is the same conclusion true for all groups?

Now use the idea of standard deviation to explore the variability in hand spans among your classmates.

8. Each member of your group should measure his or her hand span: Spread your right hand as wide as possible, place it on a ruler, and measure the distance from the end of your thumb across to the end of your little finger.

   a. Find the mean and standard deviation of the hand spans of the students in your group.

   b. Report your group's mean and standard deviation to your teacher.

   c. As a class, examine the means and standard deviations from the groups in your class. Consider the specific people in each group, and try to match each set of statistics with the correct group.

   d. Now compute the mean and standard deviation of the hand spans of all class members. Are the mean and standard deviation larger or smaller than your group's mean and standard deviation? What characteristics of the data explain these results? Is the same conclusion true for all groups?

9. Consider the heights of the people in the following two groups:

   ■ The members of the Chicago Bulls basketball team

   ■ The people in Chicago named Smith

   a. Which group would you expect to have the larger mean height? Which group would you expect to have the larger standard deviation? Explain your reasoning.

   b. Sketch or describe what you think histograms of these data would look like.

LESSON 1 • MEASURING VARIATION WITH THE STANDARD DEVIATION   **349**

Checkpoint

Look back at how you used the standard deviation to help you analyze measurement data.

ⓐ What does the standard deviation tell you about a distribution?

ⓑ Why can you think of the standard deviation of a set of data as a kind of average distance of the values from their mean?

ⓒ How is the standard deviation similar to, and different from, other measures of variation you have studied?

Be prepared to share your ideas with the entire class.

The standard deviation is the most widely used measure of variation in the practice and study of statistics. As you complete the remaining investigations in this unit, think about reasons why this is the case. You will be asked to give your reasons in the "Looking Back" lesson.

▶ On Your Own

Assess your understanding of the standard deviation as a measure of variation.

a. For each data set below, first find the mean and standard deviation *without* using the formulas. Then check your answers by actually computing these statistics using the formulas.

- 4, 4, 4, 4, 4, 4, 4
- 6, 6, 6, 10, 10, 10

b. The normal monthly precipitation (rain and snow) in inches for Portland, Maine, and for Portland, Oregon, is given in the table below.

Portland, Oregon

Normal Monthly Precipitation

	Jan.	Feb.	Mar.	Apr.	May	June	July	Aug.	Sept.	Oct.	Nov.	Dec.
Portland, ME	3.5	3.3	3.7	4.1	3.6	3.4	3.1	2.9	3.1	3.9	5.2	4.6
Portland, OR	5.4	3.9	3.6	2.4	2.1	1.5	0.6	1.1	1.8	2.7	5.3	6.1

Source: *The World Almanac and Book of Facts 2001.* Mahwah, NJ: World Almanac, 2001.

- From studying the data in the table, what comparisons can you make about the amount of precipitation for the two cities?

- Make a back-to-back stem-and-leaf plot of the precipitation in each of the cities. How do you think the mean monthly amounts of precipitation for the cities will compare? How will the standard deviations compare?

- Calculate the mean and standard deviation of the normal monthly precipitation for each city. How well did you estimate?

SHARE AND SUMMARIZE   full-class discussion

Checkpoint

See Teaching Master 129.

ⓐ The standard deviation tells us how spread out the data are.

ⓑ We have taken the square root of the average squared distance from the mean.

ⓒ The standard deviation is most similar to the MAD in that it is a kind of average distance from the mean. Both are sensitive to outliers, but the standard deviation is even more so than the MAD. About all the standard deviation has in common with the range and the IQR is that they are measures of spread. The range and IQR give the distance between just two numbers in the distribution. For the range, they are the maximum and minimum; for the IQR, they are the third and first quartiles.

Master 129

MASTER 129   Transparency Master

Checkpoint

Look back at how you used the standard deviation to help you analyze measurement data.

ⓐ What does the standard deviation tell you about a distribution?

ⓑ Why can you think of the standard deviation of a set of data as a kind of average distance of the values from their mean?

ⓒ How is the standard deviation similar to, and different from, other measures of variation you have studied?

Be prepared to share your ideas with the entire class.

Use with page 350.   UNIT 5 • PATTERNS IN VARIATION

CONSTRUCTING A MATH TOOLKIT: Following the Checkpoint discussion, students should write a thorough response to Part c in their Math Toolkits. If students do not already have formulas for the range, IQR, and MAD in their Math Toolkits, they should enter those formulas, along with the formula for the standard deviation. (See Teaching Master 196.)

APPLY   individual task

▶On Your Own

a. ■ The mean is 4; the SD is 0.

■ The mean is 8; the SD is 2.

b. ■ It looks as if Portland, Maine gets more yearly rainfall, but there is much more variation by month in Portland, Oregon, which has a dry summer and a wet winter.

■ Normal Monthly Precipitation

Portland, ME		Portland, OR
	0	6
	1	1 5 8
9	2	1 4 7
9 7 6 5 4 3 1 1	3	6 9
6 1	4	
2	5	3 4
	6	1

5|3 represents 5.3 inches.

The mean for Portland, Maine is greater, and Portland, Oregon has a larger standard deviation.

■ Normal Monthly Precipitation

	Mean	SD
Portland, ME	3.7"	0.64"
Portland, OR	3.04"	1.74"

MORE

ASSIGNMENT   *pp. 355–361*

Students can now begin Modeling Task 3 or 4; Organizing Task 1; Reflecting Task 1, 2, or 3; or any Extending task from the MORE assignment following Investigation 2.

INVESTIGATION 2 Properties of the Standard Deviation

In this investigation, students will explore the effects on the standard deviation of adding a constant to each data value, of multiplying each data value by a constant, and of outliers. They will learn that adding a constant will change the mean by that same amount while not affecting the standard deviation because the spread hasn't been changed. Students will also discover that multiplying by a constant will change both the mean and the standard deviation by that factor. Students who have developed a strong graphical sense will find it relatively easy to see that adding a constant c simply translates the graph and its mean c units, without altering the spread. The effect of multiplying may be harder for them to predict. Some students will check the extremes and discover that the range has increased by the same factor. They will then be able to deduce that the standard deviation will also change. You may wish to have students create graphs (histograms or number-line plots) to check their conjectures and calculations.

It is important for students to realize that in some cases, you do not want a summary statistic to be affected by an outlier, especially if you suspect the measurement might be a mistake. In other cases, you want to pay special attention to outliers. For example, in quality control processes an outlier can signal that a process is out of control.

Some students may recall the principle behind Activity 1. If not, or if students seem unsure, you might suggest to them that their conjectures should be tested on sets of data. In Activities 3, 4, and 5, students have the opportunity to conjecture and then calculate the effects of multiplying by or adding a constant. Depending on the ability your students have with symbol manipulation, you may decide that Activity 6 provides a good opportunity for a large group discussion to draw the class together and reach consensus on the effects of these two transformations and the reasons for the different effects.

1. **a.** It doesn't change either measure. This makes sense because the IQR and the MAD are measures of spread. Measures of spread should not be affected by a horizontal translation of the distribution.

    b. The transformation won't affect the standard deviation for the same reason given in Part a. (Students will check this conjecture in this investigation.)

    c. The IQR and the MAD are also multiplied by that same value. This makes sense because multiplying each value in a distribution by a constant changes the spread by that same factor.

    d. The transformation will change the standard deviation by that same factor for the same reason given in Part c. (Students will check this conjecture in this investigation.)

INVESTIGATION 2 ▸ Properties of the Standard Deviation

In other courses, you have examined the effect of transformations of data on the interquartile range and on the MAD. In this investigation, you will explore how transformations affect the standard deviation.

1. Working with your group, recall your previous work with data transformations.

   a. How does adding the same positive number to each value in a set of data affect the IQR? The MAD? Why does this make sense?

   b. If the standard deviation behaves like other measures of variation, how will the transformation in Part a affect it?

   c. How does multiplying each value in a data set by the same positive number affect the IQR? The MAD? Why does this make sense?

   d. If the standard deviation behaves like other measures of variation, how will the transformation in Part c affect it?

2. Ms. King polled her two senior mathematics classes to determine the hourly wage of students who had part-time jobs. The results are listed in the table below.

Student Wages

Student	Hourly Wage (in dollars)	Student	Hourly Wage (in dollars)
Neil	5.15	Mia	6.60
Bill	5.25	Tasha	6.60
Dimitri	5.30	Sarah	6.65
Jose	5.50	Vanita	6.70
Kerry	5.75	N'taka	6.70
Emerson	5.85	Olivia	6.75
Rashawnda	5.90	Katrina	6.80
Katie	5.90	Deeonna	6.90
Cleave	6.00	Jacob	7.00
Jan	6.10	Rusty	7.00
Kyle	6.25	Jennifer	7.25
Mike	6.25	Phuong	7.30
Toby	6.30	Corinna	7.45
Nafikah	6.40	John	7.50
Robert	6.40		

Here is a histogram of these data.

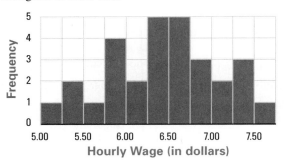

a. Estimate the average hourly wage of these students from the histogram. Compute the mean. How close was your estimate?

b. Estimate the standard deviation of the hourly wages. Compute the standard deviation. How close was your estimate?

3. Berry decided it was too much work to enter the decimal point in the wages each time in her calculator list, so she entered each wage without it.

a. What mathematical operation describes how Berry transformed the original data?

b. How will the histogram of her data be different from the one shown in Activity 2?

c. Predict the mean and standard deviation of her data. Check your predictions.

4. Suppose each student in Ms. King's class gets a 4% raise.

a. What mathematical operation transforms the original data to reflect a 4% raise in hourly wages?

b. How will the histogram of the new hourly wages be different from the original one?

c. Predict the mean and standard deviation for the new wages of the students. Check your predictions.

5. Suppose that instead of a 4% raise, each student gets a raise of 25 cents per hour.

a. What mathematical operation transforms the original data to reflect an increase in hourly wages of 25 cents per hour?

b. How will the histogram of the new hourly wages be different from the original one?

c. How will the mean and standard deviation change? Explain why this is reasonable.

2. a. The mean wage is approximately $6.40.

   b. The standard deviation is approximately $0.64.

3. a. Berry multiplied each piece of data by 100, which is the same as recording the wages in cents rather than dollars.

   b. It will have exactly the same shape but will be centered at 640 and will have a larger spread.

   c. Students should recall that this transformation also multiplies the mean by 100. So the new mean will be approximately 640. The standard deviation will also be multiplied by 100. The new standard deviation is 64.

4. a. A 4% raise transforms the data by multiplying by a factor of 1.04.

   b. The shape will be the same but more stretched out. The mean will be larger by a factor of 1.04.

   c. The new mean will be (6.40)(1.04) or approximately $6.66, and the new standard deviation will be (0.64)(1.04) or approximately $0.67.

5. a. Each piece of data will have 25 cents added to it.

   b. The shape will be exactly the same and so will the spread, but the location of the histogram will be $0.25 to the right of the original.

   c. The mean will increase by $0.25. This is reasonable because all data values have been increased by $0.25. The standard deviation will not change. This is because the spread or variation of the data is not changed by this transformation. When it comes to transformations of the data, the standard deviation behaves the same as the MAD does.

Unit 5

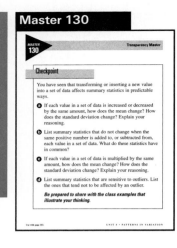
EXPLORE *continued*

6. **a.** $x_1 + c, x_2 + c, x_3 + c, x_4 + c, x_5 + c$

b. $\dfrac{(x_1 + c) + (x_2 + c) + (x_3 + c) + (x_4 + c) + (x_5 + c)}{5} = \dfrac{x_1 + x_2 + x_3 + x_4 + x_5 + 5c}{5}$

$$= \dfrac{x_1 + x_2 + x_3 + x_4 + x_5}{5} + \dfrac{5c}{5}$$

$$= \bar{x} + c$$

c. $\sqrt{\dfrac{[(x_1 + c) - (\bar{x} + c)]^2 + \ldots + [(x_5 + c) - (\bar{x} + c)]^2}{5}} = \sqrt{\dfrac{(x_1 - \bar{x})^2 + \ldots + (x_5 - \bar{x})^2}{5}}$

$$= \sqrt{\dfrac{\sum(x - \bar{x})^2}{5}}$$

d. It is the same.

e. If you add a constant c to each value in a set of data, then the mean of the transformed data is c more than the mean of the original data and the standard deviation of the transformed data is the same as the one of the original data.

7. **a.** The mean and the standard deviation will decrease slightly since Maurice's wage of $5.85 per hour is less than but relatively close to the mean, $6.40. When $5.85 is added to the list, the new mean is approximately $6.38. The previous standard deviation was approximately 0.639, and the new standard deviation is approximately 0.636.

b. Both the mean and the standard deviation will increase significantly. The new mean is approximately $6.62, and the new standard deviation is approximately $1.34.

SHARE AND SUMMARIZE full-class discussion

Checkpoint

See Teaching Master 130.

ⓐ If each value is increased or decreased by the same amount, the mean will be increased or decreased by that same amount. Think of the histogram being shifted to the right or left by that amount. The standard deviation will remain the same because the spread will not change.

ⓑ The standard deviation, mean absolute deviation, interquartile range, and range will not change when the same number is added to or subtracted from each value of a data set. All are measures of spread or variability.

ⓒ Each of these statistics is multiplied by that amount. Student explanations will vary. Encourage students to think of the transformation as a horizontal stretch (or shrink if the factor is between 0 and 1). In the next unit, students will study this type of transformation as it relates to functions.

ⓓ The mean, standard deviation, range, and MAD are all sensitive to outliers. The median and the IQR are not.

CONSTRUCTING A MATH TOOLKIT: Students should describe the properties of the standard deviation in their Math Toolkits.

6. In this activity, you will examine symbolically the effect on the standard deviation of adding the same value c to each of the five values in a set of data,

$$x_1, x_2, x_3, x_4, x_5.$$

   a. Suppose the constant c is added to each of the values in the above set of data. What are the transformed values?

   b. Let $\bar{x}$ be the mean of the original values. Compute the mean of the transformed values.

   c. Compute the standard deviation of the transformed values.

   d. How does the standard deviation of the transformed values compare to the standard deviation of the original values?

   e. Write an if-then statement of what you proved in Parts a through d.

7. Now examine the effect of inserting a new value into the hourly wages data.

   a. Suppose Maurice was absent from the class the day of the wage poll. When he returned to school, his wage of $5.85 per hour was included in the data set. How do you think this additional value will affect the mean and standard deviation? Check your conjecture.

   b. Suppose that, instead, Maurice was a computer expert and had a programming job that paid $13.00 per hour. How do you think the mean and standard deviation of the hourly wage data will change? Compute the mean and standard deviation, and explain why the results are reasonable.

Checkpoint

You have seen that transforming or inserting a new value into a set of data affects summary statistics in predictable ways.

a If each value in a set of data is increased or decreased by the same amount, how does the mean change? How does the standard deviation change? Explain your reasoning.

b List summary statistics that do not change when the same positive number is added to, or subtracted from, each value in a set of data. What do these statistics have in common?

c If each value in a set of data is multiplied by the same amount, how does the mean change? How does the standard deviation change? Explain your reasoning.

d List summary statistics that are sensitive to outliers. List the ones that tend not to be affected by an outlier.

Be prepared to share with the class examples that illustrate your thinking.

▶ **On Your Own**

In a community college class, all thirty-six students were working at jobs for which they were paid. The number of hours they worked per week is given below.

Community College Students' Employment

5	5	5	6	10	11	12	12	12
13	14	15	15	16	16	16	17	17
17	17	18	19	19	20	20	20	20
20	20	23	25	25	25	27	28	40

a. Examine this histogram of these data. Describe the distribution.

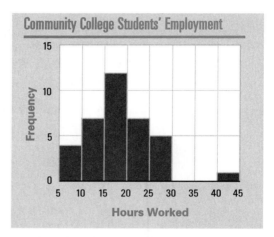

b. Find the mean and standard deviation. Locate the mean on a copy of the histogram. Locate the values one standard deviation above the mean and one standard deviation below the mean.

c. Saundra is the student who works 40 hours a week. She is thinking about reducing her work hours to 20 a week so she will have more time to study. What will happen to the mean and standard deviation if Saundra makes this change?

d. Describe two ways to find the mean and standard deviation of the number of hours worked *per semester* (15 weeks) by these students.

e. The instructor of the class expects students to do homework two hours every school night for a total of ten hours a week. If each student's homework hours are added to his or her work hours, how will the mean and standard deviation change?

▶**On Your Own**

a. All but one student works between 5 and 30 hours a week. The mean number of hours worked is between 15 and 20. Except for the one outlier, the distribution is approximately symmetric.

b. The mean number of hours these students worked per week at paid jobs was approximately 17.2 with a standard deviation of approximately 7.0 hours. One standard deviation below and above the mean will be 10.2 and 24.2 hours, respectively.

c. The mean and the standard deviation will decrease to approximately 16.7 and 5.9 hours, respectively.

d. The mean is 15(17.2) or 258 hours. The standard deviation is 15(7.0) or 105 hours. In addition to using this property of the mean and standard deviation, a second way is to multiply each data value by 15 and then recompute the mean and standard deviation.

e. The mean number of hours will increase by 10 hours to 27.2 hours, and the standard deviation will remain the same at 7.0.

Unit 5

NOTE: Be sure students recognize that the data set with the larger range is not the one with the larger standard deviation.

Modeling

1. a. Kilograms of Oranges per Tree

Fertilizer *A*		Fertilizer *B*
5 3 0	0	2 8
9 5 4 1	1	0 0 3 4 5
4	2	
1	3	3
	4	0 4
	5	
	6	
	7	2
4	8	
6 2	9	
	10	
	11	6

1|0 represents 10 kg.

b. The mean for Fertilizer *A* is about the same as the one for Fertilizer *B*: about 32 kg.

c. Student responses will vary. Fertilizer *B* has the larger range but has only one large value. Fertilizer *A* has three outliers.

d. The approximate mean and standard deviation for Fertilizer *A* are 32.8 kg and 34.5 kg and for Fertilizer *B* are 31.4 kg and 32.0 kg.

e. Fertilizer *A*:   Mean is 2.2(32.8) or 72.16 pounds.
                          Standard deviation is 2.2(34.5) or 75.9 pounds.
     Fertilizer *B*:   Mean is 2.2(31.4) or 69.08 pounds.
                          Standard deviation is 2.2(32.0) or 70.4 pounds.

MORE
Modeling • Organizing • Reflecting • Extending

Modeling

1. In an agricultural experiment, two different types of fertilizer were used on twelve orange trees each. The table below gives the number of kilograms of oranges produced per tree.

Kilograms of Oranges per Tree	
Fertilizer *A*	Fertilizer *B*
3	14
14	116
19	33
0	40
96	10
92	72
11	8
24	10
5	2
31	13
84	15
15	44

a. Make a back-to-back stem-and-leaf plot of the number of kilograms of oranges produced by trees with Fertilizer *A* and with Fertilizer *B*.

b. Use the stem-and-leaf plot to estimate the mean number of kilograms for each set of trees.

c. Which set do you think has the larger standard deviation? What clues suggest which set might have the larger standard deviation?

d. Compute the mean and standard deviation of each set. How close were your estimates in Parts b and c?

e. What are the mean and standard deviation of the number of *pounds* of oranges for Fertilizer *A*? For Fertilizer *B*? (There are about 2.2 pounds in a kilogram.)

Modeling • Organizing • Reflecting • Extending

2. The prices of used 1998 and 1999 Honda Civics advertised in a Sunday newspaper were $7,500, $8,900, $5,200, $6,000, $6,500, $8,000, and $8,995.

   a. Compute the mean and standard deviation of the prices.

   b. If the seven car owners all lower their prices by $500 for the next Sunday's edition of the paper, how will the mean and standard deviation of the prices change?

   c. Suppose that there is a 5% sales tax on used cars. How will this affect the mean and standard deviation of the costs of these cars? How would these two statistics be affected if the buyer then also had to pay a $12.00 registration fee?

   d. Suppose that another Honda Civic is listed for $4,900. How will this affect the mean and standard deviation of the listed prices?

201 Autos, Used

HONDA CIVIC, '99 – white, 68,000 miles, very clean. Only $7500. Call 555-5996.

HONDA CIVIC EX '98 – 50K, 5 spd., air, $8900 or best offer. 555-7641.

HONDA CIVIC SI '98 – hatch-back, 2 door, 5 spd., black, tint, runs excel, $5200. Call 555-1203.

HONDA CIVIC '98 – Loaded. Orchid. Moonroof. $6000. 555-0255.

HONDA CIVIC '98 – 2 dr. hatch. Green. Air. Only $6500. Call 555-5800.

HONDA CIVIC '99 – Loaded. Pwr sunroof, 5spd., 49K. $8000 obo. 555-8300.

HONDA CIVIC '99 – 43K mi, leather, sunroof, 4 dr, $8995. 555-2204.

3. Thirty-two students in a drafting class were asked to prepare a design to certain specifications, which included exact dimensions. A histogram of the perimeters of their designs is displayed below. The mean perimeter was 98.42 cm.

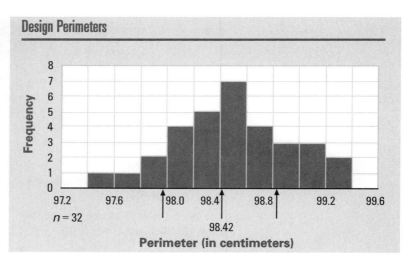

Design Perimeters

$n = 32$

98.42

Perimeter (in centimeters)

2. **a.** The mean is $7,299, and the standard deviation is $1,347. It may help students to understand the standard deviation as a measure of spread if you use language such as, "You would expect to pay $7,299, give or take $1,347 or so."

 b. The mean will decrease by $500 to $6,799 and the standard deviation will stay the same at $1,347.

 c. The mean price with sales tax added is $7,299(1.05) or approximately $7,664. The standard deviation is $1,347(1.05) or approximately $1,414. If there was a $12.00 registration fee, the mean would increase by $12.00 to $7,676, but the standard deviation would not change.

 d. Adding $4,900 to the data set will decrease the mean and increase the standard deviation. The new value for the mean is $6,999, and the standard deviation is $1,489.

3. **a.** Responses will vary. Variation could be caused by inaccuracies in the drawing or the measuring process.

   b. Estimates may vary but should be close to 0.45 cm.

   c. Percentages may vary. Without the actual data you can only estimate. One estimate using the four bars within one standard deviation of the mean is about $\frac{20}{32}$ or 62.5%.

   d. Estimates may vary. About 91% or 94% (29 or 30) of the values are within two standard deviations of the mean.

4. **a.** The mean will be larger if the smallest class size is removed. Thus, the mean with the calculus class is 35.97, and the mean without it is 37.00.

   b. The standard deviation will be smaller if the smallest class size is removed. Thus, the standard deviation with the calculus class is 6.34 and without it is 3.25.

   c. Using a mean of 35.97 and a standard deviation of 6.34, you can see that the calculus class lies $7 - 35.97$ or 28.97 units below the mean. This is 4.57 standard deviations below the mean. Using a mean of 37 and a standard deviation of 3.25, the calculus class lies 30 units, or 9.23 standard deviations, below the mean.

   d. The mean decreases by 5 to 30.97; the standard deviation remains the same at 6.34.

NOTE: The population standard deviation σ was computed in both cases.

Unit 5

a. What might explain the variation in perimeters of the design?

b. The arrows mark the mean and the points one standard deviation above the mean and one standard deviation below the mean. Use the marked plot to estimate the standard deviation for the class's perimeters.

c. Estimate the percentage of the perimeters that are within one standard deviation of the mean.

d. Estimate the percentage of the perimeters that are within two standard deviations of the mean.

4. A large urban high school has 29 math classes. The number of students enrolled in each of the classes is displayed on the plot below. The outlier is a calculus class with only 7 students enrolled.

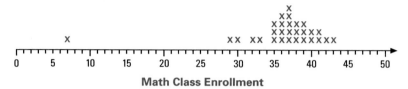

Math Class Enrollment

a. Jason computed the mean, both with and without the outlier. The two values were 35.97 and 37.00. Which value was computed with the outlier, and which was computed without the outlier?

b. Jason also computed the standard deviation, both with and without the outlier. The two values were 3.25 and 6.34. Which value was computed with the outlier, and which was computed without the outlier?

c. How many standard deviations below the mean is the enrollment in the calculus class when it is included in computing the mean and standard deviation? How many standard deviations below the mean is the enrollment in the calculus class when it is not included in the calculations?

d. Suppose five students drop out of each class. What will be the new mean and standard deviation if the calculus class is included in the computations?

Organizing

1. Match each of the following histograms of test scores in three classes, *A*, *B*, and *C*, to the best description of class performance.

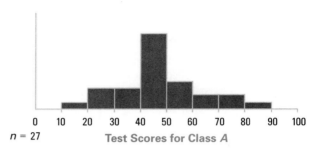

$n = 27$
Test Scores for Class *A*

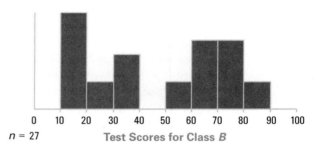

$n = 27$
Test Scores for Class *B*

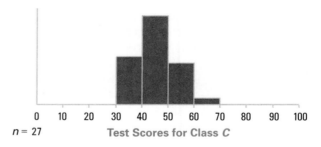

$n = 27$
Test Scores for Class *C*

a. The mean of the test scores is 46, and the standard deviation is 26.

b. The mean of the test scores is 46, and the standard deviation is 8.

c. The mean of the test scores is 46, and the standard deviation is 16.

Organizing

1. **a.** Class *B*
   b. Class *C*
   c. Class *A*

2. Responses will vary. One possible response is {0, 0, 0, 0, 0, 10, 10, 10, 10, 10} and {0, 5, 5, 5, 5, 5, 5, 5, 5, 10}. The mean for each data set is 5, and the range is 10. The standard deviations are 5 and 2.24, respectively.

3. **a.** $dx_1, dx_2, dx_3, dx_4, dx_5$

   b. $$\frac{dx_1 + dx_2 + dx_3 + dx_4 + dx_5}{5} = \frac{d(x_1 + x_2 + x_3 + x_4 + x_5)}{5}$$
   $$= d\left(\frac{x_1 + x_2 + x_3 + x_4 + x_5}{5}\right)$$
   $$= d\bar{x}$$

   c. $$SD = \sqrt{\frac{\Sigma(dx - d\bar{x})^2}{n}} = \sqrt{\frac{\Sigma d^2(x - \bar{x})^2}{n}} = d\sqrt{\frac{\Sigma(x - \bar{x})^2}{n}}$$

   d. It is d times the standard deviation of the original values.

   e. If each value in a data set is multiplied by a positive constant, then the mean and the standard deviation of the transformed data are d times the mean and standard deviation of the original data.

4. The new number should be 24 (the mean of the data set). Adding a value equal to the mean contributes 0 to the sum of squared differences. It is not possible to do better.

Reflecting

1. They are remarkably alike; both involve the square root of a sum of squared differences.

2. Different measures tell us different things. For example, the MAD tells us the average distance from the mean while the IQR tells us the range of the middle half of the data. In addition, different measures have different properties. For example, the median is resistant to outliers while the mean is not. Which measure we choose to use depends primarily on what we want to learn about the data.

3. "Deviation" is appropriate because the standard deviation measures differences or deviations from the mean. "Standard" could have resulted either from the fact that the standard deviation is the standard measure of spread or because the standard deviation is a typical (or standard) distance from the mean.

4. **a.** Responses will vary. You would like to have the standard deviations small in situations in which consistency is important: health test results, length and width of a manufactured part, the number of hours you sleep each night, and so on.

   b. Responses will vary. For example, you would like to be more than two standard deviations above the mean on a test, with your bowling score, or for the number of push-ups you can do in a given time. You would like to be two standard deviations below the mean with your golf score, the price you paid for something, your gas mileage, or the amount of time you spend waiting in line this year.

5. For the standard deviation to be zero, each deviation, $x - \bar{x}$, must be zero. Thus, each data value must be equal to the mean. In other words, all values in the data set must be the same.

2. Give an example of two data sets that each have the same number of values, the same mean, and the same range, but one data set has a standard deviation that is at least twice as big as the standard deviation of the other data set. Use at least eight data values.

3. In this task, you will examine symbolically the effect on the standard deviation of multiplying each of the values in a set of five pieces of data,

$$x_1, x_2, x_3, x_4, x_5,$$

by a positive number d.

   a. Suppose each of the five values in the set of data above is multiplied by the positive constant d. What are the transformed values?

   b. Let $\bar{x}$ be the mean of the original values. Compute the mean of the transformed values.

   c. Compute the standard deviation of the transformed values.

   d. How does the standard deviation of the transformed values compare to the standard deviation of the original values?

   e. Write an if-then statement of what you proved in Parts a through d.

4. Add one more number to the set {10, 20, 22, 32, 36} so the set has a standard deviation that is as small as possible. Explain your method.

Reflecting

1. How is the standard deviation formula like the distance formula?

2. Why is there more than one measure of center? More than one measure of variation?

3. Explain why "standard deviation" is a good name for this measure of variation.

4. Think about the meaning of a standard deviation.

   a. Describe two situations in which it would be important that the data values have a standard deviation as small as possible.

   b. Describe a situation in which you would like to be more than two standard deviations above the mean of all people. Describe a situation in which you would like to be more than two standard deviations below the mean of all people.

5. Under what conditions will the standard deviation of a data set be equal to 0? Explain your reasoning.

Extending

1. Runners in the Boston Marathon compete in divisions determined by age and gender. In a recent marathon, the mean time for the 18- to 39-year-old women's division was 225.31 minutes with a standard deviation of 26.64 minutes, and the mean time for the 50- to 59-year-old women's division was 242.58 minutes with a standard deviation of 21.78 minutes. In that marathon, a 57-year-old woman finished the race in 4:09:08 (hours:minutes:seconds), and a 34-year-old woman finished the race in 4:00:15.

   a. How many standard deviations above the mean for her division was each runner? Explain your reasoning.

   b. Write a formula that gives the number of standard deviations above the mean for a time of x minutes by a woman in the 50- to 59-year-old division.

   c. Does your formula from Part c also work for times below the mean? If not, adjust your formula.

   d. Write a formula that gives the number of standard deviations above or below the mean for a time of x minutes by a woman in the 18- to 39-year-old division.

2. A set of data consists of the numbers 2, 2, 2, 4, 7, 8, and 10. Here, the sample size, n, is 7, and the individual values that should be substituted for x in the following formulas are 2, 2, 2, 4, 7, 8, and 10.

   a. One at a time, substitute each measure of center (the mean, median, and mode) for C in the formula below. Which measure of center gives the smallest value?

   $$\sqrt{\frac{\sum (x - C)^2}{n}}$$

   b. One at a time, substitute each measure of center (the mean, median, and mode) for C in the formula below. Which measure of center gives the smallest value?

   $$\frac{\sum |x - C|}{n}$$

Extending

1. **a.** The 57-year-old woman was $\frac{249.13 - 242.58}{21.78}$ or approximately 0.30 standard deviations above the mean for her division. The 34-year-old woman was $\frac{240.25 - 225.31}{26.64}$ or approximately 0.56 standard deviations above the mean for her division.

   b. $\frac{x - 242.58}{21.78}$ = number of standard deviations x is above the mean

   c. Yes, the same formula will work. The answer will be negative, but that indicates that the score is below the mean.

   d. $\frac{x - 225.31}{26.64}$

2. The mean is 5, the median is 4, and the mode is 2.

   a. With $C = 5$, you get $\sqrt{\frac{66}{7}}$ or 3.07.

   With $C = 4$, you get $\sqrt{\frac{73}{7}}$ or 3.23.

   With $C = 2$, you get $\sqrt{\frac{129}{7}}$ or 4.29.

   The mean gives the smallest value.

   b. With $C = 5$, you get 2.86.

   With $C = 4$, you get 2.71.

   With $C = 2$, you get 3.

   The median gives the smallest value.

Unit 5

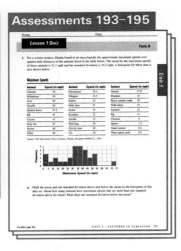

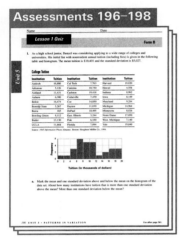

2. **c.** This formula counts the number of values in the data set that aren't equal to C.

With $C = 5$, the sum is 7.

With $C = 4$, the sum is 6.

With $C = 2$, the sum is 4.

The mode gives the smallest number.

d. If you use the measure of center that gives the smallest value, the mean is paired with the standard deviation, the median with the MAD, and the mode with the number of "errors" or nonzero deviations.

3. **a.** It is always true that $MAD \leq SD \leq \dfrac{range}{2}$.

b. All three measures are equal to 0 if all values in the data set are the same. They are also all equal with data sets like {0, 0, 0, 8, 8, 8} in which all points are the same distance from the mean.

4. **a.** (20, 20), (20, 40), (20, 90), (25, 20), (25, 40), (25, 90), (30, 20), (30, 40), (30, 90)

b. 40, 60, 110, 45, 65, 115, 50, 70, 120

c. SD ≈ 29.72

d. $883.\overline{3}$

e. Brand A: $(SD)^2 = 16.\overline{6}$

Brand B: $(SD)^2 = 866.\overline{6}$

$16.\overline{6} + 866.\overline{6} = 883.\overline{3}$

f. The sum of the variances is equal to the variance of the "sum." (This is always true, in fact, if the two selections are independent.)

g. Brand A: mean is 25.

Brand B: mean is 50.

Mean total is 75.

Yes, the sum of the means is equal to the mean of the "sum." (This is always true.)

h. Brand A: MAD is $\dfrac{10}{3}$ or $3.\overline{3}$.

Brand B: MAD is $\dfrac{80}{3}$ or $26.\overline{6}$.

Total MAD is $\dfrac{240}{9}$ or $26.\overline{6}$.

No, the sum of the MADs is not equal to the MAD of the "sum."

See Assessment Resources pages 193–198.

c. One at a time, substitute each measure of center (the mean, median, and mode) for C in the word formula below. What does this formula count? Which measure of center makes this count as small as possible?

> Start with a sum of 0.
>
> Look at each value of x.
>
> Add 0 to the sum if $x = C$.
>
> Add 1 to the sum if $x \neq C$.

d. Look over your answers to Parts a, b, and c. Which measures of center are paired with which measures of variation?

3. Compare the mean absolute deviation, standard deviation, and half the range.

   a. One of these measures is always smaller than or equal to the other two. One of the others is always larger than or equal to the other two. One is always in the middle. Which is which?

   b. Describe a situation in which all three measures of variation will be equal.

4. In this task, you will investigate one reason why the standard deviation is considered to be so important. The number of raisins in three boxes of Brand A raisins was counted, as was the number of raisins in three boxes of Brand B. The results are shown in the table below. Suppose you select one of the Brand A boxes and one of the Brand B boxes at random.

Raisin Box Contents	
Brand A	Brand B
20	20
25	40
30	90

a. List all nine of the possible pairs that you could get.

b. Compute the nine possible total numbers of raisins that you could get.

c. Compute the standard deviation of the total number of raisins.

d. Square this standard deviation. The square of the standard deviation is called the **variance**.

e. Compute the variance of the three boxes of Brand A. Compute the variance of the three boxes of Brand B. Add these two variances.

f. What can you conclude?

g. Can you add the mean of Brand A to the mean of Brand B to get the mean of the total?

h. Can you add the mean absolute deviation of Brand A to the mean absolute deviation of Brand B to get the mean absolute deviation of the total?

Lesson 2 — *The Normal Distribution*

In a science class, you may have weighed something by balancing it on a scale against a standard weight. To be sure the standard weight is reasonably accurate, its manufacturer can have it weighed at the National Institute of Standards and Technology in Washington, D.C. The accuracy of the weighing procedure at the National Institute of Standards and Technology is itself checked about once a week by weighing a known 10-gram weight, NB 10. The histogram below is based on 100 consecutive measurements of the weight of NB 10 using the same apparatus and procedure. Shown is the distribution of weighings, in micrograms *below* 10 grams. (A microgram is a millionth of a gram.) Examine this histogram and the two that follow for common features.

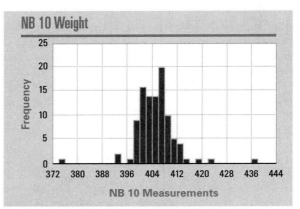

Source: Freedman, David, et al. *Statistics*, 3rd edition. New York: W. W. Norton & Company, 1998.

At the left is a picture of a device called a *quincunx*. Small balls are dropped into the device and fall through several levels of pins, which cause the balls to bounce left or right at each level. The balls are collected in columns at the bottom forming a distribution like the one shown.

The histogram at the top of the next page shows the political points of view of a sample of 1,271 voters in the United States in 1976. The voters were asked a series of questions to determine their political philosophy and then rated on a scale from liberal to conservative.

Lesson 2 *The Normal Distribution*

LESSON OVERVIEW Lesson 2 introduces students to the normal distribution and its characteristics. In a normal distribution, most values are clustered near the mean with values trailing off at each end of the distribution. In a normal distribution, the mean and median are the same, and the distribution is symmetric around the mean. Students are given three benchmarks for the distribution: 68%, 95%, and 99.7% of the data should be within one, two, and three standard deviations of the mean, respectively.

   Be aware that students tend to use the 68%-95%-99.7% rule on all distributions, not just the normal distributions for which it is valid. Activity 9 of Investigation 1 will remind them that other distributions are possible.

Lesson Objectives

■ To recognize that in a normal distribution, 68% of the data are within one standard deviation of the mean, 95% are within two standard deviations, and 99.7% are within three standard deviations of the mean

■ To describe characteristics of a normal distribution, such as its symmetry and the relationship between the mean and median

■ To understand that the number of standard deviations from the mean is a measure of location

■ To use a table of the normal distribution

LAUNCH full-class discussion

Think About This Situation

See Teaching Masters 131a–131b.

Show students each of the three distributions on the overhead projector, if you have one. Be sure that students understand that, although the distributions look different, they actually have the same general shape. To transform one into another, all you have to do is translate so that the means coincide and then stretch or shrink the distribution so that the standard deviations are the same. If you know a distribution is normal and you have its mean and standard deviation, then the distribution is uniquely determined. See Extending Task 4 on page 381.

ⓐ They all have the same basic shape although the means and standard deviations are different. The measures of the perimeters from Lesson 1 may have been approximately normal.

ⓑ Students might suggest heights of people the same age of one gender, SAT scores, IQ scores, grade point averages, heights of plants, or a variety of other things. In Lesson 1, students saw that many repeated measurements of the same object tend to be normally distributed. Distributions that students may suggest that are not normal include:

■ the distribution of heights of young men and young women together, which can be bimodal and not a normal distribution;

■ the distribution of people's weights, which is skewed right.

ⓒ Repeated measurements of the same thing are often normally distributed, as are many physical characteristics. Conversely, if we know the mean and standard deviation of a normal distribution, we can give the probability of getting a measurement in a given range. (As students will learn in this lesson, you can use the number of standard deviations from the mean to estimate how unusual (or rare) an event is.)

EXPLORE small-group investigation

INVESTIGATION 1 ► Characteristics of the Normal Distribution

In this investigation students learn the percentage of values within 1, 2, and 3 standard deviations from the mean for approximately normal distributions. They also distinguish between the sample and population standard deviations.

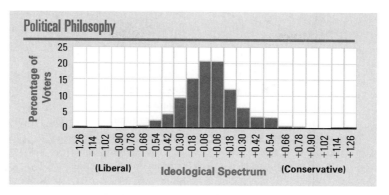

Political Philosophy

Source: Romer, Thomas, and Howard Rosenthal. 1984. Voting models and empirical evidence. *American Scientist*, 72: 465-473.

Think About This Situation

Compare the histogram above and the two on the previous page.

a What do the three distributions have in common? What other distributions have you seen in this unit or in other units that have approximately the same overall shape?

b What other sets of data might have this same shape?

c How might understanding this shape be helpful in studying variation?

INVESTIGATION 1 ▸ Characteristics of the Normal Distribution

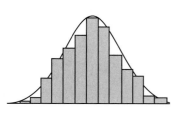

Many naturally occurring characteristics, such as human heights or the lengths or weights of supposedly identical objects produced by machines, are approximately **normally distributed**. Their histograms are "bell-shaped," with the data clustered symmetrically about the mean and tapering off gradually on both ends.

In this lesson, you will explore how the standard deviation is related to normal distributions. In Lesson 3, you will see how this relationship is used in industry to study the variability in a quality control process. In these lessons, as in the "Modeling Public Opinion" unit, distinguishing between a population and a sample taken from that population is important. The symbol for the mean of a population is μ, the lower case Greek letter "mu." As in the case of $\bar{x}$, the mean of a sample, it is calculated by dividing the sum of the data values by n, the number of values.

There are two types of standard deviation on many calculators and statistical software: σ (lower case Greek letter "sigma") and s. Like μ, the standard deviation σ is used for a population; that is, compute σ when you have all the values from a particular population or you have a theoretical distribution. The standard deviation s is used for a sample; that is, compute s when you have only some of the values from the population. The formulas for σ and s differ in only one small way. When computing σ, you divide by n. When computing s, you divide by $(n-1)$. (A technical argument shows that dividing by $n-1$ makes s^2, for the sample, a better estimate of σ^2, for the population from which the sample was drawn.) You will gain some experience interpreting and calculating the sample standard deviation s in the activities that follow.

The first three activities provide data about weights of nickels, heights of women in a college course, and the times for a solute to dissolve. Your teacher will assign one of the three activities to your group. Study your distribution and think about its characteristics. Be prepared to share and compare your group's results with the rest of the class.

1. **Weights of Nickels** The data below and the accompanying histogram give the weights, to the nearest hundredth of a gram, of a sample of 100 new nickels. The mean weight is 4.9941 grams and the standard deviation s is approximately 0.0551 gram.

Nickel Weights (in grams)

4.87	4.92	4.95	4.97	4.98	5.00	5.01	5.03	5.04	5.07
4.87	4.92	4.95	4.97	4.98	5.00	5.01	5.03	5.04	5.07
4.88	4.93	4.95	4.97	4.99	5.00	5.01	5.03	5.04	5.07
4.89	4.93	4.95	4.97	4.99	5.00	5.02	5.03	5.05	5.08
4.90	4.93	4.95	4.97	4.99	5.00	5.02	5.03	5.05	5.08
4.90	4.93	4.96	4.97	4.99	5.01	5.02	5.03	5.05	5.09
4.91	4.94	4.96	4.98	4.99	5.01	5.02	5.03	5.06	5.09
4.91	4.94	4.96	4.98	4.99	5.01	5.02	5.04	5.06	5.10
4.92	4.94	4.96	4.98	5.00	5.01	5.02	5.04	5.06	5.11
4.92	4.94	4.96	4.98	5.00	5.01	5.02	5.04	5.06	5.11

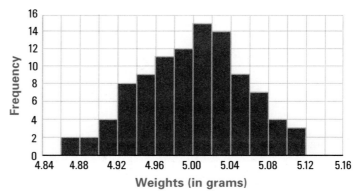

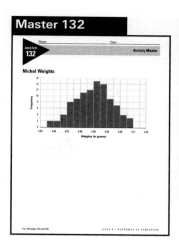

Master 132

The reason for the distinction between σ and s is quite technical. Standard practice is to use σ (dividing by n) for the standard deviation of a population and for the standard deviation of a theoretical distribution. For a sample, the sample standard deviation s is used. Usually, the standard deviation of a sample is computed in order to estimate the standard deviation of the population. Dividing by $n - 1$ makes the variance (the square of the standard deviation) an unbiased estimate of the variance of the population. That means that the average value of the variances of all possible samples from a given population (dividing by $n - 1$) is exactly equal to the variance of the population. If you divide by n to compute the sample variance, then it tends, on average, to be too small. (It is impossible to get an unbiased estimate of both the standard deviation and the variance at the same time.)

For a proof that s^2 is an unbiased estimator of σ^2, see "Why $n - 1$ in the Formula for the Sample Standard Deviation?" by Stephen A. Book, *The College Mathematics Journal* 10 (1979): 330–333.

Each group of students should investigate exactly one of the three situations in the text (Activities 1–3). Have the groups report their results to the rest of the class. Allow groups to choose the activity, but try to assure that each activity is done by at least two groups. Based on these three distributions, the class will then make conjectures about the characteristics of a normal distribution.

1. See Teaching Master 132.

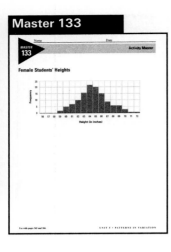

1. a. The mean is given as 4.9941 grams, and the median is 5.0 grams. The mean and the median are almost exactly the same. They vary by only 0.0059 gram.

b. Students should place marks at 4.8288, 4.8839, 4.9390, 5.0492, 5.1043, and 5.1594 as shown below.

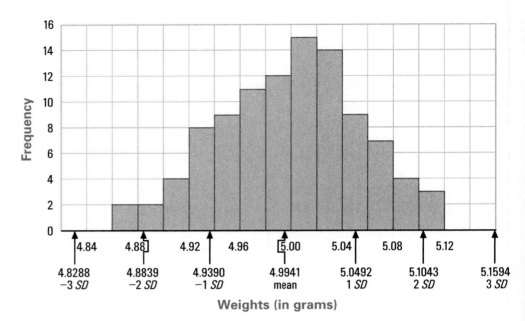

c. $\frac{67}{100}$ = 67% of the nickels are within one standard deviation of the mean.

$\frac{95}{100}$ = 95% of the nickels are within two standard deviations of the mean.

100% of the nickels are within three standard deviations of the mean.

d. 0.95

2. See Teaching Master 133.

a. How do the mean weight and the median weight compare?

b. On a copy of the histogram, mark points along the horizontal axis that correspond to the mean, one standard deviation above the mean, one standard deviation below the mean, two standard deviations above the mean, two standard deviations below the mean, three standard deviations above the mean, and three standard deviations below the mean.

c. What percentage of the data are within one standard deviation of the mean? Within two standard deviations? Within three standard deviations?

d. Suppose you weigh a randomly chosen nickel from this collection. Find the probability its weight would be within two standard deviations of the mean.

2. Heights of Female Students The table and histogram below give the heights of 123 women in a statistics class at Penn State University in the 1970s. The mean height of the women in this sample is approximately 64.626 inches, and the standard deviation s is approximately 2.606 inches.

Female Students' Heights

Height (inches)	Frequency	Height (inches)	Frequency
59	2	66	15
60	5	67	9
61	7	68	6
62	10	69	6
63	16	70	3
64	22	71	1
65	20	72	1

Source: Joiner, Brian L. 1975. Living histograms. *International Statistical Review* 3: 339–340.

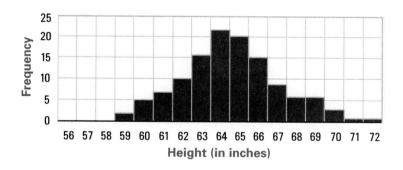

a. How do the mean and the median of the women's heights compare?

b. On a copy of the histogram, mark points along the horizontal axis that correspond to the mean, one standard deviation above the mean, one standard deviation below the mean, two standard deviations above the mean, two standard deviations below the mean, three standard deviations above the mean, and three standard deviations below the mean.

c. What percentage of the data are within one standard deviation of the mean? Within two standard deviations? Within three standard deviations?

d. Suppose you pick a female student from the class at random. Find the probability that her height would be within two standard deviations of the mean.

3. **Dissolution Times** For a chemistry experiment, students measured the time for a solute to dissolve. The experiment was repeated 50 times. The results are shown in the following chart and histogram. The mean time for the 50 experiments is 11.8 seconds, and the standard deviation s is approximately 3.32 seconds.

Dissolution Time (in seconds)

12	10	10	12	17	10	13	11	12	17
10	6	5	16	8	8	15	7	11	10
14	14	9	14	19	4	16	9	12	19
12	13	11	14	13	12	9	11	14	15
8	8	11	13	10	12	13	12	12	17

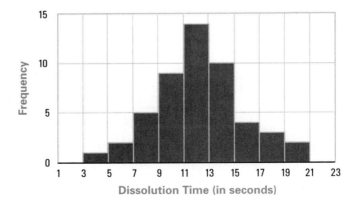

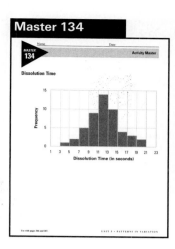

2. a. The mean is given as 64.626 inches, and the median is about 64 inches. They differ by only 0.626 inch. Note, however, that the tallest person categorized as 64 inches may be as tall as 64.49 inches, so the difference is most likely even smaller.

b. Students should place arrows at 56.808, 59.414, 62.020, 67.232, 69.838, and 72.444 as shown below.

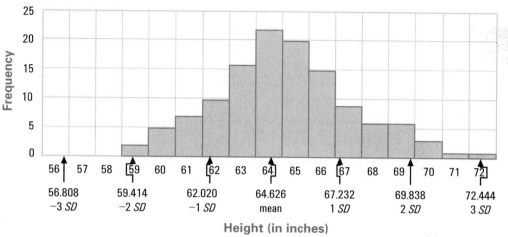

c. Approximately $\frac{82}{123}$ or 67% are within one standard deviation of the mean.

Approximately $\frac{116}{123}$ or 94% are within two standard deviations of the mean.

Approximately 100% are within three standard deviations of the mean.

d. 0.94

3. **See Teaching Master 134.**

This is the actual data from a chemistry lab. Like the two previous distributions, the data are only approximately normal.

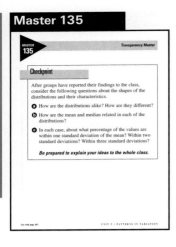

EXPLORE *continued*

3. **a.** The mean is given as 11.8 seconds, and the median is 12. Again, the mean and the median are very close, which is what we would expect from a distribution that is nearly symmetric.

b. Students should place arrows at 1.84, 5.16, 8.48, 15.12, 18.44, and 21.76 as shown below.

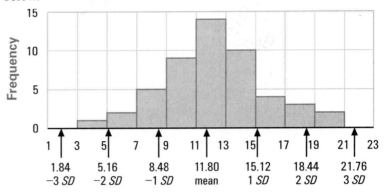

c. Approximately $\frac{35}{50}$ or 70% of the data are within one standard deviation of the mean; approximately $\frac{46}{50}$ or 92% of the data are within two standard deviations of the mean; and 100% of the data are within three standard deviations of the mean.

d. 0.92

SHARE AND SUMMARIZE   full-class discussion

Checkpoint

See Teaching Master 135.

ⓐ They both have an approximately normal shape and 67%–70% of the values within one standard deviation of the mean, 92%–95% of the values within two standard deviations of the mean, and all of the values within three standard deviations of the mean. Each has a different mean and standard deviation.

ⓑ They are approximately equal. We would expect this with distributions that are nearly symmetric.

ⓒ About 68%, 95%, and 100%, respectively.

MORE
ASSIGNMENT   *pp. 375–383*

Students can now begin Organizing Task 1 from the MORE assignment following Investigation 2.

NOTE: In the class discussion following the "On Your Own" task, be sure that students understand that σ and s are almost the same given a large n.

APPLY   individual task

▶ **On Your Own**

a. s is larger. The only difference in the two formulas is that you divide by n to compute σ and by $n - 1$ to compute s. Since dividing by a smaller number makes the quotient larger, s is larger than σ for any given data set.

b. $\sigma = \sqrt{\frac{1,500}{15}} = 10$ $s = \sqrt{\frac{1,500}{14}} \approx 10.35$

$\sigma = \sqrt{\frac{1,500}{100}} \approx 3.87$ $s = \sqrt{\frac{1,500}{99}} \approx 3.89$

If n is large, the values of σ and s are almost the same. Even if n isn't very large, σ and s don't vary a lot.

a. How do the mean and the median of the times compare?

b. On a copy of the histogram, mark points along the horizontal axis that correspond to the mean, one standard deviation above the mean, one standard deviation below the mean, two standard deviations above the mean, two standard deviations below the mean, three standard deviations above the mean, and three standard deviations below the mean.

c. What percentage of the data are within one standard deviation of the mean? Within two standard deviations? Within three standard deviations?

d. Suppose you repeat this experiment. Estimate the probability that the time for the solute to dissolve will be within two standard deviations of the mean.

Checkpoint

After groups have reported their findings to the class, consider the following questions about the shapes of the distributions and their characteristics.

ⓐ How are the distributions alike? How are they different?

ⓑ How are the mean and median related in each of the distributions?

ⓒ In each case, about what percentage of the values are within one standard deviation of the mean? Within two standard deviations? Within three standard deviations?

Be prepared to explain your ideas to the whole class.

On Your Own

If the set of data is the entire population you are interested in studying, you use σ, the population standard deviation. If you are looking at the set of data as a sample from a larger population of data, you use s. (See page 364.)

a. For a given set of data, which is larger: σ or s? Explain your reasoning.

b. Suppose you are computing the standard deviation, and the sum of the squared differences is 1,500. Assume there are 15 values and find σ and s. Assume there are 100 values and find σ and s. What do you conclude?

All normal distributions have the same overall shape, differing only in mean μ and standard deviation σ. Some look tall and skinny; others look more spread out. All normal distributions, however, have certain characteristics in common. They are symmetric about the mean; 68% of the data values lie within one standard deviation of the mean; 95% of the data values lie within two standard deviations of the mean; and 99.7% of the data values lie within three standard deviations of the mean. The distributions in Activities 1 through 3 were *approximately normal*. Each was a sample taken from a larger population that is more nearly normal.

4. The normal distribution shown here has mean μ of 125 and standard deviation σ of 8.

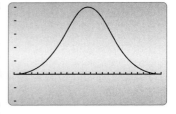

   a. On three copies of this distribution, mark points along the horizontal axis that correspond to the mean, one standard deviation above and below the mean, two standard deviations above and below the mean, and three standard deviations above and below the mean.

   b. On one copy of the distribution, shade and label the region under the curve that represents 68% of the data values.

   c. On another copy of the distribution, shade and label the region that represents 95% of the data values.

   d. On the third copy of the distribution, shade and label the region that corresponds to 99.7% of the data values.

   e. Compare your graphs to those of other groups. Resolve any differences.

5. Suppose that the distribution of the weights of newly minted nickels is a normal distribution with mean μ of 5 grams and standard deviation σ of 0.10 gram.

   a. Draw a sketch of this distribution and label the points on the horizontal axis that correspond to the mean, one standard deviation above and below the mean, two standard deviations above and below the mean, and three standard deviations above and below the mean.

   b. What can you conclude about the middle 68% of the weights of these newly minted nickels? About the middle 95% of the weights? About the middle 99.7% of the weights?

   c. Explain or illustrate your answers in Part b in terms of your sketch.

6. Think about the overall shape of a normal distribution as you answer the following questions. Then draw sketches illustrating your answers.

   a. What percentage of the values in a normal distribution lie above the mean?

   b. What percentage of the values in a normal distribution lie more than two standard deviations away from the mean?

   c. What percentage of the values in a normal distribution lie more than two standard deviations above the mean?

   d. What percentage of the values in a normal distribution lie more than one standard deviation away from the mean?

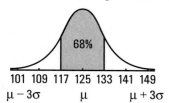 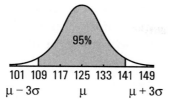 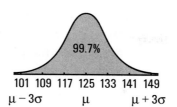

4. See Teaching Master 136.

5. a.

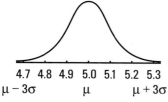

b. 68% of the nickels weigh between 4.9 and 5.1 grams; 95% of the nickels weigh between 4.8 and 5.2 grams; and 99.7% of the nickels weigh between 4.7 and 5.3 grams.

c.

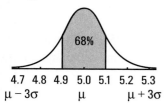 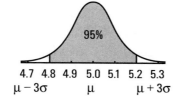 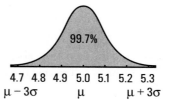

6. a. 50%   **b.** 5%

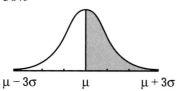 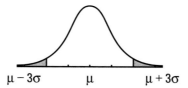

c. 2.5%   **d.** 100% − 68% = 32%

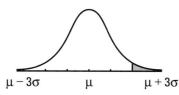 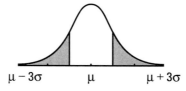

7. The standard deviation for Figure B is approximately 1 because it is about half the standard deviation of Figure A. The standard deviation for Figure C is approximately 5 because it is about 2.5 times the standard deviation of Figure A.

8. **a.** **Notice that the distribution of weights of babies at either age is approximately normally distributed, while the distribution of adults' weights is skewed right.**

Distribution of Weights of Baby Boys

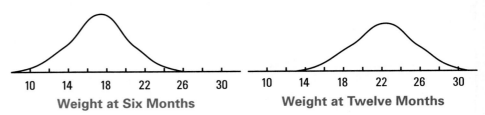

Weight at Six Months   Weight at Twelve Months

The shapes are similar since both distributions are normal. The distribution of weights at twelve months has a higher mean and is spread out slightly more than the distribution at six months.

b. 26.9 pounds is two standard deviations above the mean, so about 2.5% of twelve-month-old boys weigh more than 26.9 pounds.

c. 15.25 pounds is one standard deviation below the mean and 19.25 pounds is one standard deviation above the mean. Thus, about 68% of the weights of six-month-old boys fall in this interval.

d. 24.7 pounds is one standard deviation above the mean, so about 84% of the weights are below this. The baby is in the 84th percentile.

e. This weight is two standard deviations above the mean. Thus, the baby is at about the 98th percentile.

7. Three very large sets of data have approximately normal distributions, each with a mean of 10. Sketches of the overall shapes of the distributions are shown below. The scale on the horizontal axis is the same in each case. The standard deviation of the distribution in Figure A is 2. Estimate the standard deviations of the distributions in Figures B and C.

Figure A   **Figure B**   **Figure C**

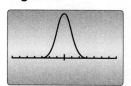 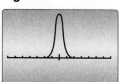 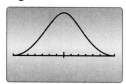

8. The weights of babies of a given age and gender are approximately normally distributed. This fact allows a doctor or nurse to use a baby's weight to find the weight percentile to which the child belongs. The table below gives information about the weights of six-month-old and twelve-month-old baby boys.

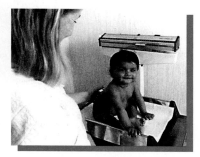

Weights of Baby Boys

	Weight at Six Months (in pounds)	Weight at Twelve Months (in pounds)
Mean μ	17.25	22.50
Standard Deviation σ	2.0	2.2

Source: Tannenbaum, Peter, and Robert Arnold. *Excursions in Modern Mathematics*. Englewood Cliffs, New Jersey: Prentice Hall. 1992.

a. On separate sets of axes with the same scales, draw sketches that represent the distribution of weights for six-month-old boys and the distribution of weights for twelve-month-old boys. How do the distributions differ?

b. About what percentage of twelve-month-old boys weigh more than 26.9 pounds?

c. About what percentage of six-month-old boys weigh between 15.25 pounds and 19.25 pounds?

d. A twelve-month-old boy who weighs 24.7 pounds is at what percentile for weight?

e. A six-month-old boy who weighs 21.25 pounds is at what percentile?

9. The producers of a movie did a survey of the ages of the people attending one screening of the movie. The data are shown here in the table and histogram.

Saturday Night at the Movies	
Age	Frequency
12	2
13	26
14	38
15	32
16	22
17	10
18	8
19	8
20	6
21	4
22	1
23	3
27	2
32	2
40	1

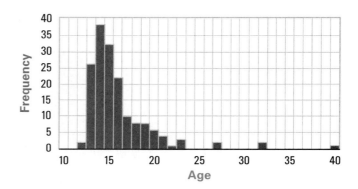

a. Compute the mean and standard deviation for these data. Find a way to do this without entering each of the individual ages (for example, entering the age "14" thirty-eight times) into a calculator or computer software.

b. What percentage of values fall within one standard deviation of the mean? Within two standard deviations of the mean? Within three standard deviations of the mean?

c. Compare the percentages from Part b to those from a normal distribution. Explain your findings in terms of the shapes of the two distributions.

d. What kind of a movie do you think was playing?

9. **This activity reminds students that not all distributions are normal.**

a. The mean age is 16 years, and the standard deviation is 3.7 years. The mean can be found using the formula $\bar{x} = \frac{\sum xf}{n}$, where n is 165 and each value of x is multiplied by its frequency f. The corresponding formula for the standard deviation is $s = \sqrt{\frac{\sum (x - \bar{x})^2 f}{n - 1}}$. Also, many calculators and computer software will calculate these values using two data lists, one being the frequencies of the other.

b. The percentage of ages that fall within one, two, and three standard deviations of the mean are approximately 87.3%, 97%, and 98%, respectively.

c. The ages are not normally distributed. This can best be seen from the plot of the data. The histogram is not symmetric. For example, only $\frac{67}{165}$ or approximately 40.6% of the ages lie at or above the mean. The 87.3% of ages within one standard deviation of the mean is quite a bit more than the 68% of ages that would be within one standard deviation of the mean in any normal distribution.

d. Student responses will vary. The movie playing appeals to high school students; the attendees may also have been some type of youth group accompanied by parents, with a few extra young adults (perhaps younger siblings) in attendance also.

Master 137

MASTER 137   Transparency Master

Checkpoint

In this investigation, you examined connections between the overall shape of a distribution and its mean and standard deviation.

a Describe and illustrate with sketches some of the characteristics of a normal distribution.

b Estimate the mean and the standard deviation of this normal distribution. Explain how you found your estimate. The scale on the horizontal axis is 5 units per tick mark.

Be prepared to explain your ideas to the entire class.

SHARE AND SUMMARIZE full-class discussion

Checkpoint

See Teaching Master 137.

ⓐ A normal distribution is symmetric with 68% of values within one standard deviation of the mean, 95% within two standard deviations, and 99.7% within three standard deviations:

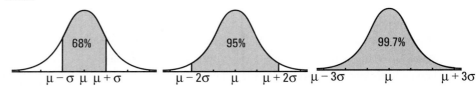

ⓑ The mean is clearly 10; estimates of the standard deviation should be around 3.5 but may vary. Explanations may vary but should refer to the percentage of data values that fall in a given interval for a normal distribution. One possible response is the following: Mark the points on the number line that are symmetrical about the mean and between which about 95% of the values fall. These points fall at about 3 and 17. Divide the distance between these two points by 4. That gives $\frac{14}{4}$ or 3.5 for an estimate of the standard deviation.

CONSTRUCTING A MATH TOOLKIT: Following the Checkpoint discussion, students should write in their toolkits a description of the normal distribution and illustrate with sketches the percentages of the data within each standard deviation as in Part a of the Checkpoint.

JOURNAL ENTRY: When examining the graph of a distribution, what characteristics might lead you to conclude that it is not a normal distribution? Give some examples.

MORE
ASSIGNMENT   pp. 375–383

Students can now begin Reflecting Task 1, 2, or 4 or Extending Task 1 from the MORE assignment following Investigation 2.

APPLY   individual task

▶On Your Own

a. 68%
b. $\frac{1}{2}(32\%) = 16\%$
c. $100\% - 16\% = 84\%$

EXPLORE   small-group investigation

INVESTIGATION 2 Standardizing Scores

In the previous investigation, students learned a rule of thumb about normal distributions:

68% of the values lie within one standard deviation of the mean,

95% of the values lie within two standard deviations of the mean, and

99.7% of the values lie within three standard deviations of the mean.

See additional Teaching Notes on page T419D.

Checkpoint

In this investigation, you examined connections between the overall shape of a distribution and its mean and standard deviation.

ⓐ Describe and illustrate with sketches some of the characteristics of a normal distribution.

ⓑ Estimate the mean and the standard deviation of this normal distribution. Explain how you found your estimate. The scale on the horizontal axis is 5 units per tick mark.

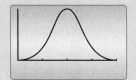

Be prepared to explain your ideas to the entire class.

▶On Your Own

Scores on the verbal section of the SAT I are approximately normally distributed with mean μ of 500 and standard deviation σ of 100.

a. What percentage of students score between 400 and 600 on the verbal section of the SAT I?

b. What percentage of students score over 600 on the verbal section of the SAT I?

c. What percentage of students score less than 600 on the verbal section of the SAT I?

INVESTIGATION 2 Standardizing Scores

In a previous course, you learned how to describe the location of a value in a distribution by giving its *percentile*, that is, the percentage of values that are smaller than or equal to the one given. In this investigation, you will explore how to use the standard deviation to describe the location of a value in a distribution that is normal, or approximately so.

1. Examine the chart below, which gives approximate information about the heights of young Americans aged 18 to 24. Each distribution is approximately normal.

Heights of American Young Adults

	Men	Women
Mean μ	68.5"	65.5"
Standard Deviation σ	2.7"	2.5"

a. Sketch the two distributions. Include a scale on the horizontal axis.

b. What can you conclude about the following?

- The percentage of young adult American women who are within one standard deviation of the average in height.
- The percentage of young adult American men who are within one standard deviation of the average in height.
- The percentage of young adult American women who are within two standard deviations of the average in height.
- The percentage of young adult American men who are within two standard deviations of the average in height.

c. On what assumptions are your conclusions in Part b based?

d. Alex is 3 standard deviations above average in height. How tall is she?

e. Miguel is 2.1 standard deviations below average in height. How tall is he?

f. Marcus is 74" tall. How many standard deviations above average height is he?

g. Jackie is 62" tall. How many standard deviations below average height is she?

h. Mary is 68" tall. Steve is 71" tall. Who is relatively taller for her or his gender, Mary or Steve? Explain your reasoning.

The **standardized value** or **z-score** is the number of standard deviations a given value lies from the mean. For example, in Activity 1 Part d, since Alex is 3 standard deviations *above* average in height, the z-score for her height is 3. Similarly, in Activity 1 Part e, since Miguel is 2.1 standard deviations *below* average in height, the z-score for his height is –2.1.

2. Look more generally at how standardized values are computed.

a. Compute the standardized values for Marcus's height and for Jackie's height.

b. Write a formula for computing the standardized value z of a data point if you know the value of the data point x, the mean of the population μ, and the standard deviation of the population σ.

3. Now consider how standardizing scores can help you make comparisons.

a. Find the standardized value for the height of a young woman who is 5' tall.

b. Find the standardized value for the height of a young man who is 5'2" tall.

c. Is the young woman in Part a or the young man in Part b shorter, relative to his or her own gender?

1. a.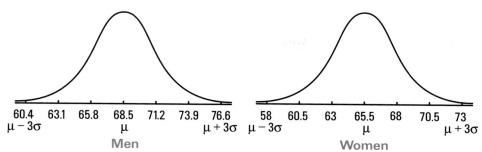

   Heights of American Young Adults

60.4	63.1	65.8	68.5	71.2	73.9	76.6
$\mu - 3\sigma$			μ			$\mu + 3\sigma$

   Men

58	60.5	63	65.5	68	70.5	73
$\mu - 3\sigma$			μ			$\mu + 3\sigma$

   Women

   b. ■ 68%; 68%

   ■ 95%; 95%

   c. The assumption is that the distributions are normal.

   d. $65.5" + 3(2.5") = 73"$

   e. $68.5" - 2.1(2.7") = 62.83"$

   f. $\frac{74 - 68.5}{2.7} \approx 2.04$

   g. $\frac{62 - 65.5}{2.5} = -1.4$ or 1.4 standard deviations below average

   h. Mary is $\frac{68 - 65.5}{2.5}$ or 1 standard deviation above average, and Steve is $\frac{71 - 68.5}{2.7}$ or approximately 0.926 standard deviation above average. Mary is relatively taller than Steve is because her height is farther above the mean as measured by the standard deviation for the appropriate distribution.

2. a. Marcus: $z = \frac{74 - 68.5}{2.7} \approx 2.04$; Jackie: $z = \frac{62 - 65.5}{2.5} = -1.4$

   b. $z = \frac{x - \mu}{\sigma}$

3. a. $z = \frac{60 - 65.5}{2.5} = -2.2$

   b. $z = \frac{62 - 68.5}{2.7} \approx -2.41$

   c. The young man is relatively shorter because he is farther below the mean of his distribution as measured by the standard deviation than the young woman is from the mean of her distribution.

Unit 5

Unit 5

The following table gives the proportion of values in a normal distribution that are less than the given standardized value z.

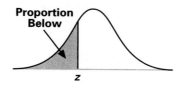

Proportion Below

Proportion of Values Below Standardized Value

z	Proportion Below	z	Proportion Below	z	Proportion Below
−3.5	0.0002	−1.1	0.1357	1.3	0.9032
−3.4	0.0003	−1.0	0.1587	1.4	0.9192
−3.3	0.0005	−0.9	0.1841	1.5	0.9332
−3.2	0.0007	−0.8	0.2119	1.6	0.9452
−3.1	0.0010	−0.7	0.2420	1.7	0.9554
−3.0	0.0013	−0.6	0.2743	1.8	0.9641
−2.9	0.0019	−0.5	0.3085	1.9	0.9713
−2.8	0.0026	−0.4	0.3446	2.0	0.9772
−2.7	0.0035	−0.3	0.3821	2.1	0.9821
−2.6	0.0047	−0.2	0.4207	2.2	0.9861
−2.5	0.0062	−0.1	0.4602	2.3	0.9893
−2.4	0.0082	0.0	0.5000	2.4	0.9918
−2.3	0.0107	0.1	0.5398	2.5	0.9938
−2.2	0.0139	0.2	0.5793	2.6	0.9953
−2.1	0.0179	0.3	0.6179	2.7	0.9965
−2.0	0.0228	0.4	0.6554	2.8	0.9974
−1.9	0.0287	0.5	0.6915	2.9	0.9981
−1.8	0.0359	0.6	0.7257	3.0	0.9987
−1.7	0.0446	0.7	0.7580	3.1	0.9990
−1.6	0.0548	0.8	0.7881	3.2	0.9993
−1.5	0.0668	0.9	0.8159	3.3	0.9995
−1.4	0.0808	1.0	0.8413	3.4	0.9997
−1.3	0.0968	1.1	0.8643	3.5	0.9998
−1.2	0.1151	1.2	0.8849		

LESSON 2 • THE NORMAL DISTRIBUTION   **373**

4. As you complete this activity, think about the relation between the table entries and the graph of a normal distribution.

  a. If a value from a normal distribution is 2 standard deviations below the mean, what percentage of the values are below it? Above it? Draw sketches illustrating your answers.

  b. If a value from a normal distribution is 1.3 standard deviations above the mean, what percentage of the values are below it? Above it? Illustrate your answers with sketches.

  c. Based on the table, what percentage of values are within one standard deviation of the mean? Within two standard deviations of the mean? Within three standard deviations of the mean? What do you notice?

5. Now practice converting between heights and percentiles for Americans aged 18 to 24.

  a. Marcus is 74" tall. What is Marcus's percentile for height? (That is, what percentage of young men are the same height or shorter than Marcus?)

  b. Jackie is 62" tall. What is Jackie's percentile for height?

  c. Abby is 68" tall. What percentage of young women are between Jackie (Part b) and Abby in height?

  d. Cesar is at the 20th percentile in height. What is his height?

6. There are different scales for Intelligence Quotients (IQs). Scores on the Wechsler Intelligence Scale for Children are (within each age group) approximately normally distributed with a mean of 100 and standard deviation of 15.

  a. Draw a sketch of the distribution of these scores, with a marked scale on the horizontal axis.

  b. What percentage of children of a given age group have IQs above 150?

  c. What IQ score would be at the 50th percentile?

  d. Javier's IQ was at the 75th percentile. What was his IQ score on this test?

Checkpoint

Think about the meaning and use of standardized values.

a What is the purpose of standardizing scores?

b Kua earned a grade of 50 on a normally distributed test with a mean of 45 and a standard deviation of 10. On another normally distributed test with a mean of 70 and a standard deviation of 15, she earned a 78. On which of the two tests did she do better, relative to the others who took the tests? Explain your reasoning.

c How would your reasoning for Part b change if the distributions weren't normal?

Be prepared to explain your thinking to the entire class.

4. **See Teaching Master 138.**

   a. $0.0228 = 2.28\%$ $1 - 0.0228 = 97.72\%$

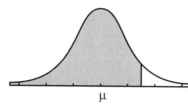 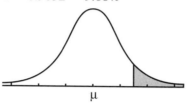

   b. $0.9032 = 90.32\%$ $1 - 0.9032 = 9.68\%$

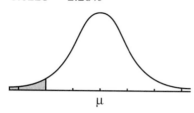 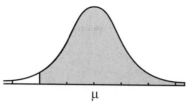

   c. 68.26%; 95.44%; 99.74%

      The values we used before, 68%, 95%, and 99.7%, are rounded from these values.

5. **a.** The standardized value for Marcus' height is approximately 2.0. This gives a percentile for height of about 97.72.

   b. The standardized value for Jackie's height is approximately -1.4. This gives a percentile for height of about 8.08.

   c. For Abby, $z = \frac{68 - 65.5}{2.5} = 1$. Her percentile is 84.13.

      So $84.13 - 8.08$ or 76.05% of young women are between Jackie and Abby in height.

   d. His z-score is closest to -0.8. Solve $-0.8 = \frac{x - 68.5}{2.7}$ to find that Cesar's height is about 66.34".

6. **a.** See the graph at the right.

   b. $z = \frac{150 - 100}{15} \approx 3.3$

      So $1 - 0.9995$ or 0.05% of children have scores above 150.

   c. 100

   d. His z-score is about 0.7. Solve $0.7 = \frac{x - 100}{15}$ to find Javier's score was about 110.5.

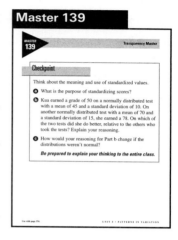

SHARE AND SUMMARIZE   full-class discussion

Checkpoint

See Teaching Master 139.

  ⓐ A standardized score tells us how many standard deviations from the mean the original score lies. When the distribution is normal, you can use the table on page 373 to find the percentile for the original score. Standardizing scores helps make comparisons between original scores from two normal distributions that have different means and/or standard deviations.

  ⓑ For the first test, $z = \frac{50 - 45}{10} = 0.5$. For the second test, $z = \frac{78 - 70}{15} \approx 0.53$. Kua's z-score and percentile ranking are higher for the second test, so she did better on it, relative to the other students.

  ⓒ If the distributions weren't normal, it would be possible for Kua to be in a higher percentile on the first test or on the second test.

CONSTRUCTING A MATH TOOLKIT: Students should explain the purpose of standardized scores in their Math Toolkits and provide an example using the formula they developed in this investigation.

ASSIGNMENT   *pp. 375–383*

APPLY   individual task

▶On Your Own

a. Her score was $\frac{608-462}{100}$ or 1.46 standard deviations above average.

b. Her percentile was about 93.

c. No.

d. Jim's standardized score is $\frac{75-100}{15}$ or approximately -1.7. Jim would not be considered to have even mild mental retardation.

e. $1 - 0.0446 \approx 95.54\%$

MORE   independent assignment

Modeling: 2 and choice of one*
Organizing: 2 and choice of one*
Reflecting: 1 and 3
Extending: 1 and choice of one*

*When choice is indicated, it is important to leave the choice to the student.
NOTE: It is best if Organizing tasks are discussed as a whole class after they have been assigned as homework.

Modeling

1. a.

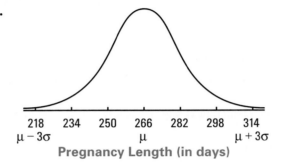

Pregnancy Length (in days)

b. About 16% last less than 250 days. (If students use the table on page 373, they will get 15.87%.)

c. Approximately 2.5% (2.28% using the table)

The standard deviation is the measure of variability most often paired with the mean, particularly for investigating measurement data. By standardizing values, you can use the table on page 373 for *any* normal distribution. If the distribution is not normal, the percentages given in the table do not necessarily hold.

▶ **On Your Own**

Mensa is an organization for people who score very high on certain tests. You can become a member by scoring at or above the 98th percentile on an IQ test or, for example, the math section of the SAT.

a. It was reported that Brooke Shields, the actress, scored 608 on the math section of the SAT. When she took the SAT, the scores were approximately normally distributed with an average on the math section of about 462 and a standard deviation of 100. How many standard deviations above average was her score?

b. What was Brooke's percentile on the math section of the SAT?

c. Can Brooke get into Mensa on the basis of this test?

The clinical definition of mental retardation includes several levels of severity. People who score between two and three deviations below average on the Stanford-Binet intelligence test are generally considered to have mild mental retardation. The IQ scores on the Stanford-Binet intelligence test are approximately normal with a mean of 100 and a standard deviation of 15.

d. Suppose Jim has an IQ of 75. Would Jim be considered to have mild mental retardation?

e. What percentage of people have an IQ higher than Jim's?

MORE

Modeling • Organizing • Reflecting • Extending

Modeling

1. The length of a human pregnancy is often said to be 9 months. Actually, the length of pregnancy from conception to natural birth varies according to a distribution that is approximately normal with mean 266 days and standard deviation 16 days.

   a. Draw a sketch of the distribution of pregnancy lengths. Include a scale on the horizontal axis.

   b. What percentage of pregnancies last less than 250 days?

   c. What percentage of pregnancies are longer than 298 days?

d. To be in the shortest 2.5% of pregnancies, what is the longest that a pregnancy can last?

e. What is the median length of pregnancy?

2. In April 1995, scores on the mathematics section of the SAT were "recentered" so that they are approximately normally distributed with mean 500 and standard deviation 100. Scores on the mathematics part of the ACT are approximately normally distributed with mean 18 and standard deviation 6.

   a. Sketch graphs of the distribution of scores on each test. Include a scale on the horizontal axis.

   b. What percentage of the SAT scores lie between 400 and 600? Between what two ACT scores would this same percentage of scores lie?

   c. What percentage of SAT scores lie above 600?

   d. Find the percentile of a person who gets an SAT score of 450.

   e. One of the colleges to which Ellen is applying accepts either SAT or ACT mathematics scores. Ellen scored 680 on the mathematics part of the SAT and 27 on the mathematics section of the ACT. Should she submit her SAT or ACT mathematics score to this college? Explain your reasoning.

3. Many body dimensions of adult males and females in the United States are approximately normally distributed. Approximate means and standard deviations for two such measurements are given in the table below.

Adult Height and Shoulder Width		Male	Female
Height (in.)	Mean	68.8	63.6
	Standard Deviation	2.65	2.5
Shoulder Width (in.)	Mean	17.7	16.0
	Standard Deviation	0.85	0.85

   a. What percentage of American women are taller than the average height for American men?

   b. What percentage of adult males will be uncomfortable in an airplane seat designed for people with shoulder width less than 18.5 inches? What percentage of adult females will be uncomfortable?

   c. If you sampled 100,000 American males, approximately how many would you expect to be taller than 6'5"?

   d. What percentage of women have a shoulder width of less than 15.5 inches? Of more than 15.5 inches?

   e. What percentage of men have a shoulder width between 16 and 18 inches?

1. **d.** The shortest 2.5% of pregnancies are less than 234 days.

   e. In a normal distribution, the median and mean are equal. So the median length of pregnancy is 266 days.

2. **a.**

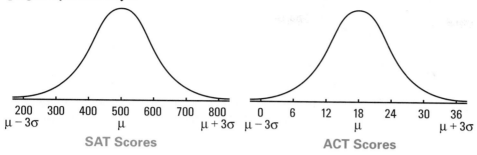

   b. 68% (68.26%) of the SAT scores lie between 400 and 600. 68% of the ACT scores lie between 12 and 24.

   c. Approximately 16% (15.87%) of the SAT scores lie above 600.

   d. About the 31st percentile, since a score of 450 is half of a standard deviation below the mean. (See the chart on page 373.)

   e. Ellen's 680 on the SAT is 1.8 standard deviations $\left(\frac{680 - 500}{100}\right)$ above the mean. Her ACT score is only 1.5 standard deviations $\left(\frac{27 - 18}{6}\right)$ above the mean. So she should submit the SAT score.

3. **Stress again to students that they should make a sketch of the normal distribution involved and locate the area they are trying to find.**

   a. A woman whose height is the average for men would have a z-score of $\frac{68.8 - 63.6}{2.5}$ or approximately 2.1. Thus, the proportion of women with heights less than 68.8 inches is 0.9821. Since $1 - 0.9821 = 0.0179$, the percentage of American women taller than the average height for American men is about 1.79%.

   b. For men, $z = \frac{18.5 - 17.7}{0.85} \approx 0.9$. Thus, the proportion of men with shoulder widths less than 18.5 inches is 0.8159. Since $1 - 0.8159 = 0.1841$, the percentage of adult males that will be uncomfortable is about 18.41%. For women, $z = \frac{18.5 - 16.0}{0.85} \approx 2.9$. So about $1 - 0.9981$ or 0.19% of adult women will be uncomfortable.

   c. $z = \frac{77 - 68.8}{2.65} \approx 3.1$. Thus, the proportion of men shorter than 77 inches is 0.9990. Since $1 - 0.9990 = 0.001$, we would expect approximately $0.001 \cdot 100{,}000$ or 100 men to be taller than 77 inches.

   d. $z = \frac{15.5 - 16.0}{0.85} \approx -0.6$. The percentage of women with shoulder widths less than 15.5 inches is about 27.43%, and the percentage of women with shoulder widths more than 15.5 inches is about $100\% - 27.43\%$ or 72.57%.

   e. The standardized score for a man's shoulder width of 18 inches is $\frac{18 - 17.7}{0.85}$ or approximately 0.35, which corresponds to a proportion of men with shoulder widths less than 18 inches of about 0.63. The standardized score for a man's shoulder width of 16 inches is $\frac{16 - 17.7}{0.85}$ or -2, which corresponds to a proportion of men with shoulder widths of less than 16 inches of about 0.02. So about $63\% - 2\%$ or about 61% of men have shoulder widths between 16 and 18 inches.

4. **For this activity, students will need to collect the heights of 30 mothers. Students might do this as a group.**

    a. Yes. The distribution is bell-shaped, symmetric, and clustered about the mean and tapers off at the ends of the distribution.

    b. The mothers will probably be taller than those in 1903.

    c. Students might conjecture that the heights of mothers today are greater. They might also conjecture that the heights are still about the same. Their plan might include obtaining a larger sample of mothers. If they do not think of selecting the mothers randomly, ask them to consider whether mothers in some ethnic groups or age groups seem to be taller than in others and whether this would affect the results if students didn't take a random sample.

4. Karl Pearson and Alice Lee collected the heights of 1,052 mothers. Their data are summarized in the table below. A mother who was exactly 53 inches tall, for example, would be in the 53–54 inches row.

Heights of Mothers

Height (in.)	Number of Mothers	Height (in.)	Number of Mothers
52–53	1	62–63	183
53–54	1	63–64	163
54–55	1	64–65	115
55–56	2	65–66	78
56–57	7	66–67	41
57–58	18	67–68	16
58–59	34	68–69	7
59–60	80	69–70	5
60–61	135	70–71	2
61–62	163		

Source: Pearson, Karl and Alice Lee. 1903. On the laws of inheritance in man. *Biometrika*: 364.

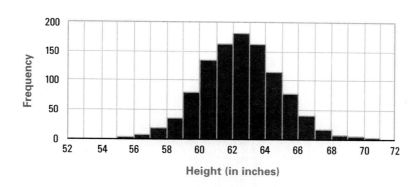

a. Is this distribution of heights approximately normal? Why or why not?

b. Collect the heights of 30 mothers. How does the distribution of your sample compare to the distribution generated in 1903?

c. What hypothesis might you make? Design a plan you could use to test your hypothesis.

Organizing

1. Make a rough sketch of the overall shape of each distribution below. Indicate an appropriate scale on the horizontal axes. Explain why you believe the distribution has the shape you sketched.

   a. The ages of everyone who died in the United States last year

   b. The weights of all adult men in the United States

   c. The prices of all pairs of blue jeans sold in the United States last week

2. In this task, "standard deviation" refers to the population standard deviation σ.

   a. For each condition below, try to find a set of 10 numbers which fit it.

      ■ All of the numbers are less than one standard deviation from the mean.

      ■ All of the numbers are exactly one standard deviation from the mean.

      ■ All of the numbers are more than one standard deviation from the mean.

   b. Try to find a set of numbers so that none of them are more than two standard deviations from the mean.

   c. Try to find a set of numbers so that half of the values are more than two standard deviations from the mean.

   d. What is the largest percentage of values that you were able to find in Part c that are more than two standard deviations from the mean? Compare your results to those of other students completing this task.

3. Is it true that in all symmetric distributions, exactly 68% of the values are within one standard deviation of the mean? Give an example to illustrate your answer.

4. Examine how a normal distribution and the distribution of its standardized values are related.

   a. Suppose a normal distribution has a mean of 100 and a standard deviation of 15. Now suppose every value in the distribution is converted to a standardized value. What is true about the mean of the standardized values? What is true about the standard deviation of the standardized values?

   b. Describe geometrically how a normal distribution and the distribution of its standardized values are related.

Reflecting

1. Make a list of all of the types of distributions you have studied, including those from previous courses, and illustrate each with a sketch. Then look back at the shapes of the distributions you constructed in the "Modeling Public Opinion" unit. What types of distributions did you find?

2. What variables studied in your other school subjects might have distributions that are approximately normal?

Organizing

1. **Responses will vary. The point of this task is to make students think about the general shape of each distribution, not to have them sketch perfect graphs. This important task is usually surprisingly difficult for students. For example, in Part a, students often make a distribution like this:**

0   100

Help them see that this would mean that more 100-year-olds died than people of any other age. In fact, relatively few 100-year-olds die because there are very few 100-year-olds.

   a. Actual data show the ages are skewed left with a bump around age 20. The safest of all ages is 11. This is the low point of the distribution. Look for reasonable student explanations of distributions.

   b. The weights are skewed right.

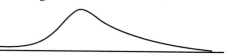

   c. Students will know best here! Have them discuss their sketches.

2. a. ■ This is impossible. Some students may suggest a data set like {2, 2, 2, 2, 2} in which the standard deviation is 0. This doesn't work, as no value is less than one standard deviation from the mean.
      ■ One example is {1, 1, 1, 1, 1, 2, 2, 2, 2, 2}; $\mu = 1.5$ and $\sigma = 0.5$.
      ■ This is impossible.

   b. The example in Part a will do.

   c. This is impossible.

   d. Responses will vary. The largest percentage must be less than 25%. The set {0, 5, 5, 5, 5, 5, 5, 5, 10} has a mean of 5 and a standard deviation σ of 2.36. Two of the nine values (or 22.2%) are more than two standard deviations from the mean. It is difficult to get a larger percentage.

3. This is not true. Examples may vary. For the distribution {5, 5, 5}, which has $\mu = 5$ and $\sigma = 0$, 100% of the values are within one standard deviation of the mean.

4. a. The mean is 0, and the standard deviation is 1.

   b. The shape of the distribution of standardized scores will still be normal, but it will be translated so that the mean is 0 and rescaled so that the standard deviation is 1.

See additional Teaching Notes on page T419D.

3. **a.** This often means that the number of As is the same as the number of Fs; similarly the number of Bs is the same as the number of Ds. There would be more Cs than any other grade and fewer As and Fs.

    b. A teacher could give the 68% of the students whose scores fell within one standard deviation of the mean a C, the 13.5% between one and two standard deviations above the mean a B, the 13.5% between one and two standard deviations below the mean a D, the 2.5% more than two standard deviations above the mean an A, and the 2.5% more than two standard deviations below the mean an F.

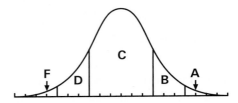

    c. The grading scheme in Part b probably would lower the grades of most students! This can be a good discussion: Grading on a curve means that in every class there have to be some As and some Fs. Some students think this is fine, because they think it means the teacher will give people good grades to make the "curve" work out. Others will recognize that on a given test everyone may do well, yet with this scheme some will be forced to get a low grade. Encourage students to calculate the number of As, Bs, Cs, Ds, and Fs in a class of their class size. In a class of 30 students, the distribution would be 0.75 As, 4.05 Bs, 20.4 Cs, 4.05 Ds, and 0.75 Fs.

4. Empirical science is research-based and involves measurements. The distribution of different measurements of the same thing is often normal, and the standard deviation is the measure of spread associated with a normal distribution. (Karl Gauss, an eighteenth-century mathematician, was interested in the normal distribution, sometimes called the Gaussian distribution, because he found that repeated astronomical measurements were normally distributed.)

Extending

1. **a.** $\bar{x} = 2$, $s_x = 1$, $\bar{y} = 3$, $s_y \approx 2.6458$

x	y	$\dfrac{x - \bar{x}}{s_x}$	$\dfrac{y - \bar{y}}{s_y}$	$\dfrac{x - \bar{x}}{s_x} \cdot \dfrac{y - \bar{y}}{s_y}$
1	1	-1	-0.7559	0.7559
2	2	0	-0.3780	0
3	6	1	1.1339	1.1339

$r = \frac{1}{2} \cdot 1.8898 = 0.9449$

(Finding the correlation using a calculator also gives 0.9449.)

    b. The correlation coefficient is the average product of the standardized x-scores and the standardized y-scores (with the exception that we divide by $n - 1$ rather than by n when computing the average).

See additional Teaching Notes on page T419D.

3. ACT and SAT scores have a normal distribution. Scores on classroom tests are sometimes assumed to have a normal distribution.

   a. What do teachers mean when they say they "grade on a curve"?

   b. Explain how a teacher might use a normal distribution to "grade on a curve."

   c. Do you think this is a fair way to grade? Why or why not?

4. Why is the standard deviation important in science?

Extending

1. One formula for the correlation coefficient is

$$r = \frac{1}{n-1} \sum \left(\frac{x - \bar{x}}{s_x} \right) \left(\frac{y - \bar{y}}{s_y} \right).$$

   Here, n is the sample size, $\bar{x}$ is the mean of the values of x, $\bar{y}$ is the mean of the values of y, s_x is the standard deviation of the values of x, and s_y is the standard deviation of the values of y.

   a. Use this formula to find the correlation between x and y for the following data.

x	y
1	1
2	2
3	6

   b. Explain the meaning of the correlation coefficient in the context of standardized scores.

2. Discuss whether the situations below are consistent with what you know about normal distributions and IQ tests. What could account for any inconsistencies you see?

   a. The Los Angeles Unified School District is one of the largest K–12 districts in the country, with between 700,000 and 800,000 children. In this district, there are special magnet schools for "highly gifted" children. The only way for a child in this district to be classified as highly gifted is to score 145 or above on an IQ test given by a school psychologist. Recently at the Portola Highly Gifted Magnet School, one of two such middle schools in Los Angeles, there were 61 students in the ninth-grade class.

   b. One way for a child to be identified as gifted in California is to have an IQ of 130 or above. A few years ago, El Camino Real High School in Los Angeles had a total enrollment of 2,830 students, of whom 410 were identified as gifted.

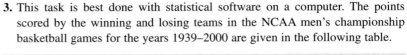
3. This task is best done with statistical software on a computer. The points scored by the winning and losing teams in the NCAA men's championship basketball games for the years 1939–2000 are given in the following table.

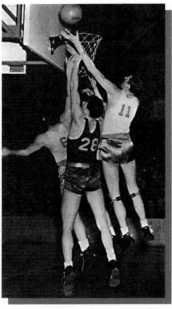

1939 NCAA Championship

NCAA Men's Basketball Championships

Year	Champion	Score	Year	Champion	Score
1939	Oregon	46–33	1970	UCLA	80–69
1940	Indiana	60–42	1971	UCLA	68–62
1941	Wisconsin	39–34	1972	UCLA	81–76
1942	Stanford	53–38	1973	UCLA	87–66
1943	Wyoming	46–34	1974	North Carolina State	76–64
1944	Utah	42–40	1975	UCLA	92–85
1945	Oklahoma State	49–45	1976	Indiana	86–68
1946	Oklahoma State	43–40	1977	Marquette	67–59
1947	Holy Cross	58–47	1978	Kentucky	94–88
1948	Kentucky	58–42	1979	Michigan State	75–64
1949	Kentucky	46–36	1980	Louisville	59–54
1950	CCNY	71–68	1981	Indiana	63–50
1951	Kentucky	68–58	1982	North Carolina	63–62
1952	Kansas	80–63	1983	North Carolina State	54–52
1953	Indiana	69–68	1984	Georgetown	84–75
1954	LaSalle	92–76	1985	Villanova	66–64
1955	San Francisco	77–63	1986	Louisville	72–69
1956	San Francisco	83–71	1987	Indiana	74–73
1957	North Carolina	54–53	1988	Kansas	83–79
1958	Kentucky	84–72	1989	Michigan	80–79
1959	California	71–70	1990	UNLV	103–73
1960	Ohio State	75–55	1991	Duke	72–65
1961	Cincinnati	70–65	1992	Duke	71–51
1962	Cincinnati	71–59	1993	North Carolina	77–71
1963	Loyola (Illinois)	60–58	1994	Arkansas	76–72
1964	UCLA	98–83	1995	UCLA	89–78
1965	UCLA	91–80	1996	Kentucky	76–67
1966	UTEP	72–65	1997	Arizona	84–79
1967	UCLA	79–64	1998	Kentucky	78–69
1968	UCLA	78–55	1999	Connecticut	77–74
1969	UCLA	92–72	2000	Michigan State	89–76

Idea from Don Bentley, Pomona College. Source: *The World Almanac and Book of Facts 2001*. Mahwah, NJ: World Almanac, 2001.

3. a. The best way to tell is to look at the histogram below. The scores are only approximately normal, at best, as the distribution is skewed left.

NCAA Men's Basketball Championship

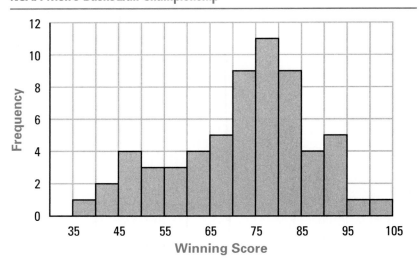

b. The scores have a mean of 72.1 and a standard deviation of 14.8. Thus, scoring 100 points would be approximately 1.9 standard deviations above the mean $\left(\frac{100 - 72.1}{14.8} \approx 1.9\right)$. The probability of scoring more than 100 points would be $1 - 0.9713$ or 0.0287. Scoring 80 points would be approximately 0.5 standard deviations above the mean $\left(\frac{80 - 72.1}{14.8} \approx 0.5\right)$. The probability of scoring fewer than 80 points would be 0.6915.

c. See the plot below. The number of points scored by the winner is increasing over time, at least up to about 1964. The scoring was very low in the early years, resulting in the histogram being skewed to the left. (This means that the probability a team will score more than 100 points next year is larger than you estimated in Part b by looking at the entire set of scores in the histogram. The probability of scoring fewer than 80 points is less than estimated.)

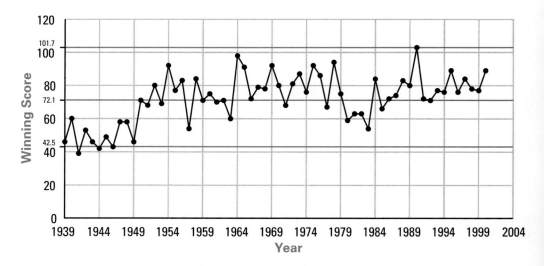

See additional Teaching Notes on page T419E.

a. Are the points scored by the winning team approximately normally distributed?

b. Assuming a normal distribution, estimate the probability that the winner of the next championship game will score more than 100 points. Estimate the probability that the winner will score fewer than 80 points.

c. Often, plots over time reveal additional interesting trends. Plot the points scored by the winning teams over time. Draw horizontal lines at the mean, at two standard deviations above the mean, and at two standard deviations below the mean. Comment on any patterns or trends you observe.

The table below gives the scores for the NCAA Division I women's basketball championships for the years 1982–2001.

NCAA Division I Women's Basketball Championships

Year	Champion	Score	Year	Champion	Score
1982	Louisiana Tech	76–62	1992	Stanford	78–62
1983	Southern California	69–67	1993	Texas Tech	84–82
1984	Southern California	72–61	1994	North Carolina	60–59
1985	Old Dominion	70–65	1995	Connecticut	70–64
1986	Texas	97–81	1996	Tennessee	83–65
1987	Stanford	67–44	1997	Tennessee	68–59
1988	Louisiana Tech	56–54	1998	Tennessee	93–75
1989	Tennessee	76–60	1999	Purdue	62–45
1990	Stanford	88–81	2000	Connecticut	71–52
1991	Tennessee	70–67	2001	Notre Dame	68–66

Source: *The World Almanac and Book of Facts 2001*. Mahwah, NJ: World Almanac, 2001.

1982 NCAA Women's Championship

d. Do the scores for the winning teams appear to be approximately normal?

e. How does the distribution of the women's winning scores compare to the distribution of the men's winning scores?

4. Following is the equation of a curve that describes a normal distribution:

$$f(x) = \frac{1}{\sigma\sqrt{2\pi}} e^{-\frac{1}{2}\left(\frac{x-\mu}{\sigma}\right)^2}$$

In this formula, μ is the mean of the distribution, σ is the standard deviation, and the number e is approximately equal to 2.71828.

a. On your calculator, graph the normal curve that has a mean of 0 and a standard deviation of 1.

b. What is the total area under the normal curve and above the x-axis?

c. Describe what happens to the distribution if you change the mean. Describe what happens if you change the standard deviation.

d. There is a "bend," or **point of inflection**, in the curve where the graph changes from curved up to curved down. Estimate the point where the "bend" seems to occur. What relation does this point have to the mean and standard deviation?

5. Ozone is one of the pollutants in smog. Ozone is toxic to most living organisms and often causes eye irritations and breathing problems. In most cities, the amount of ozone in the air is carefully monitored. The following data are the daily high readings for May 16, 2001 to June 14, 2001 at a station in Washington, D.C. The readings are for the number of parts per billion (ppb). The mean was 68.4 ppb and the standard deviation was 19.57 ppb.

Highest Daily Ozone Reading (in ppb) at Washington, D.C.

68	46	40	63	48	48	50	67	84	65
53	66	67	64	55	58	58	64	47	66
81	90	59	70	74	86	87	117	124	87

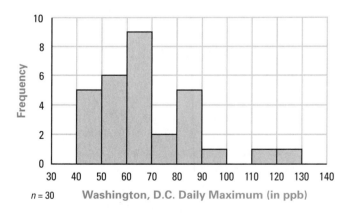

n = 30

4. d. The point of inflection occurs one standard deviation on each side of the mean.

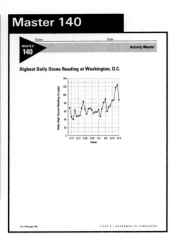

Master 140

5. a. $\frac{124 - 68.4}{19.57} \approx 2.8$ standard deviations above the mean.

b. See Teaching Master 140.

The ozone level generally was rising, although there was quite a bit of variation from day to day. The ozone level was below the mean or only slightly above it until June 5. It was above the mean for all but one of the days between June 5 and June 14.

c.

Highest Daily Ozone Reading at Washington, D.C.

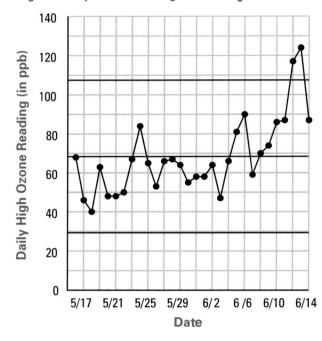

d. See the plot above. Two values, 117 and 124, are above 107.54.

e. Q_1 is 55 and Q_3 is 81, giving an IQR of 26. The median is 65.5. Both of the values in Part c, 117 and 124, are outliers according to the 1.5(IQR) rule. There are no other outliers. This is reasonable since these two values are much greater than the next highest value.

See Assessment Resources pages 199–204.

Assessments 199–201

Assessments 202–204

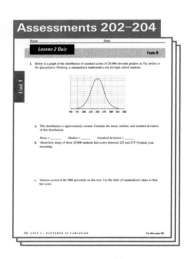

a. How many standard deviations above the mean was the highest reading?

b. A plot over time of the daily high readings in Washington, D.C. is given below. What can you see from this plot that you couldn't see from the histogram?

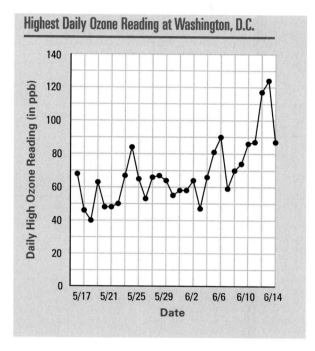

Highest Daily Ozone Reading at Washington, D.C.

c. On a copy of this plot, draw a horizontal line that represents the mean of the daily high readings. How do the readings vary around the mean?

d. Draw horizontal lines two standard deviations above the mean and two standard deviations below the mean. How many values are outside this band?

e. Are these values outliers (1.5 IQR beyond the quartiles)? Are there other outliers? Is this reasonable?

Lesson **3** *Statistical Process Control*

A major West Coast metal producer received the following complaint from a customer. The customer said that the metal they had recently received had an impurity in it. (The impurity was a trace element in the metal that affected how the metal performed.) Since this particular impurity hadn't been a problem in the past, the metal producer hadn't been monitoring it. The metal producer looked up the records on metal shipped recently to that customer. The percentage of the impurity in the metal for each week's shipment is given in the table below.

Metal Impurity

Week Ending	Percentage	Week Ending	Percentage	Week Ending	Percentage
4/7	0.000533	5/26	0.000721	7/14	0.002192
4/14	0.000472	6/2	0.000331	7/21	0.002205
4/21	0.000426	6/9	0.000537	7/28	0.002372
4/28	0.000481	6/16	0.000458	8/4	0.001866
5/5	0.000351	6/23	0.000420	8/11	0.002691
5/12	0.000471	6/30	0.000500	8/18	0.002721
5/19	0.000661	7/7	0.001976	8/25	0.002887

Source: From "Metal Impurity" by Lynda Finn. Copyright © Oriel Incorporated (formerly Joiner Associates), 1993. All rights reserved. Reprinted with permission.

The metal producer graphed the data on a plot over time (called a **run chart** when used for an industrial process). The run chart is shown below.

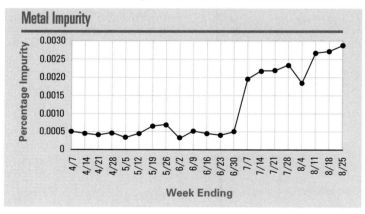

Lesson 3 Statistical Process Control

LESSON OVERVIEW In this lesson, students apply their knowledge of the normal distribution to study the tests commonly used by industry to signal that a manufacturing process has gone out of control. One of the more subtle points of this lesson is the fact that even though a process is under control, the tests will eventually signal that it is out of control. This is because rare events will happen, given enough time. For example, suppose we are monitoring the width of jar lids produced on a manufacturing line and find one that is more than three standard deviations from the mean. Test 1 (see page 390) signals that the process is out of control. Students will learn that this means one of two things:

■ The process has gone out of control.

■ The process has not gone out of control, but a rare event has occurred.

In Investigation 3, we will call the latter situation a false alarm. Depending on the costs of each action, the machine operator can:

■ immediately call a halt to production to see if something has gone out of adjustment.

■ watch the line for awhile to determine if a false alarm has occurred.

Lesson Objectives

■ To recognize when the mean and standard deviation change on a plot over time

■ To use control charts and tests for out-of-control behavior

■ To understand why it is best to watch a process for awhile before trying to adjust it

■ To compute the probability of a false alarm on a set of readings, that is, the probability that a test will give an out-of-control signal for a process that is under control

■ To understand the Addition Rule for mutually exclusive events

Master 141

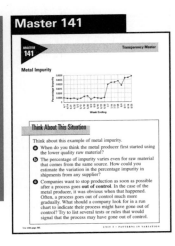

Think About This Situation

See Teaching Master 141.

ⓐ Early in the week ending July 7

ⓑ To estimate the variation of the percentage impurity, you would have to collect data over time and then calculate the variation. The range, IQR, MAD, or standard deviation might be used to measure the variation.

ⓒ Responses will vary. Be sure to encourage a variety of student responses. A student may suggest a rule like "the percentage goes up a little bit each time." That is the right idea for a rule, but students need to understand that their rules must be very explicit. Students need to define both what is meant by "a little bit" and how many times the percentage would need to go up for the rule to indicate an out-of-control process. Help students make their rules operational.

Master 142

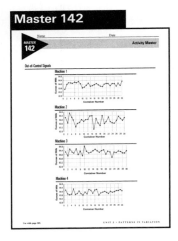

INVESTIGATION 1 ▶ Out-of-Control Signals

The activities in this investigation are quite accessible to most students without any intervention from the teacher. However, it makes sense to stop after Activity 5 and draw the class together for a summary of what has been learned by that point. Ask students to explain in their own words how control charts work and how they are related to normal distributions. Then discuss the eight tests given on page 390 and why each one may signal that either the mean or standard deviation is changing. See additional notes about these tests on page T390.

1. See Teaching Master 142.
   a. Machines 2 and 3 appear to be out of control.
   b. Machine 3
   c. Machine 2

The metal producer checked with its supplier and found that the supplier had substituted a different raw material, which contained the impurity, in place of its regular raw material. The metal producer now routinely plots impurity levels of all types of impurities so that the customer will never again be the first to know!

Think About This Situation

Think about this example of metal impurity.

a When do you think the metal producer first started using the lower quality raw material?

b The percentage of impurity varies even for raw material that comes from the same source. How could you estimate the variation in the percentage impurity in shipments from any supplier?

c Companies want to stop production as soon as possible after a process goes **out of control**. In the case of the metal producer, it was obvious when that happened. Often, a process goes out of control much more gradually. What should a company look for in a run chart to indicate its process might have gone out of control? Try to list several tests or rules that would signal that the process may have gone out of control.

INVESTIGATION 1 ▸ Out-of-Control Signals

In this investigation, you will examine what the run charts of out-of-control processes look like. You will then explore some of the tests employed by industry to signal that a process may have gone out of control.

1. A process of filling milk containers is supposed to give a mean of 64 ounces and a standard deviation of 0.2 ounces. The four run charts on the next page come from four different machines. For each machine, 30 milk containers were filled and the number of ounces of milk measured. Two of the four machines are out of control.

   a. Which two machines appear to be out of control?

   b. On which of these machines did the mean change?

   c. On which of these machines did the standard deviation change?

Machine 1

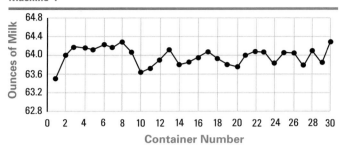

Machine 2

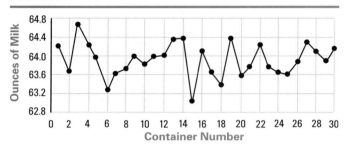

Machine 3

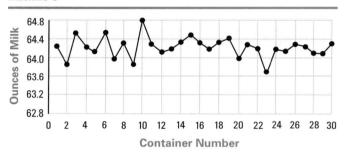

Machine 4

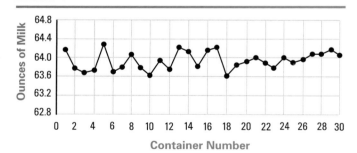

2. **Since students know the effect on the mean and standard deviation of trans-forming data by multiplication, they might choose to code the data by multiply-ing by 1,000,000 and using integers like 533 in place of 0.000533.**

   a. Students might make a histogram or a stem-and-leaf plot to display the values. The stem-and-leaf plot below shows the ten-thousandth and hundred-thousandth places. Student estimates will vary, but students should estimate the mean around 0.0005% and a very small standard deviation ($\approx 0.0001\%$). The calculated value of the mean is 0.000489%, and the calculated value of the standard deviation is 0.000109%.

   ```
   3 | 3 5
   4 | 2 2 5 7 7 8
   5 | 0 3 3
   6 | 6
   7 | 2              7|2 represents 0.000720%–0.000729%
   ```

   b. $\dfrac{0.001976 - 0.000489}{0.000109} = \dfrac{1{,}976 - 489}{109} = 13.64$ standard deviations

   c. The probability of getting a percentage as high or higher than the July 7 reading is very close to 0. (The proportion above 3.5 standard deviations is only 0.0002.)

In Activity 1, you saw two ways that an out-of-control machine might behave. Since the people who monitor machines want to stop the machine as soon as possible after it has gone out of control, they have signs and patterns they look for in run charts.

2. Reexamine the data from the West Coast metal producer, reproduced below.

Metal Impurity

Week Ending	Percentage	Week Ending	Percentage	Week Ending	Percentage
4/7	0.000533	5/26	0.000721	7/14	0.002192
4/14	0.000472	6/2	0.000331	7/21	0.002205
4/21	0.000426	6/9	0.000537	7/28	0.002372
4/28	0.000481	6/16	0.000458	8/4	0.001866
5/5	0.000351	6/23	0.000420	8/11	0.002691
5/12	0.000471	6/30	0.000500	8/18	0.002721
5/19	0.000661	7/7	0.001976	8/25	0.002887

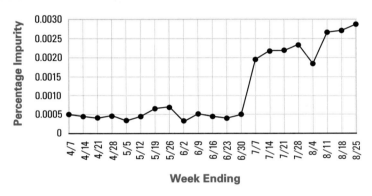

a. In the first 13 weeks of metal production, the percentage of the impurity was under control. That is, the percentage of the impurity varied a little but was of a level acceptable to the customer. Make a plot that displays the variability in these 13 percentages, and estimate the mean and standard deviation. Compare your estimates to calculated values.

b. Now look at the percentage of impurity for the 14th week, which ended July 7. How many standard deviations from the mean computed in Part a is this percentage?

c. Assume that when the level of impurity is under control, the percentages of impurity are normally distributed with the mean and standard deviation you calculated in Part a. If the level of impurity is under control, what is the probability of getting a percentage as high or higher than the one for July 7?

One test, often used, is to declare a process out of control when a single value is more than three standard deviations from the mean. This test assumes that the individual values are approximately normally distributed.

3. In a normal distribution, what is the probability that a single value will be more than three standard deviations away from the mean?

4. Each of the run charts below and on the next page was made from a process that was supposed to be normally distributed with a mean of 5 and a standard deviation of 1. The charts were made by the statistical software *Minitab*.

Chart 1

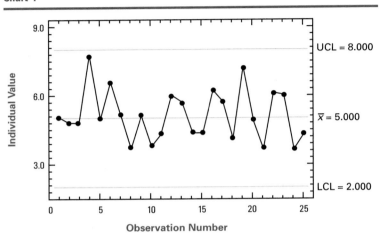

Chart 2

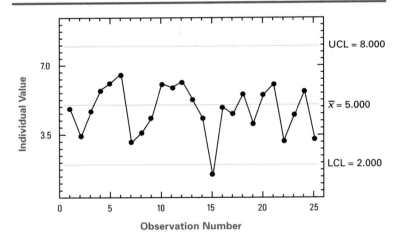

3. The probability is 0.003. Using the rule of thumb that 99.7% of the data values are within three standard deviations of the mean, approximately 0.3% of the data values are more than 3 standard deviations from the mean.

4. **a.** They are three standard deviations from the mean. $UCL = \bar{x} + 3s$ and $LCL = \bar{x} - 3s$.

   b. Chart 2 has a value more than three standard deviations from the mean.

5. Responses may vary. Nine points in a row above the mean seems unlikely to have occurred just by chance. It is a good possibility that the mean of the process changed.

Chart 3

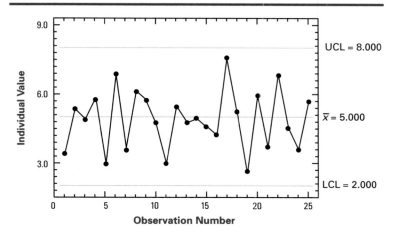

a. UCL means "upper control limit" and LCL means "lower control limit." How were these limits computed?

b. On which chart is there a point where the process should be suspected to be out of control, using the test of three standard deviations or more from the mean?

5. The process documented on the run chart below is supposed to be normally distributed with a mean of 5 and a standard deviation of 1. The small "2" below the final point, where the process was stopped, indicates that the process may have gone out of control. Why do you think *Minitab* has declared the process out of control?

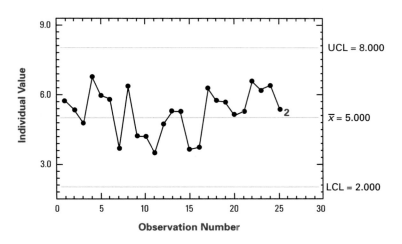

On the chart "Illustrations of Tests," reproduced below, are eight tests used by industry to signal that a process may have changed. This chart is from Western Electric's *Statistical Quality Control Handbook*. The zones are marked off in standard deviations. For example, if a value falls in Zone A, it is more than two, but less than three standard deviations from the mean $\bar{x}$. The small x marks the value at which the process is first declared out of control. Each of these tests assumes that the individual values come from a normal distribution.

Illustration of Tests

Test 1. One observation beyond either Zone A. (Two examples are shown.)

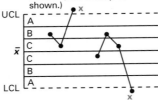

Test 2. Nine observations in a row on one half of the chart.

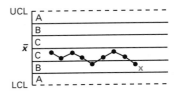

Test 3. Six observations in a row steadily increasing or decreasing. (Two examples are shown.)

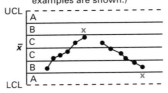

Test 4. Fourteen observations in a row alternating up or down.

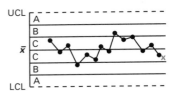

Test 5. Two out of three observations in a row on one half of the chart and in Zone A or beyond. (Three examples are shown.)

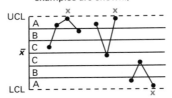

Test 6. Four out of five observations in a row on one half of the chart and in Zone B or beyond. (Two examples are shown.)

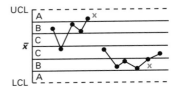

Test 7. Fifteen observations in a row within the two C zones.

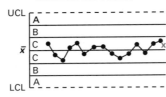

Test 8. Eight observations in a row with none in either Zone C.

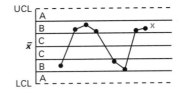

Source: Western Electric. *Statistical Quality Control Handbook*. Chicago: American Telephone and Telegraph Company, 1956.

See Teaching Master 143.

It would be helpful to discuss Activities 1–5, as well as the eight tests shown here, before students continue on to Activity 6. Two of the tests may cause your students some puzzlement. They may believe the process shown in Test 7 exhibits acceptable behavior. Test 7 gives an out-of-control signal because it detects a pattern that we would not expect for a process with the specified mean and standard deviation. This situation should be investigated promptly because decreased variation is beneficial and the cause should be identified and duplicated if possible. However, Test 7 can also indicate that the control limits have been miscalculated, the points misplotted, or the data tampered with. In fact, Test 7 is not typically used in practice for the purpose of detecting an out-of-control process. (Similarly, Test 8 is not typically used for that purpose.)

If students haven't had much experience with random behavior, they may also be puzzled by Test 4. Its regular pattern of up-down-up is what many people think of as random, when in fact it would rarely occur in a true random situation. Imagine how unusual it would be to pick fourteen digits at random and get a sequence like 2, 5, 3, 8, 6, 9, 1, 3, 2, 9, 0, 1, 0, 7, which alternates smaller, larger, smaller….

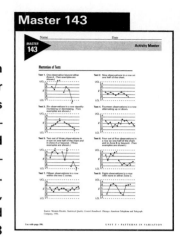

Master 143

6. Note that some of the illustrations contain one example (Tests 2, 4, 7, and 8), while others contain two (Tests 1, 3, and 6) or three examples (Test 5).
    a. Test 3
    b. Test 1
    c. Test 5
    d. Test 6
    e. Test 2
    f. Test 7
    g. Test 8
    h. Test 4
7. a. Test 1
    b. Test 2
8. a. Test 6
    b. Test 3
    c. Test 5

6. Match each of the eight tests to the best description below.

   a. The observations are gradually getting larger (or smaller).

   b. One observation is very far from the mean.

   c. Two of three observations are unusually high (or low).

   d. Four of five observations are all somewhat high (or low).

   e. The mean seems to have decreased (or increased).

   f. The standard deviation seems to have decreased.

   g. The standard deviation seems to have increased.

   h. The process shows a nonrandom pattern that should be explained.

7. Look back at how these tests relate to your previous work in this investigation.

   a. What is the number of the test that signals when a single value is more than three standard deviations from the mean?

   b. Which test signaled the point marked "2" in Activity 5 (page 389)?

8. For each of the run charts below and on the next page, there is an x at the point when the process first was declared to be out of control. Give the number of the test used to decide that the process was out of control.

   a.

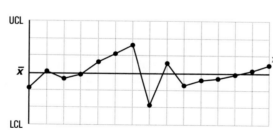

   b.

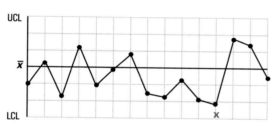

   c.

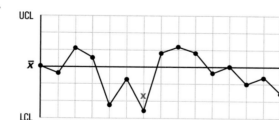

Unit 5

d.

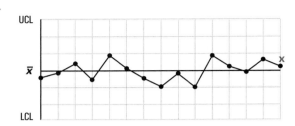

9. Here is a run chart for a process that is supposed to have a mean of 28 and a standard deviation of 2.

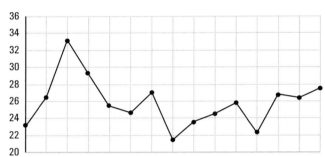

a. On a copy of the chart, identify and label the horizontal lines dividing the zones.

b. When did the process first go out of control? By which test?

c. Has the mean or the standard deviation changed?

Checkpoint

In this investigation, you have examined eight tests used by industry to signal that a process may have gone out of control.

ⓐ Describe each of these tests in your own words.

ⓑ Name three tests that will detect a change in the mean of a process.

ⓒ Which tests will detect a change in the standard deviation of a process?

ⓓ Suppose you are monitoring a process that is in control. What is the probability that Test 1 will signal on the very next value that the process is out of control?

Be prepared to share your descriptions and thinking with the class.

8. d.   Test 7

9.   See Teaching Master 144.

a.

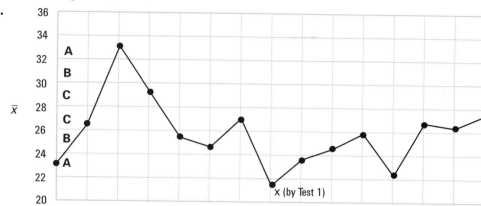

b.   The process first went out of control at the eighth point by Test 1.

c.   Student responses may vary. Test 1 may signal that either the mean or the standard deviation has changed. For this process, it appears that both the mean and standard deviation may have changed.

SHARE AND SUMMARIZE   full-class discussion

Checkpoint

See Teaching Master 145.

a   Responses will vary. Having students describe the rules in their own words is one method that helps you to know that they understand them and also will help make students more familiar with the rules.

b   Tests 1, 2, 3, 4, 5, and 6 can all signal a change in the mean.

c   Tests 1, 4, 7, and 8 can detect a change in the standard deviation.

d   The probability is 0.003 if the values are normally distributed. So this reading is possible, although a rare occurrence, when the process is in control. (Stress again to students that the 68%-95%-99.7% rule can be used only with a normal distribution. In the rest of this unit, we will assume that all of the values plotted on the control charts follow a normal distribution, and students should continue to state that as an assumption.)

JOURNAL ENTRY:
Reflecting Task 1, 4, or 5 would make a good journal entry.

MORE
ASSIGNMENT   *pp. 396–402*

Students can now begin any task except Reflecting Task 3 from the MORE assignment following Investigation 2.

▶ On Your Own

a. Test 4
b. The process should be declared out of control at the next to last point by Test 3.

The run charts that you have been examining are sometimes called Shewhart control charts. Dr. Walter A. Shewhart invented these charts during the late 1920s and early 1930s while he worked for Bell Laboratories. These charts provide a quick, visual check if a process has changed or gone "out of control." When there is change in an industrial process, the machine operator wants to know why and may have to adjust the machine.

On Your Own

Carefully examine each of the following run charts.

a. For this run chart, there is an asterisk (*) below the observation at which the statistical software warned that the process may have gone out of control. Give the number of the test used.

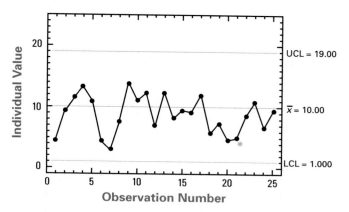

b. The process graphed on the run chart below is supposed to have a mean of 8 ounces and a standard deviation of 1 ounce. Find the point at which the process should first be declared out of control. Give the number of the test used.

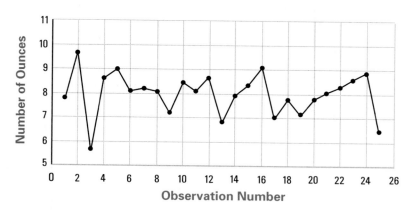

INVESTIGATION 2 ▸ Getting Things under Control

You are now familiar with several tests commonly used by industry to signal that a process may have gone out of control. Once you have determined that a process is out of control, you are faced with determining the best way to get things back under control. Consider a process such as throwing darts or bowling.

1. In bowling, most bowlers put a slight spin on the ball when they roll it down the lane. This causes the ball to curve eventually, rather than always following a straight line, which actually makes it easier to make a strike (knock down all ten pins). By hitting a "pocket" between the lead pin and one of the two pins on either side, the ball and any pins knocked down are more likely to knock down other pins as well. Because of the curve, bowlers usually aim not for the pins themselves but for one of a series of arrows on the lane floor.

Whenever a bowler uses a lane for the first time and aims toward the usual arrow, it's difficult to tell just where the ball will hit the pins. Lane conditions, such as how slick the floor is, can cause slight changes in what the bowler might expect from previous experience. One way a bowler can increase his or her accuracy is to observe where the ball hits the pins and adjust where to roll the ball in relation to the arrows.

The bowler has several possibilities for deciding how to adjust his or her roll:

- Roll once, decide which arrow to aim for, and then always aim at that arrow.
- After every roll, readjust which arrow to aim for, based on the last roll.
- Roll a number of times, observe the results, and then decide which arrow to aim for.

a. Which strategy do you think is the best? Explain your choice.

Suppose a bowler's spin always causes the ball to curve to the left. The best pocket to hit for such a spin is the pocket to the right of the lead pin, so the ball continues toward the center of the pins after it first hits. This bowler aims for the second arrow from the right and gets the pattern at the right for where the ball hits the pins.

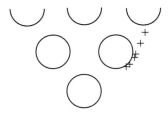

b. Suppose the bowler chooses the third strategy above to adjust his or her aim. Describe how the bowler can decide what adjustments to make.

INVESTIGATION 2 Getting Things under Control

The purpose of this investigation is to show students that it is often better to assess a situation for awhile before trying to make corrections. As you listen to students discuss these activities, you might want to ask in what way the "process" seems to be out of control for the bowling situation. (The center is off, but the spread is small.) Most students will intuitively believe that basing adjustments on several observations is a more reliable process than adjusting after a single reading.

1. **a.** The best strategy is the third: Roll a number of times, observe the results, and then decide which arrow to aim for.

   b. Responses may vary. The pattern of hits shows that the ball is hitting to the right of where the bowler wants it to hit. The bowler probably should aim more to the left, toward the third arrow from the right rather than the second one.

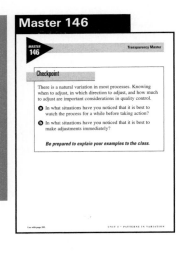

EXPLORE *continued*

2. **a.** Student strategies will vary but should suggest examining several containers, for example, 10 containers, finding the mean number of ounces in those 10 containers, and then adjusting accordingly.

   b. Based on the strategy in Part a, wait and measure 9 more containers before adjusting.

SHARE AND SUMMARIZE **full-class discussion**

Checkpoint

See Teaching Master 146.

ⓐ Responses will vary. Perhaps students will suggest a one-pound difference in their weight, shooting a basketball, a minor argument with a friend, a mild temperature, or a minor rattle in a car.

ⓑ Responses will vary. Perhaps students will suggest a failing grade on a test, a temperature of 103°, or a burning smell from an oven.

APPLY **individual task**

On Your Own

Since Mrs. Carter can't expect to be exactly on time every day, she should wait a few more days before deciding if she tends to be early or late.

2. Now refer back to the milk-container-filling process at the beginning of Investigation 1 (page 385).

a. Suppose that an operator is trying to adjust the machine that fills milk containers so that there is an average of 64 ounces per container. The operator measures the volume of milk in each container as it is filled. If the container has less than 64 ounces in it, the operator increases the amount of milk that goes into the next container. If the container has more than 64 ounces in it, the operator decreases the amount of milk that goes into the next container. Can you suggest a better strategy for the operator?

b. Based on your strategy, what action would you suggest the operator take if the next container has 64.5 ounces in it?

Checkpoint

There is a natural variation in most processes. Knowing when to adjust, in which direction to adjust, and how much to adjust are important considerations in quality control.

a In what situations have you noticed that it is best to watch the process for a while before taking action?

b In what situations have you noticed that it is best to make adjustments immediately?

Be prepared to explain your examples to the class.

▶ **On Your Own**

Mrs. Carter is a new bus driver for Orchard View Public Schools. Her bus is scheduled to arrive at school at 7:46 A.M. On Monday morning, the bus arrives at 7:44 A.M. Mrs. Carter suggests that she pick up all the students two minutes later on Tuesday. What would you say to her?

LESSON 3 • STATISTICAL PROCESS CONTROL **395**

MORE
Modeling • Organizing • Reflecting • Extending

Modeling

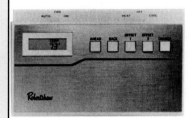

1. The thermostat in the Silvermans' apartment is set at 70° Fahrenheit. Mr. Silverman checks the temperature in the apartment every day at noon. The table and plot below give his observations over the last 25 days. At noon today, the temperature in his apartment was 63°. Should Mr. Silverman call building maintenance? Explain why or why not, in terms of statistical process control methods.

Temperature Observations

Day	Temp in °F	Day	Temp in °F
1	72	14	67
2	71	15	72
3	67	16	73
4	72	17	71
5	72	18	70
6	71	19	70
7	73	20	67
8	72	21	69
9	69	22	68
10	70	23	72
11	68	24	71
12	65	25	70
13	68		

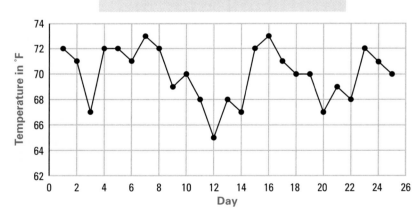

Modeling

MORE
ASSIGNMENT   *pp. 396–402*

Modeling: 3 and choice of one*
Organizing: 1 and 3
Reflecting: 3 and 4
Extending: Choose one*

*When choice is indicated, it is important to leave the choice to the student.
NOTE: *It is best if Organizing tasks are discussed as a whole class after they have been assigned as homework.*

Unit 5

1. Yes, Mr. Silverman should call maintenance. On previous days, the mean temperature was 70° with a standard deviation of 2.16°. This morning's temperature was $\frac{63 - 70}{2.16}$ or 3.2 standard deviations below the average. Even if the temperatures aren't normally distributed, this would be a fairly unusual occurrence. The temperature is out of control by Test 1.

2. Responses will vary. The car probably got a tune-up around tank 10. Before tank 11, the average gas mileage was about 23.9 mpg with a standard deviation of 1.1 mpg. Using the eight tests, Test 1 will signal that the process is out of control at tank 12, which is more than three standard deviations above that average. (For tanks 10–20, the average gas mileage was about 27 mpg.)

3. a.

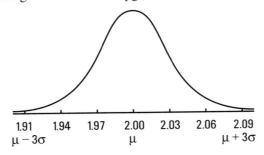

   b. $\frac{100\% - 95\%}{2} = 2.5\%$

   Since 95% of the nails will have lengths from 1.94 inches to 2.06 inches, 5% of them will be either longer than 2.06 inches or shorter than 1.94 inches. Since the distribution should be symmetric, 2.5% will be longer than 2.06 inches and 2.5% will be shorter than 1.94 inches.

   c. $\frac{100\% - 99.7\%}{2} = 0.15\%$

   So 0.15% will be more than 2.09 inches long, and 0.15% will be less than 1.91 inches long.

   d. It doesn't look like the machine is out of adjustment. None of the eight tests signals that the process may be out of control. The machinist should continue working but keep watching the control chart.

4. Responses will vary. Note that the tests are meant to be used with a process that results in measurements that follow a normal distribution. Thus, it is important that students graph their first ten observations to check for outliers or other indications that the underlying distribution isn't normal.

2. The plot below gives the gas mileage for a car for 20 consecutive tanks of gas. During this time, the owner drove the car only to work and back. Do you think that at any point the car got a tune-up, which generally improves gas mileage? If so, when and why do you think so? If not, why not?

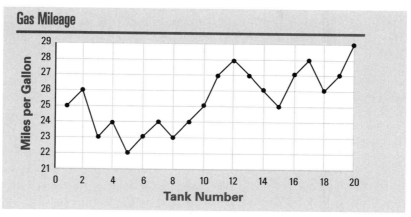

Gas Mileage

3. A person is running a machine that makes nails. The nails are supposed to have a mean length of 2 inches. But, as in all processes, the nails don't come out *exactly* 2 inches long each time. The machine is supposed to be set so the distribution of the lengths of the nails is normal and the standard deviation of the lengths of the nails is 0.03 inch.

   a. Sketch the distribution of the lengths of the nails when the machine is under control. Mark the mean and one, two, and three standard deviations from the mean on the horizontal axis.

   b. If the machine is set correctly, what percentage of the nails will be more than 2.06 inches long? Less than 1.94 inches long?

   c. What percentage of the nails will be more than 2.09 inches long? Less than 1.91 inches long?

   d. Suppose the machinist turns on the machine one morning after it has been cleaned and finds these lengths for the first ten nails: 2.01, 2.08, 1.97, 1.99, 1.92, 2.00, 2.03, 1.99, 1.97, and 1.95. Explain what your advice would be and why.

4. Think of a process for which you can collect data that you think will be approximately normally distributed and for which you can make at least 35 observations. For example, you might count the number of raisins in small boxes or the number of drops of water that will fit on a penny. To estimate the mean and standard deviation of your process, make 10 observations of the process when you have reason to believe that it is behaving in a typical manner. Compute the mean and standard deviation from those 10 observations. Make a run chart of the next 25 observations. Did the process go out of control according to any of the eight tests? If so, do you have an explanation?

Organizing

1. Suppose you are operating a machine that fills cereal boxes. The boxes are supposed to contain 16 ounces. The machine fills the boxes so that the distribution of weights is normal and the standard deviation is 0.2 ounce. You can adjust the mean.

   Cleaning a cereal machine

   a. If you set the machine so that the mean is 16 ounces, what percentage of customers will get a box of cereal that weighs less than 16 ounces?

   b. Explain where you would set the mean and why.

   c. Suppose you are buying a new box-filling machine. All else being equal, should you buy one with a standard deviation of 0.2 ounce or 0.4 ounce? Explain your reasoning.

2. If a process is in control and data collected from the process are approximately normally distributed, what is the probability that the next reading on a control chart lies outside the control limits?

3. A paper clip machine makes 4,000,000 paper clips each month. The machinist measures every 10,000th paper clip to be sure the machine is still set correctly. When the machine is set correctly, the measurements follow a normal distribution. The machinist uses *only* Test 1 (one value more than three standard deviations from the mean). Suppose the machine remains set correctly for a month. How many times would you expect the operator to stop production anyway?

4. Make a run chart with at least 25 observations on it that have an obvious pattern but for which none of the eight tests signal that the process may have gone out of control. Invent a test that would give an out-of-control signal for your run chart. Copy your chart and explanation of your test onto a larger piece of paper that can be displayed in your classroom.

Reflecting

1. What types of data can be displayed on a run chart?

2. A machinist is making video game tokens that are supposed to be a certain diameter.

   a. What might cause the mean diameter to change?

   b. What might cause the standard deviation of the diameter to change while the mean stays the same?

Organizing

1. **a.** Approximately 50% because the mean and median are equal in a normal distribution.
    b. Responses may vary. If you set the mean at 16.4 ounces, only 2.5% of the customers will get less than one pound. But half of the customers will get more than 0.4 ounce extra, and that is costly to the cereal company.
    c. You should buy the one with the smaller standard deviation of 0.2 ounce. With 0.4 ounce, for Part b you would have to set the mean at 16.8 ounces so that 97.5% of the customers would get at least a pound. However, in this case, half the customers would get more than 0.8 ounce extra of cereal.
2. A reading is outside of the control limits if it is more than three standard deviations from the mean. Assuming a normal distribution, the probability of this happening is only 0.3%.
3. The machinist will measure $\frac{4,000,000}{10,000}$ or 400 paper clips, and for approximately 400(0.003) or 1.2 of them, Test 1 will cause the operator to stop the machine.
4. Students' charts and tests will vary. One possibility is a chart that shows a pattern similar to that detected by Test 4, only instead of up, down, up, down, …, the pattern is up, up, down, down, up, up, ….

Reflecting

1. A run chart is a type of plot over time. On the *x*-axis, "observation number" is plotted. On the *y*-axis, the measurement is plotted. The type of data commonly plotted is measurements from an industrial process taken over time, for example, once per hour.
2. **a.** The mean might change if the adjustment for the diameter of the tokens slips away from the required diameter, the operator doesn't set the adjustment quite right, the operator isn't paying attention, and so on.
    b. The standard deviation might decrease as the operator gets more skilled or if there is not enough oil, making the machine "tight." The standard deviation might increase if some parts get a bit loose or if a new, less-skilled operator takes over.

3. The word *micromanage* is used when a manager or supervisor pays attention to details that should be watched by a subordinate. When managers do this, they often miss the big picture that is their real responsibility because either they don't have time for it or they are overwhelmed by too many details. Adjusting a process too often is somewhat like micromanaging in that you are trying to get every detail perfect at the expense of losing overall control.

4. Generally, a decrease in variation is a good thing. Parts will fit better, packages of food won't be too light or too heavy, and so on. So if variation decreases, a company would want to determine what caused the decrease so that it could be implemented elsewhere as well.

5. Responses will vary. Students should select at least one test that signals when the mean is changing and at least one that signals when the standard deviation is changing.

Extending

1. **This task introduces students to the Central Limit Theorem.**

   a.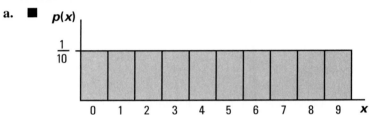

      ■ The mean of the distribution is 4.5.
      ■ The standard deviation is approximately 2.87.

   b. Neither Test 1 nor Test 5 would ever signal that the process was out of control, as all possible random digits are within two standard deviations of the mean. That is, an observation could never fall in or beyond Zone A.

   c. Answers will vary. For example, if the random digits are 5, 4, 1, 4, and 9, then the sum is 23.

   d. The smallest possible sum is $0 + 0 + 0 + 0 + 0$ or 0. The largest possible sum is $9 + 9 + 9 + 9 + 9$ or 45. (Neither of these happened in Noah's 1,400 trials in Part e.)

Unit 5

3. Find out what businesspeople mean when they use the word "micromanage." In what way is adjusting a process too often like micromanaging?

4. Why might a company want to detect a decrease in variation in the manufacturing of a product or in the processing of a service?

5. Suppose you had to select four of the tests to use for a process of filling milk containers so that the mean is 8 ounces. Explain which four tests you would choose.

Extending

1. The eight tests assume that observations come from a distribution that is approximately normal. For individual observations, this is not always the case. For example, suppose the Random Digit Company has a machine that produces random digits from the set {0, 1, 2, 3, 4, 5, 6, 7, 8, 9}.

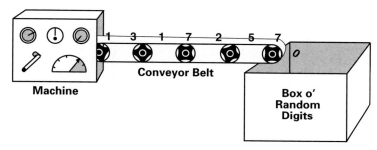

a. Suppose the machine produces one random digit.
   ■ Make a graph of the probability distribution of all possible outcomes.
   ■ What is the mean of the distribution?
   ■ What is the standard deviation of the distribution?

b. Of the eight tests, are there any by which the process could never be classified "out of control"? Explain.

Since the distribution isn't approximately normal, the Random Digit Company shouldn't use the eight tests. In Parts c through f, you will explore what the Random Digit Company might do so it *can* use the tests.

c. Using a table of random digits or your calculator, select 5 digits at random and find their sum.

d. Noah repeated Part c 1,400 times on his computer. That is, his computer selected 5 digits at random and found the sum. The computer repeated this process until it had 1,400 sums. What is the smallest sum Noah could have gotten? The largest?

e. The histogram below shows the 1,400 sums that Noah got. About how many times did he get a sum of 10? Of 21?

Random Digits Sums

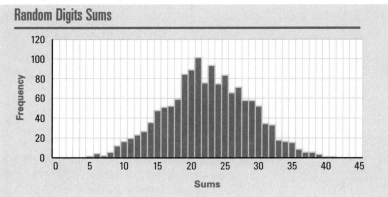

f. How could the Random Digit Company use sums to meet the normality assumption of the eight tests?

2. In Lesson 3 of the "Modeling Public Opinion" unit, you used simulation to construct sampling distributions. A sampling distribution for the situation of flipping a coin 20 times and counting the number of heads appears at the right. This sampling distribution of 2,500 trials was constructed using computer software.

Coin Flips

a. Describe how to construct this sampling distribution using a table of random digits. Perform one trial of the simulation.

b. What is the shape of the sampling distribution shown?

c. For your trial of the simulation in Part a, code each head as a 1 and each tail as a 0. That is, suppose your simulation began H, T, T, H, H, H. You would code this as 1, 0, 0, 1, 1, 1. What is the sum of the digits from your trial?

d. Suppose you perform many trials, code the results, and make a histogram of the sums. What would this histogram look like?

e. How is this task like Extending Task 1? What statement can you make about the distribution of sums?

1. **e.** Noah got a sum of 10 about 18 times and a sum of 21 about 101 times.

    f. The Random Digit Company could plot the sum of consecutive groups of 5 random digits on a control chart. As we can see from Noah's picture, these sums are approximately normal with mean 5(4.5) or 22.5 and standard deviation $2.87\sqrt{5}$ or approximately 6.42. If, for example, Noah's next five digits were 9, 9, 8, 9, and 9, which have a sum of 44, he would declare the process out of control by Test 1.

2. **a.** Start at a random spot in the table and look at the next 20 digits. For example, let the even digits represent heads and the odd digits represent tails. Count how many of the 20 digits are even. That represents the number of heads in 20 flips of a fair coin. Continuing in the table, repeat this process 2,499 more times so that you have a total of 2,500 trials.

    Suppose the first 20 random digits are

    $$5, 3, 3, 0, 1, 4, 8, 0, 2, 0, 3, 0, 3, 7, 1, 0, 7, 0, 2, 1.$$

    This represents

    $$T, T, T, H, T, H, H, H, H, H, T, H, T, T, T, H, T, H, H, T$$

    or 10 heads.

    b. Approximately normal

    c. The results above,

    $$T, T, T, H, T, H, H, H, H, H, T, H, T, T, T, H, T, H, H, T,$$

    would be coded as

    $$0, 0, 0, 1, 0, 1, 1, 1, 1, 1, 0, 1, 0, 0, 0, 1, 0, 1, 1, 0.$$

    The sum is 10.

    d. It would be approximately normal since the histogram should look like the one given in the student text (subject to the vagaries of simulation). Counting the number of heads produces exactly the same results as coding and then taking the sum.

    e. Coding the coin flips is like a Random Digit Company that makes 20 random digits from the set {0, 1} and finds the sum. Thus, the two problems illustrate the same general principle. If you take random samples of a fixed size from a population of digits and find the sum, the distribution of the sums is approximately normal (if the sample size is large enough).

3. **The authors would like to thank Tom Walters of Wilson High School in Los Angeles for suggesting these data.**

    a. The maximum ozone reading of the year in Los Angeles is generally decreasing rapidly. The level in 1998 is less than a third of what it was in the 1950s. There is also a trend for the year-to-year fluctuations to become smaller. The decline in ozone is rather remarkable in light of a big increase in population over these years. The main reason for the decline is the very strict emissions-control standards in California.

    b. Responses may vary. Using the third dot and the last dot (the first two dots look atypically high and low, respectively), the estimate for the slope of the regression line would be $\frac{(0.15 - 0.53)}{(98 - 57)}$ or approximately -0.01. This means that the maximum ozone reading in Los Angeles has tended to drop approximately 0.01 parts per million per year from 1955 to 1998.

    c. Since students don't have all of the original data and can't compute the actual regression line, they must make an estimate of the ozone level in the year 2005. One way to do this is to estimate the level in 1998, 0.15 ppm (parts per million), and subtract 0.01 from it seven times (once for each year between 1998 and 2005). This gives an estimate of 0.08 ppm.

    d. 0.68 ppm means 0.68 parts of ozone per million parts of air. Ozone comprised a proportion $\frac{0.68}{1,000,000}$ or 0.00000068 of the air. This is $6.8 \times 10^{-5}\%$.

    e. The median is 0.3 ppm. A horizontal line for the median is marked on the plot over time below.

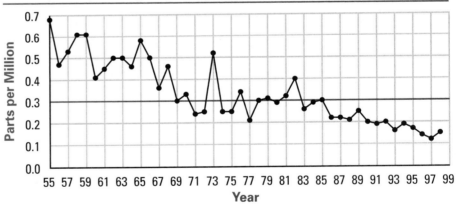

Maximum Ozone Readings in Los Angeles, 1955-1998

    f. The values for 1969, 1978, and 1985 are at the median. Excluding those, there are 20 years above the median and 21 below. There were 13 consecutive years before and including 1998 where the ozone reading was below the median.

    g. Since the set of numbers is large, the numbers selected are essentially independent. You can approximate with the Multiplication Rule for Independent Events: $(0.5)^{13} \approx 0.0001220703125$. (A calculator may give the answer as 1.220703125E–4, so you might want to discuss scientific notation with your students.)

See additional Teaching Notes on page T419F.

3. When we say we want to get things under control, sometimes we mean making things better. In that case, we need statistical techniques other than the eight tests. The graph below gives the highest recorded ozone reading in parts per million for each year from 1955 through 1998 in downtown Los Angeles. (Ozone is a component of smog.)

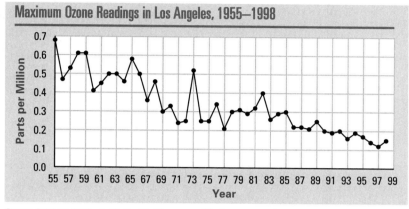

Maximum Ozone Readings in Los Angeles, 1955–1998

Source: Southern California Air Quality Management District. *www.aqmd.gov*

a. This graph shows several interesting trends. Describe what is happening to the highest recorded ozone levels in Los Angeles during the period from 1955 to 1998. Do you know any possible explanations for this trend?

b. Estimate the slope of the regression line. Describe, in words, what this slope means in terms of ozone levels.

c. Estimate the parts per million for ozone in the year 2005.

d. In 1955, the worst year, the maximum ozone level was 0.68 part per million (ppm). What proportion of the air was ozone? What percentage?

e. Estimate the median of the highest ozone readings for Los Angeles for the 44 years from 1955 to 1998.

f. For how many years immediately following and including 1955 was the maximum ozone level above the median? For how many years immediately before and including 1998 was the maximum ozone level below the median?

g. If thirteen numbers are selected at random from a large set of numbers, what is the probability that they are all below the median?

h. What do you conclude from observing where the points lie in relation to the median?

4. In the case of Los Angeles (Extending Task 3), it is easy to see that the ozone problem is getting better because there are so many years of data and the trend is so strong. In some cases, it's not so easy to tell. For example, records of ozone have been kept in Lancaster, California, only since 1970. Lancaster is a rapidly growing community in the desert north of the mountains that rim Los Angeles. The plot below shows maximum ozone levels in Lancaster.

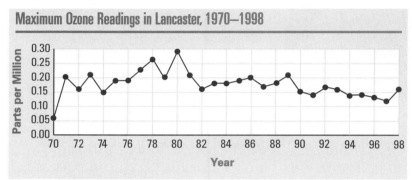

Maximum Ozone Readings in Lancaster, 1970–1998

Source: Southern California Air Quality Management District. *www.aqmd.gov; www.arb.ca.gov/aqd/ozone/A153007.htm*

a. Describe what you see in the plot above.

b. Estimate the median of these maximum ozone levels.

c. How do the values in the last few years in Lancaster compare to the median for the entire 28 years? Was any other long consecutive set of readings either all above or all below the median?

d. If nine numbers are selected at random from a large set of numbers, what is the probability that they are all below the median of the set?

e. If seven numbers are selected at random from a large set of numbers, what is the probability that they are all above the median of the set?

f. From your results in Parts d and e, what can you conclude about the ozone levels in Lancaster?

g. Why is the median used as the measure of center in the Los Angeles (Extending Task 3) and Lancaster ozone problems?

INVESTIGATION 3 False Alarms

Even a process that is under control exhibits variation. Consequently, the eight tests on page 390 occasionally will give an out-of-control signal, called a **false alarm**, for a process that is under control. For example, if you watch a process that is in control long enough, eventually one observation will be beyond one of the A zones. Eventually six observations in a row will be steadily increasing, and so on. The tests have been designed so that false alarms occur very rarely. If you have been monitoring a process that is under control, the probability of a false alarm on the next set of observations is very small.

4. a. The first year, 1970, had the lowest maximum ozone reading. But then the ozone concentration tended to rise through 1980. Then it dropped and remained fairly constant between 0.12 and 0.21 ppm until 1998. Since the last 9 years are relatively low it may be that the ozone level has decreased slightly from what it was in the 1980s.

b. The median is approximately 0.18 ppm. See the plot in Part c below.

c. The median for the 24 years, 0.18 ppm, is drawn horizontally on the plot below. Each of the last nine years was below the median. The seven years from 1975 through 1981 were all above the median.

Maximum Ozone Readings in Lancaster, 1970-1998

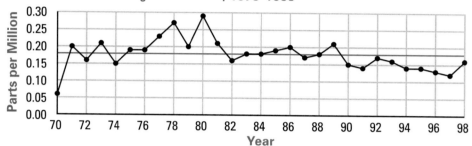

d. Since the set of numbers is large, you can use the Multiplication Rule for Independent Events: $P(\text{all nine below the median}) = (0.5)^9 = 0.001953125$.

e. The probability that seven randomly selected numbers from a large set of numbers are all above the median is $(0.5)^7$ or 0.0078125.

f. From the results in Parts d and e, you can conclude that it isn't very likely that the pattern of numbers in this time series plot would occur by chance. Since a run of seven numbers above the median is unlikely, you can conclude that the ozone levels got worse up until about 1980, probably because of the rapid growth of Lancaster. Since then, the ozone levels have fallen back to what they were before. The fact that the last nine years are all below the median looks promising.

   Again, it is important to realize that if you have a long enough string of years, eventually you will get a string of any given length above the median or below the median.

g. We used the median as the measure of center because otherwise you would have been unable to compute the probabilities in Extending Task 3 Part g and Extending Task 4 Parts d and e. It is not necessarily the case that the probability is $\frac{1}{2}$ that a randomly selected point is above the mean. For example, the distribution of the Los Angeles ozone levels is skewed right. The mean will be larger than the median. The probability that a randomly selected point is above the mean is less than $\frac{1}{2}$.

NOTE: The Introduction to Investigation 3 is on page T419F.

See additional Teaching Notes on page T419F.

NOTE: This table uses the 68%, 95%, 99.7% rule and not the chart on p. 373.

NOTE: Tell students that they are not expected to fill in the entire chart now, only the first line. Results for the chart here are compiled from the activities and tasks noted.

EXPLORE *continued*

1. See Teaching Master 147.

	Number of Standard Deviations from Mean	Percentage of Values in Zone
	Beyond Zone A	0.15%
UCL	**3**	
	Zone A	2.35%
	2	
	Zone B	13.5%
	1	
	Zone C	34%
Mean	**0**	
	Zone C	34%
	1	
	Zone B	13.5%
	2	
	Zone A	2.35%
LCL	**3**	
	Beyond Zone A	0.15%

2. See Teaching Master 148.

$1 - 0.997 = 0.003$

The probability is 0.003 that the weight of the next carton will be beyond either Zone A.

False Alarms

Test	Probability of a False Alarm on the Next Set of Observations of a Process under Control
1 One observation beyond either Zone A	0.003 (from Activity 2)
2 Nine observations in a row on one half of the chart	0.0039 (from Activity 4)
3 Six observations in a row steadily increasing or decreasing	0.0028 (from Extending Task 3)
4 Fourteen observations in a row alternating up and down	0.0046 (from Modeling Task 2)
5 Two out of three observations in a row on one half of the chart and in Zone A or beyond	0.0037 (from Modeling Task 3)
6 Four out of five observations in a row on one half of the chart and in Zone B or beyond	0.0057 (from Modeling Task 4)
7 Fifteen observations in a row within the two C zones	0.0031 (from Activity 3)
8 Eight observations in a row with none in either Zone C	0.0001 (from Modeling Task 1)

1. Assuming that the observations of a process are normally distributed, fill in the "Percentage of Values" entries on a copy of the chart and graph below. You can then refer to the chart when working on the remaining activities.

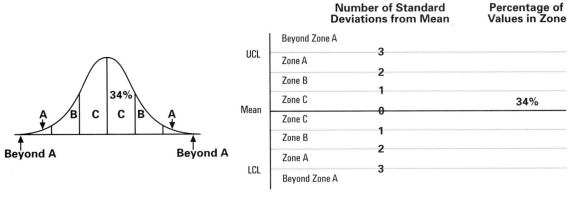

	Number of Standard Deviations from Mean	Percentage of Values in Zone
Beyond Zone A		
UCL — Zone A	3	
Zone B	2	
Zone C	1	
Mean — Zone C	0	34%
Zone C		
Zone B	1	
Zone A	2	
LCL — Beyond Zone A	3	

2. Suppose a machine is filling cartons of ice cream and is under control. The operator uses only Test 1 to signal that the weight of the ice cream may have gone out of control. What is the probability of a false alarm on the very next carton of ice cream being filled? Place your result in the appropriate row of a copy of the table below. Keep your table; you will fill out the other rows in subsequent activities.

False Alarms

Test		Probability of a False Alarm on the Next Set of Observations of a Process under Control
1	One observation beyond either Zone A	
2	Nine observations in a row on one half of the chart	
3	Six observations in a row steadily increasing or decreasing	
4	Fourteen observations in a row alternating up and down	
5	Two out of three observations in a row on one half of the chart and in Zone A or beyond	
6	Four out of five observations in a row on one half of the chart and in Zone B or beyond	
7	Fifteen observations in a row within the two C zones	
8	Eight observations in a row with none in either Zone C	

3. Now suppose the ice cream machine operator is using only Test 7. The machine continues to stay in control.

   a. What is the probability that a single observation will fall either within Zone C in the top half of the chart or within Zone C in the bottom half of the chart?

   b. What is the probability that the observations from each of the next 15 cartons filled will all fall within either of the two C zones? Explain how you calculated this.

   c. What is the probability that the ice cream machine operator will get a false alarm from the next 15 cartons being filled? Place your result in the appropriate row of your copy of the table, rounding to the nearest ten-thousandth.

4. Now suppose the ice cream machine operator is using only Test 2. The machine continues to stay in control.

   a. What is the probability that the next nine observations are all in the bottom half of the chart?

   b. What is the probability that the next nine observations are all in the top half of the chart?

   c. What is the probability that the next nine observations are all in the top half of the chart *or* all in the bottom half of the chart?

   d. What is the probability that the operator will get a false alarm from the next nine cartons being filled? Place your result in the appropriate row of your copy of the table, rounding to the nearest ten-thousandth.

5. A ceramic plate machine makes 20,000 plates in a year. It is under control. If the operator uses Test 1 only and measures every hundredth plate, what is the probability the operator will get through the year without having to stop the machine?

Checkpoint

In this investigation, you examined the likelihood of a false alarm when using quality control tests.

a What is a false alarm? Why do false alarms occur occasionally if the process is under control?

b Suppose you are monitoring a manufacturing process that is under control. Describe how to find the probability that the next five observations will all be in Zone C in the top half of the chart.

Be prepared to explain your thinking and method to the class.

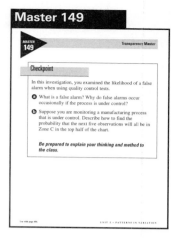

3. **a.** 0.68

   b. Using the Multiplication Rule for independent events: $(0.68)^{15} \approx 0.0031$.

   NOTE: You may wish to point out to students that the assumption of independence is usually not true in practice, so these calculations are approximations.

   ---

   c. Approximately 0.0031. This result should be placed on line 7 of the chart from Activity 2.

4. **a.** $(0.5)^9 = 0.001953125$

   b. 0.001953125

   c. $2(0.001953125) \approx 0.0039$

   d. 0.0039. The result should be placed on line 2 of the chart from Activity 2.

5. The probability of Test 1 stopping the process on any one plate is 0.003, and the probability it doesn't is 0.997. The operator tests 200 plates. The probability that all 200 are less than three standard deviations from the mean is $(0.997)^{200}$ or approximately 0.548.

SHARE AND SUMMARIZE full-class discussion

Checkpoint

See Teaching Master 149.

ⓐ A false alarm occurs when a test signals that a process is out of control when it is actually in control. False alarms occur because even an event with a very small probability of occurring will happen eventually, if given enough opportunities.

ⓑ In a normal distribution, the probability a single observation is in the upper Zone C is 0.34. You want the probability that the first observation will be in the upper Zone C *and* the second observation will be in the upper Zone C *and* ... *and* the fifth observation will be in the upper Zone C. Assuming these are independent events, you can use the Multiplication Rule for independent events and find that the probability that each of five observations will be in the upper Zone C is $(0.34)^5$ or approximately 0.0045.

MORE

ASSIGNMENT   *pp. 411–415*

Students can now begin Modeling Task 1 or 2; Organizing Task 1, 2, or 3; or Reflecting Task 1, 2, 3, or 4 from the MORE assignment following Investigation 4.

APPLY   individual task

▶ On Your Own

a. $(0.135)^6 \approx 0.000006$

b. $(0.135)^6 \approx 0.000006$

c. $2(0.000006) = 0.000012$

EXPLORE   small-group investigation

INVESTIGATION 4 ▶ The Addition Rule

In this investigation, students learn the following version of the Addition Rule: If *A* and *B* are mutually exclusive events, then $P(A \text{ or } B) = P(A) + P(B)$. Be sure students understand that we are using "*A* or *B*" in the sense of "either *A* occurs, *B* occurs, or both *A* and *B* occur."

The purpose of Activity 1 is to show students in a very concrete manner that probabilities cannot be added unless the events are *mutually exclusive* (sometimes called *disjoint*). Adding probabilities for events that aren't disjoint is a common mistake. For example, to compute the probability of getting doubles in the next six rolls of a pair of dice, students sometimes reason:

$P(\text{doubles in the next six rolls}) = P(\text{doubles on first roll } or \text{ doubles on second roll } or$
$\text{doubles on third roll } or \text{ doubles on fourth roll } or$
$\text{doubles on fifth roll } or \text{ doubles on sixth roll})$
$= P(\text{doubles on first roll}) + P(\text{doubles on second}$
$\text{roll}) + P(\text{doubles on third roll}) + P(\text{doubles on}$
$\text{fourth roll}) + P(\text{doubles on fifth roll}) + P(\text{doubles}$
$\text{on sixth roll})$
$= \frac{1}{6} + \frac{1}{6} + \frac{1}{6} + \frac{1}{6} + \frac{1}{6} + \frac{1}{6}$
$= 1$

It is certainly possible to roll a pair of dice six times and not get doubles, so this reasoning is incorrect. (Notice that if we had used the same reasoning with 12 rolls, the probability would have been an impossible 2!) Addition cannot be used, as the events aren't mutually exclusive. For example, it is possible to get doubles on the third roll and also on the fifth roll. (See Activity 8 in which students work this problem.)

Activity 1 is a whole-class activity that involves a situation for which we cannot add probabilities because to do so we would be counting some observations twice. Activities 2–5 can be completed by most students without help from the teacher. You may want to draw the class together for Activity 6, which also provides a good opportunity to make sure students can distinguish between mutually exclusive and independent events. Unfortunately, the ability of students to quote the Addition Rule and the Multiplication Rule is no guarantee that they really understand when each should be applied. A Checkpoint question asks them to think of original examples. Activities 7 and 8 are quite challenging applications of both these rules. Those activities are good opportunities for student-led presentations, ensuring all the intricacies are discussed by the class.

The eight tests were all devised so that, when you are monitoring a process that is in control, the probability of a false alarm on the next set of observations tested is about 0.005 or less. You will determine the probability of a false alarm for the remaining five tests in the next MORE section.

▶On Your Own

A machine operator is using the following rule as an out-of-control signal: six observations in a row in Zone B in the top half of the chart or six observations in a row in Zone B in the bottom half of the chart. Assume the machine is in control.

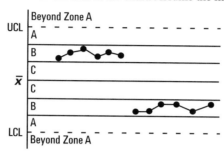

(Two examples are shown.)

a. What is the probability that the next six values are all in Zone B in the top half of the chart?

b. What is the probability that the next six values are all in Zone B in the bottom half of the chart?

c. What is the probability that the operator gets a false alarm from the next six values?

INVESTIGATION ▶ 4 ▶ The Addition Rule

In the previous investigation, you probably used the Multiplication Rule for independent events to estimate the probabilities of false alarms for processes under control. In completing the "On Your Own" task above, you may have used another rule for calculating a probability. In particular, to find the probability of a false alarm because six observations are in Zone B in the top half of the chart or six observations are in Zone B in the bottom half of the chart, you may have *added* the probabilities of the two events. In this investigation, you will explore more carefully when you can add probabilities to find the probability that one event happens or another event happens (or that both happen).

1. As a class, complete the following activity on clothing colors.

   a. Each member of your class should raise his or her hand when the appropriate category is called. (If your class wears uniforms, answer the question according to what you last wore before your uniform.) Record frequencies on a copy of the table below on the blackboard or overhead projector.

Current Clothing Colors	
Principal Color of Pants or Skirt That You Are Wearing Today	Number of Students
Blue	
Black	
White	
Brown or Beige	
Gray	
Green	
Other	

   b. Some students have pants or skirts of many different colors, while other students prefer one or two colors and so have all of their pants or skirts in just those colors. Fill in the following chart. Students should raise their hands for each category for which they own pants or skirts of that color. For example, a student who has all pants in the colors blue and white would raise his or her hand for those two colors.

General Clothing Colors	
Principal Color of Pants or Skirts That You Own	Number of Students
Blue	
Black	
White	
Brown or Beige	
Gray	
Green	
Other	

   Consider these two questions about the information you gathered.

   ■ What is the probability that a randomly selected student from your class is wearing a skirt or pants that are black or white?

   ■ What is the probability that a randomly selected student from your class owns pants or skirts that are black or white?

1. **See Teaching Master 150.**

   a–b. Frequencies will depend on the class.

1. c. The first question can be answered using just the data in the first table. Add the number of students in the two categories (black clothing and white clothing) and divide by the total number of students in the class.

d. The other question requires the second table. If you just add the numbers in those two categories, you will be counting some students twice. Some students may have raised their hands more than once when the second table was constructed.

e. Responses will vary. Ask students to raise their hand if they own any pants or skirts that are black or white. Be sure students are clear about the fact that they should raise their hand if they own both colors, as well as if they own clothing of one or the other color.

2. a. 0.56

b. 0.244

c. This question cannot be answered from the given information. You can't add the percentages, as you would be counting twice the students who took both classes. (This question is a good place to remind students that by a graduate who "has taken chemistry or physics," we mean a graduate who has taken chemistry, physics, or both.)

d. This question cannot be answered from the given information. You can't add the percentages, as you would be counting twice the students who took both classes.

e. This question cannot be answered from the given information. You can't use the Multiplication Rule for independent events because undoubtedly these aren't independent events. A student who has taken biology is more likely to take chemistry than a student selected at random. (In fact, the percentage of students who have taken both biology and chemistry was 53.8% according to the study of high school transcripts. As we would predict, $0.538 \neq (0.935)(0.56) = 0.5236$.)

c. Which question from Part b can be answered using just the data in the tables?

d. Why can't the other question be answered using just the information in the tables?

e. Find the answer to that question by asking students directly.

2. The table below gives the percentage of high school graduates who have taken selected science courses in high school. The information was gathered from high school transcripts.

Science Course Enrollment	
Science Course	**Percentage of Graduates**
Biology	93.5
Chemistry	56.0
Physics	24.4

Source: National Center for Education Statistics. *The Condition of Education 1997.* Washington, D.C.: U.S. Dept. of Education, 1997.

Use the data in the table to answer, if possible, each of the following questions. If a question cannot be answered, explain why not.

a. What is the probability that a randomly selected graduate has taken chemistry?

b. What is the probability that a randomly selected graduate has taken physics?

c. What is the probability that a randomly selected graduate has taken chemistry or physics?

d. What is the probability that a randomly selected graduate has taken chemistry or biology?

e. What is the probability that a randomly selected graduate has taken chemistry and biology?

3. Companies must not only manufacture products, they must also market them. One study asked 299 randomly selected people in a large city to complete a personality questionnaire and then classified each person as a *cautious conservative*, a *middle-of-the-roader*, or a *confident explorer*. Each person was also asked how he or she felt about small cars. The number of people in each category is shown in the table below.

Small Car Survey

		Personality Type			
		Cautious Conservative	Middle-of-the-Roader	Confident Explorer	Total
Opinion	Favorable	79	58	49	186
	Neutral	10	8	9	27
	Unfavorable	10	34	42	86
	Total	99	100	100	299

Source: Jacobson, Eugene, and Jerome Kossoff. "Self-percept and Consumer Attitudes Toward Small Cars," in *Consumer Behavior in Theory and in Action*. Steuart Henderson Britt (Ed.). New York: Wiley, 1970.

a. Estimate the probability that a randomly selected person in the city is a cautious conservative.

b. Estimate the probability that a randomly selected person in the city is a middle-of-the-roader.

c. Estimate the probability that a randomly selected person in the city will be favorable to small cars.

d. Estimate the probability that a person in the city will be a cautious conservative or a middle-of-the-roader.

e. Can you find the answer to Part d using your probability estimates from just Parts a and b? Why or why not?

f. Estimate the probability that a person in the city is a cautious conservative or has a favorable opinion of small cars.

g. Can you find the answer to Part f by just adding two probabilities? Why or why not?

3. a. $\frac{99}{299} \approx 0.331$

   b. $\frac{100}{299} \approx 0.334$

   c. $\frac{186}{299} \approx 0.622$

   d. $\frac{199}{299} \approx 0.666$

   e. Yes. You can add the two probabilities. Since nobody could be both a cautious conservative and a middle-of-the-roader, you aren't counting any person twice. (The slight difference between $\frac{199}{299}$ and $0.331 + 0.334$ is due to rounding error.)

   f. $\frac{99 + 58 + 49}{299} = \frac{206}{299} \approx 0.689$

   g. No, if you added, $\frac{99 + 186}{299}$, you would count twice the 79 people who are cautious conservatives and have a favorable opinion of small cars.

4. **a.** Yes. Each person was classified as just one of the three personality types.
   b. No. There were nine people who fit into both of these categories.
   c. No. There are students who take both chemistry and physics.
   d. No. Some students own both a white and a black skirt or pair of pants.
   e. Yes. A student wears only one skirt or pair of pants at a time, so he or she can fit into only one of the two categories.
   f. Yes. Rolling doubles will produce a sum of 2, 4, 6, 8, or 12, never a sum of 7.
   g. No. It is possible to roll double fours, which will give a sum of 8.

5. **a.** They are mutually exclusive because no value can be both above and below the mean. The probability is 0.05.
   b. They are mutually exclusive for the same reason given in Part a.
   $P(\text{below mean}) = 0.5$
   $P(\text{more than two standard deviations above the mean}) = 0.025$
   Since these events are mutually exclusive, the probability is $0.50 + 0.025$ or 0.525.

6. When A and B are mutually exclusive events, the probability of A or B happening is equal to the probability of A happening plus the probability of B happening. Symbolically, $P(A \text{ or } B) = P(A) + P(B)$.

7. **a.** $\left(\frac{1}{6}\right)^3 \approx 0.0046$
   b. $\left(\frac{1}{2}\right)^4 = 0.0625$
   c. $(0.5)^5 + (0.5)^5 = 0.0625$
   d. $(0.025)^4 \approx 0.00000039$
   e. $(0.16)^5 + (0.16)^5 \approx 0.0002097$
   f. $(0.5)^6 = 0.015625$

Two events are said to be **mutually exclusive** if it is impossible for both of them to occur on the same trial.

4. In your group, discuss which of the following pairs of events are mutually exclusive. Be sure everyone understands the reasoning behind your conclusions.

   a. Being a cautious conservative or being a confident explorer

   b. Being a confident explorer or having a neutral opinion of small cars

   c. Chemistry on a high school transcript or physics on a high school transcript

   d. A student owning white pants or skirts or a student owning black pants or skirts

   e. A student wearing white pants or a white skirt today or a student wearing black pants or a black skirt today

   f. Rolling a sum of 7 with a pair of dice or rolling doubles with a pair of dice

   g. Rolling a sum of 8 with a pair of dice or rolling doubles with a pair of dice

5. For each situation below, explain why the two events are mutually exclusive, and then determine the probability.

   a. If you pick one value at random from a normal distribution, what is the probability that it will be more than two standard deviations above the mean or more than two standard deviations below the mean?

   b. If you pick one value at random from a normal distribution, what is the probability that it will be below the mean or more than two standard deviations above the mean?

6. Suppose two events A and B are mutually exclusive. Write a symbolic rule for computing $P(A$ or $B)$. This rule is called the **Addition Rule** for mutually exclusive events.

7. Now consider probabilistic situations in which there are more than two events.

   a. If you roll a pair of dice three times, what is the probability that you will get doubles on all three rolls?

   b. If you flip a coin four times, what is the probability that you will get heads on all four flips?

   c. If you pick five values at random from a normal distribution, what is the probability that all five values will be above the mean or all will be below the mean?

   d. If you pick four values at random from a normal distribution, what is the probability that all four values will be more than two standard deviations above the mean?

   e. If you pick five values at random from a normal distribution, what is the probability that all five values will be more than one standard deviation above the mean or all will be more than one standard deviation below the mean?

   f. If you pick six values at random from a normal distribution, what is the probability that all six values will be below the mean?

8. In the Monopoly® game, a player who gets sent to jail gets three turns to roll doubles. If one of the three rolls is doubles, the player gets out of jail. If none of the three rolls is doubles, the player has to pay $50 and gets out of jail. Gina has been sent to jail. She wants to know the probability that she will get out of jail without having to pay $50.

She computes this way:

P(doubles) = P(doubles on 1st roll, doubles on 2nd roll, or doubles on 3rd roll)

$\qquad$ = P(doubles on 1st roll) + P(doubles on 2nd) + P(doubles on 3rd)

$\qquad$ = $\frac{1}{6} + \frac{1}{6} + \frac{1}{6}$

$\qquad$ = $\frac{3}{6}$

$\qquad$ = $\frac{1}{2}$

a. Use Gina's method to compute the probability of rolling doubles in seven rolls of the dice. Is her method correct?

b. What would you say to Gina about her reasoning?

c. What is the probability of rolling doubles at least once in three tries?

Checkpoint

In this investigation, you explored conditions for which it is appropriate to add probabilities and reexamined conditions for multiplying probabilities.

a If you select two values at random from a normal distribution, what is the probability that they both are more than two standard deviations above the mean or that they both are more than two standard deviations below the mean? How did you use the rules of probability in finding your answer?

b In general, under what conditions would you add probabilities? Multiply probabilities?

c Give an original example of two mutually exclusive events. Give an original example of two independent events.

Be prepared to share and explain your responses to the entire class.

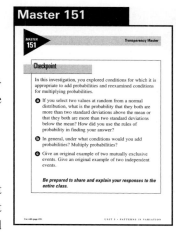

8. a. $\frac{1}{6} + \frac{1}{6} + \frac{1}{6} + \frac{1}{6} + \frac{1}{6} + \frac{1}{6} + \frac{1}{6} = \frac{7}{6}$

No, a probability cannot be greater than 1.

b. Gina can't use the Addition Rule because the events of getting doubles on the different rolls are not mutually exclusive. She could get doubles on any number of the seven rolls.

c. P(doubles at least once in three tries) $= 1 - P$(no doubles on three tries)

$$= 1 - \left(\frac{5}{6}\right)^3$$

$$\approx 0.421$$

An alternative way to calculate this follows: On the first roll, you would expect to get doubles $\frac{1}{6}$ of the time. For the remaining $\frac{5}{6}$ of the time, you would expect to get doubles on the second roll $\frac{1}{6}$ of the time. Then for the remaining times, you would expect to get doubles $\frac{1}{6}$ of those times.

So, you get doubles on the first roll $\frac{1}{6}$ of the time, on the second roll $\frac{5}{6} \cdot \frac{1}{6}$ of the time, and on the third roll $\frac{5}{6} \cdot \frac{5}{6} \cdot \frac{1}{6}$ of the time. Thus,

$$P\text{(doubles at least once in three tries)} = \frac{1}{6} + \frac{5}{6} \cdot \frac{1}{6} + \frac{5}{6} \cdot \frac{5}{6} \cdot \frac{1}{6} \approx 0.421$$

SHARE AND SUMMARIZE   full-class discussion

Checkpoint

See Teaching Master 151.

ⓐ $(0.025)^2 + (0.025)^2 = 0.00125$

You use the Multiplication Rule for independent events to find the probability that both values are more than two standard deviations above the mean. Then, you use it again to find the probability that both values are more than two standard deviations below the mean. Finally, since those two sets of events are mutually exclusive, you use the Addition Rule for mutually exclusive events to find the probability that one or the other happens.

ⓑ You add probabilities if you want the probability that one or more of the events occur and the events are mutually exclusive; that is, they can't occur on the same trial. You multiply probabilities of the events if you want the probability that they all occur and they are independent; that is, knowing that one has occurred doesn't change the probability the other has occurred.

ⓒ Responses will vary. Make sure students can explain why their events are mutually exclusive or independent.

CONSTRUCTING A MATH TOOLKIT: Students should record the Addition Rule, with examples, in their Math Toolkits. After a whole-class discussion about students' responses for Reflecting Task 5 from the MORE set on page 414, students should also write a thorough response to the task in their Math Toolkits.

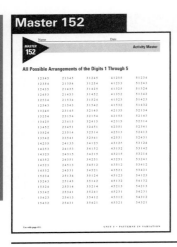

Master 152

ASSIGNMENT   *pp. 411–415*

Modeling: 1, 2, and 3
Organizing: 1 and choice of one*
Reflecting: 5 and choice of one*
Extending: 4

When choice is indicated, it is important to leave the choice to the student.
NOTE: *It is best if Organizing tasks are discussed as a whole class after they have been assigned as homework.*

APPLY individual task

On Your Own

a. ■ Mutually exclusive: If one die has a 6, the sum can't be 6.
■ Not mutually exclusive: If you get 5 heads, you also have at least 3 heads.

b. Assuming that the free throws are independent of each other, the probability that Janet scores only one point is $(0.6)(0.4) + (0.4)(0.6) = 0.48$.

MORE independent assignment

Modeling

1. a. 0.32
b. $(0.32)^8 \approx 0.00011$
c. 0.0001. This result should be placed on line 8 of the chart from Investigation 3, Activity 2 (page 403).

2. See Teaching Master 152.

Students may need some help understanding why, for the purposes of this problem, selecting a random order for the digits from 1 to 5 is equivalent to randomly selecting five measurements from a normal distribution. They may notice that each digit is equally likely, while some measurements are less likely than others.

Suppose you randomly select five measurements from a normal distribution. To determine whether the measurements alternate in size, it is enough to know how those measurements are ranked by size. Every possible ranking by size of five measurements from a normal distribution is equally likely since there is no reason for the largest measurement to be selected third, for example, rather than second. Thus, if you replace the smallest measurement with a 1, the next smallest with a 2, and so on, every possible listing of the digits from 1 to 5 is equally likely. The simulation models this situation by randomly generating a possible listing of the digits from 1 to 5.

a. Students might suggest writing the digits 1, 2, 3, 4, and 5 on cards, shuffling the cards, writing the five digits out in the order they appear, and seeing if the digits alternate. Alternatively, students may use their calculators to select the order of the five digits.

b. Estimates will vary. (The theoretical probability is $\frac{32}{5!}$ or approximately 0.267. Since students use simulation with 20 trials, they will not get 0.267 exactly.)

c. There are 5! or 120 orderings of the digits. Making a list of all orderings is not difficult, but it is tedious, so you may choose to distribute Teaching Master 152. Students can then count those orderings where the digits alternate larger, smaller, larger, smaller, larger or smaller, larger, smaller, larger, smaller. There are 32 of these, so the probability is $\frac{32}{120}$ or approximately 0.267.

NOTE: If students want to know more about how to determine that there are 120 orderings, you may wish to refer them to Extending Task 3, page 415. This idea will also be further explored in Course 4.

▶ **On Your Own**

Assess your understanding of mutually exclusive and independent events.

a. Which of the following pairs of events are mutually exclusive? Explain your reasoning.

- Rolling a pair of dice and getting a sum of 6
  Rolling a pair of dice and getting one die with a 6 on it
- Flipping a coin 7 times and getting at least 3 heads
  Flipping a coin 7 times and getting at least 5 heads

b. Janet, a 60% free-throw shooter, finds herself in a two-shot foul situation. What is the probability that she will score only one point? What assumptions did you make?

MORE
Modeling • Organizing • Reflecting • Extending

Modeling

1. In Investigation 3, page 403, you explored the probabilities of false alarms in the context of a machine filling cartons of ice cream, with the process under control. Suppose now that the operator is using only Test 8 on page 390.

   a. What is the probability that the next observation isn't in either Zone C?

   b. What is the probability that none of the next eight observations are in either Zone C?

   c. What is the probability that the operator will get a false alarm from the next eight cartons being filled? Place your result in the appropriate row of your copy of the table from Investigation 3. Round your answer to the nearest ten-thousandth.

2. Suppose that the ice cream machine in Investigation 3, page 403, is under control and the operator is using only Test 4. In this task, you will use simulation to estimate the probability of a false alarm with the next fourteen observations.

   a. First, describe a simulation to estimate the probability that if the digits 1, 2, 3, 4, and 5 are listed in a random order, they will alternate larger, smaller, larger, smaller, larger (for example: 5, 1, 3, 2, 4) or they will alternate smaller, larger, smaller, larger, smaller (for example: 4, 5, 2, 3, 1).

   b. Perform your simulation 20 times. What is your estimate of the probability that the digits will alternate?

   c. Make or obtain a listing of all possible sequences of {1, 2, 3, 4, 5}. What is the theoretical probability that if these digits are listed at random, they will alternate?

d. Design and carry out a simulation to estimate the probability that if the digits 1 through 14 are listed in a random order, they will alternate. Place your result on the appropriate row of your copy of the table from Investigation 3, rounding to the nearest ten-thousandth.

3. Suppose that the ice cream machine in Investigation 3, page 403, is under control and the operator is using only Test 5. You will now find the probability of a false alarm with the next three observations.

a. What is the probability that an observation will fall in Zone A at the top of the chart or beyond?

b. There are four ways that at least two of the next three observations can be in Zone A at the top of the chart or beyond. Three ways are described here:

■ The first observation is in Zone A or beyond; so are the second and third.

■ The first observation is not in Zone A or beyond; the second and third are.

■ The first observation is in Zone A or beyond; the second is not; the third is.

What is the fourth way?

c. Find the probability of each of the four ways in Part b. Are these four ways mutually exclusive?

d. What is the probability that at least two of the next three observations will be in Zone A at the top of the chart or beyond?

e. What is the probability that at least two of the next three observations will be in Zone A at the *bottom* of the chart or beyond?

f. Are the events described in Parts d and e mutually exclusive?

g. What is the probability that the ice cream machine operator will get a false alarm from the next three cartons being filled? Place your result in your copy of the table from Investigation 3. Round your answer to the nearest ten-thousandth.

4. Suppose that the ice cream machine in Investigation 3, page 403, is under control and the operator is using only Test 6. Find the probability of a false alarm from the next five observations. Place your result in your copy of the table from Investigation 3, rounding to the nearest ten-thousandth.

Organizing

1. In Course 2, you learned that the expected waiting time for a success in a waiting-time distribution is $\frac{1}{p}$, if p is the probability of a success on any one trial.

a. Suppose a machine operator is using only Test 1. If the process is under control, what is the expected number of items tested until a false alarm is given by Test 1? This is called the **average run length** or **ARL**.

b. If a machine operator uses both Test 1 and Test 2, is the ARL longer or shorter than if he or she uses just Test 1? Explain.

2. d. Estimates will vary. The theoretical probability is $\frac{398,721,962}{14!}$ or approximately 0.0046. The estimate should be entered on line 4 of the chart from Investigation 3, Activity 2 (page 403). This problem is hard to do theoretically; see the references below for more information.

Comtet, Louis. *Advanced Combinatorics*. Boston: D. Reidel Publishing Company, 1974.

David, F. N., M. G. Kendall, and D. E. Barton. *Symmetric Functions and Allied Tables*. Cambridge: Cambridge University Press, 1966.

Sloane, N. J. A. *Encyclopedia of Integer Sequences*. San Diego: Academic Press, 1995. See the online version at *www.research.att.com/~njas/sequences/index.html*.

3. a. 0.025

b. The first observation is, the second is, and the third isn't.

c. ■ $(0.025)(0.025)(0.025) \approx 0.000016$

    ■ $(0.975)(0.025)(0.025) \approx 0.000609$

    ■ $(0.025)(0.975)(0.025) \approx 0.000609$

    ■ $(0.025)(0.025)(0.975) \approx 0.000609$

Yes, these four events are mutually exclusive. If one of them happens, none of the other three can happen.

d. Adding the probabilities in Part c, you get 0.001843.

e. 0.001843

f. Yes. If the observations are in the top half of the chart, they cannot also be in the bottom half of the chart.

g. $2(0.001843) \approx 0.0037$. This number should be placed on line 5 of the chart from Investigation 3, Activity 2 (page 403).

4. $2[(0.16)^5 + 5(0.16)^4(0.84)] \approx 0.0057$. This number should be placed on line 6 of the chart from Investigation 3, Activity 2 (page 403).

Organizing

1. a. The probability of a false alarm using only Test 1 is 0.003. So the ARL is $\frac{1}{0.003}$ or approximately 333 items.

b. The probability of a false alarm is greater when you use more than one test, so the ARL is shorter.

2. Responses may vary. For example, Test 6 and Test 8 are not independent. If eight observations fail Test 8, all of the points are in Zone B or beyond. This means there is a better chance that the observations also fail Test 6.

3. If you use five observations in a row, the probability of a false alarm would be $(0.32)^5$ or approximately 0.0034, which is closer to the others.

4. a. **Sum of Tetrahedral Dice**

NOTE: On a tetrahedral die, the number that appears at the base of each side when it lands is the number you have rolled. The photo in the student text shows that two 3s have been rolled.

Die 1

	1	2	3	4
1	2	3	4	5
2	3	4	5	6
3	4	5	6	7
4	5	6	7	8

Die 2

b. There are four ways to roll a 5 and four ways to roll doubles. Since the events are mutually exclusive, the probability is $\frac{8}{16}$ or 0.5.

Reflecting

1. a. Responses will vary. False security is an appropriate term.

   b.

Result of Test

		Gives Alarm	Doesn't Give Alarm
Condition of Machine	In Control	False Alarm	Correct Decision
	Not in Control	Correct Decision	False Security

Unit 5

2. Give an example of two tests from the "Illustration of Tests" chart, page 390, that are *not* independent. That is, if a set of observations triggers a warning from one of the tests, it is more likely or less likely to trigger a warning by the other. Explain why you selected these two tests.

3. The probability of a false alarm using Test 8 is much smaller than the probability of a false alarm using any of the other tests. Describe how you could change Test 8 in order to make the probability of a false alarm closer to those of the other tests.

4. Imagine rolling a pair of tetrahedral dice.

  a. Make a chart showing all possible outcomes for the sum when you roll a pair of tetrahedral dice.

  b. What is the probability that if you roll a pair of tetrahedral dice, you get a sum of 5 or doubles? Are these two events mutually exclusive?

Reflecting

1. A false alarm occurs when a machine is in control and a test warns that it may not be.

  a. What could you call a situation for which the machine isn't in control and no test has given a warning?

  b. The following chart has four empty cells. Two of the cells should contain the words "correct decision." Another cell should contain the words "false alarm." The fourth cell should contain your answer from Part a. Write these words in the correct cells on a copy of the chart.

	Result of Test	
	Gives Alarm	**Doesn't Give Alarm**
In Control		
Not in Control		

Condition of Machine

Modeling • Organizing • Reflecting • Extending

2. Why is it best if a machine operator does not use all eight tests but rather picks out just a few to use?

3. If you pick six values at random from a distribution with unknown shape, what is the probability that all six values are more than the median? Can you answer this question for the mean? Explain.

4. If a person started flipping a coin and got heads on each flip, how many heads would it take before you were confident that the person had a two-headed coin? What is the probability that a person who begins to flip a fair coin will get this many heads in a row just by chance?

5. What is the difference between independent events and mutually exclusive events?

Extending

1. Invent another out-of-control signal that is different from the eight tests you have studied. That is, design another test that signals when the observations don't seem to be following a random pattern in their variation around the mean. If you can, compute the probability of a false alarm in a set of observations of appropriate size.

2. The Ford Motor Company lists these four signals on its control charts:

   ■ Any point outside of the control limits (more than three standard deviations from the mean)

   ■ Seven points in a row that are all above or all below the central line

   ■ Seven points in a row that are either increasing or decreasing

   ■ Any other obviously nonrandom pattern

   Source: Ford Motor Company, *Continuing Process Control and Process Capability Improvement.* December, 1987.

   Assume that a manufacturing process is in control.

   a. Which of these tests is exactly the same as one of the tests on page 390, taken from the Western Electric handbook?

   b. If you are using only Ford's first test, what is the probability of a false alarm on the next observation?

   c. What is the probability of a false alarm on the next seven observations, if you are using only Ford's second test?

   d. Is Ford's second test more or less likely to produce a false alarm than the corresponding test from the Western Electric handbook? Explain.

   e. Is Ford's third test more or less likely to produce a false alarm than the corresponding test from the Western Electric handbook? Explain.

2. The more tests you use, the greater the chance of getting a false alarm (out-of-control signal when the process is actually in control). Too many false alarms will affect productivity.

3. Since half of all values are above the median, the probability is $(0.5)^6$ or 0.015625. You can't calculate a similar probability for the mean because you don't know the probability that a single value is above the mean.

4. Responses will vary. Investigations have shown that people start to get suspicious after about five heads in a row. The probability of five heads in a row is $(0.5)^5$ or 0.03125. Such an investigation would make a good project for students.

5. Two events are independent if the occurrence of one on a given trial doesn't change the probability the second will occur on that same trial. Two events are mutually exclusive if they can't both occur on the same trial. Note that if two events are mutually exclusive, they can't be independent (unless the probability of one of the events is zero). If events A and B are mutually exclusive, then $P(A \text{ and } B) = 0$. Now suppose A and B are also independent. By the definition of independence, $P(A \text{ and } B) = P(A) \cdot P(B)$. Since $P(A \text{ and } B) = 0$, we must have $P(A) = 0$ or $P(B) = 0$.

   The situation of rolling two dice provides examples of all possible relationships between independence and mutually exclusive.

   ■ Mutually exclusive and independent: This is the situation that is impossible.
   ■ Mutually exclusive and not independent: Let A be the event of getting doubles and B be the event of getting a sum of 7. These are mutually exclusive events: $P(A \text{ and } B) = 0$. They are not independent: $P(A) = \frac{6}{36} \neq 0 = P(A|B)$.
   ■ Not mutually exclusive and independent: Let A be the event of getting a sum of 7 and B be the event of getting a 1 on the first die. These aren't mutually exclusive events since you can roll a 1 on the first die and a 6 on the second die. They are independent events since $P(A) = \frac{6}{36} = \frac{1}{6} = P(A|B)$.
   ■ Not mutually exclusive and not independent: Let A be the event of getting doubles and B be the event of getting a sum of 8. These aren't mutually exclusive events since you can roll a 4 on each die. They also aren't independent because $P(A) = \frac{6}{36}$ while $P(A|B) = \frac{1}{5}$.

Extending

1. Responses will vary. Students may want to use their test from Organizing Task 4 in the previous MORE set, page 398.

2. **a.** The first Ford test is the same as Test 1.
    b. 0.003
    c. $(0.5)^7 + (0.5)^7 = 0.015625$
    d. Ford's test, which requires seven observations in a row, is more likely to produce a false alarm than Test 2, which requires nine observations.
    e. Ford's test is less likely than Test 3, which requires only six observations in a row.

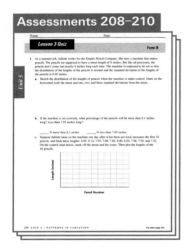
MORE *continued*

3. **a.** They can be ordered as follows: 123, 132, 231, 213, 312, and 321. There are 6 ways.

   b. 24 ways. Students will probably need to list the orders. Encourage students to be systematic as they write their lists.

   c. The values should be the same. 4! = 24 and 3! = 6.

   d. 6! = 720

   e. There is only one ordering from smallest to largest. So the probability is $\frac{1}{6!}$ or approximately 0.0014.

   f. $\frac{1}{720} \approx 0.0014$

   g. Yes; $\frac{2}{720} \approx 0.0028$

   h. The probability that the operator will get a false alarm from Test 3 is 0.0028. This result should be placed on line 3 of the chart from Investigation 3, Activity 2. (See page T403.)

4. **a.** If two events are not mutually exclusive and we add the probability of the first to the probability of the second, the probability of an event in the intersection is counted twice. We can compensate for this by subtracting the probability that both events occur from the total.

   b. $P(A \text{ or } B) = P(A) + P(B) - P(A \text{ and } B)$

   c. Student problems and solutions will vary. For example, from Activity 3 of Investigation 4 (page 408), find the probability that a randomly selected person is a middle-of-the-roader or has a neutral opinion of small cars.

   $P(\text{middle or neutral}) = P(\text{middle}) + P(\text{neutral}) - P(\text{middle and neutral})$

   $$= \frac{100}{299} + \frac{27}{299} - \frac{8}{299}$$
   $$= \frac{119}{299}$$
   $$\approx 0.3980$$

See Assessment Resources pages 205–210.

3. Suppose that the ice cream machine in Investigation 3, page 403, is under control and the operator is using only Test 3 from the chart on page 390. To find the probability of a false alarm, you can use the idea of permutations or ordered arrangements.

    a. In how many different orders can the digits 1, 2, and 3 be listed?

    b. In how many different orders can the digits 1, 2, 3, and 4 be listed?

    c. Compute 4! and 3! using the factorial function (!) on a calculator. Compare the calculator values of 4! and 3! to your answers in Parts a and b.

    d. Use the factorial function to compute the number of different orders in which the digits 1, 2, 3, 4, 5, and 6 can be listed.

    e. If the digits 1, 2, 3, 4, 5, and 6 are listed in a random order, what is the probability that they are in order from smallest to largest?

    f. If the digits 1, 2, 3, 4, 5, and 6 are listed in a random order, what is the probability that they are in order from largest to smallest?

    g. Are the two events described in Part e and Part f mutually exclusive? If any six numbers are listed at random, what is the probability that they are in order from largest to smallest or in order from smallest to largest?

    h. What is the probability that the ice cream machine operator will get a false alarm using only Test 3 with the next six cartons filled? Place your result in the appropriate row of your copy of the table from Investigation 3. Round your answer to the nearest ten-thousandth.

4. Refer back to your work for Activity 3 of Investigation 4 (page 408).

    a. Describe how to find the probability that event *A* or event *B* occurs if *A* and *B* are not mutually exclusive.

    b. Write a symbolic rule for *P*(*A* or *B*) in the case that *A* and *B* are not mutually exclusive.

    c. Pose and solve a probability problem involving two events that are not mutually exclusive.

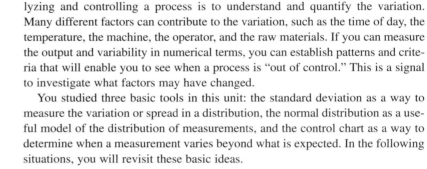

Lesson **4** ▶ *Looking Back*

In this unit, you have learned about quality control and some of the statistical ideas that are important in a quality control process. The essential element in analyzing and controlling a process is to understand and quantify the variation. Many different factors can contribute to the variation, such as the time of day, the temperature, the machine, the operator, and the raw materials. If you can measure the output and variability in numerical terms, you can establish patterns and criteria that will enable you to see when a process is "out of control." This is a signal to investigate what factors may have changed.

You studied three basic tools in this unit: the standard deviation as a way to measure the variation or spread in a distribution, the normal distribution as a useful model of the distribution of measurements, and the control chart as a way to determine when a measurement varies beyond what is expected. In the following situations, you will revisit these basic ideas.

1. A machine produces calculator buttons. When it is in control, the widths of the buttons are normally distributed with mean 8 mm and standard deviation 0.1 mm.

   a. Make a sketch of the distribution of the widths. Include a scale on the horizontal axis.

   b. The buttons work best if they are between 7.85 mm and 8.15 mm wide. What percentage of the buttons are between 7.85 mm and 8.15 mm wide?

   c. What are the mean and standard deviation of the widths, measured in centimeters? (There are 10 millimeters in a centimeter.)

   d. What widths would cause the process to be declared out of control by Test 1 on page 390?

   e. Which of the following pairs of events are mutually exclusive on the same observation?

   ■ The process is declared out of control by Test 1.
   The process is declared out of control by Test 2.

   ■ The process is declared out of control by Test 1.
   The process is declared out of control by Test 7.

   ■ The process is declared out of control by Test 7.
   The process is declared out of control by Test 4.

Lesson 4 *Looking Back*

SYNTHESIZE UNIT IDEAS   small-group activity

1. a.

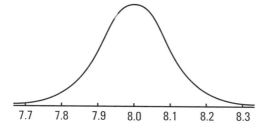

b.   For 7.85 mm, $z = -1.5$, and for 8.15 mm, $z = 1.5$. The area between these values of z under a normal curve is $0.9332 - 0.0668$ or 0.8664. The percentage of buttons with widths between 7.85 mm and 8.15 mm is 86.64%.

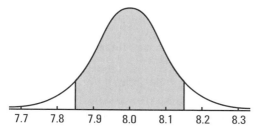

c.   The mean is 0.8 cm, and the standard deviation is 0.01 cm. (Students should use the fact that the new mean and standard deviation will be 0.1 times the originals, and not recompute the mean and standard deviation from the transformed data.)

d.   Any width larger than 8.3 mm or smaller than 7.7 mm

e.   Only the second pair of events is mutually exclusive. A process can't be declared out of control on the same observation by Test 1 and Test 7, because for Test 1, the observation would have to be in Zone A, and for Test 7, it would have to be in Zone C.

Unit 5

2. **a.** The mileage was low the first week and then was relatively consistent except during the 8th and the 21st weeks, when it was higher than the other weeks.

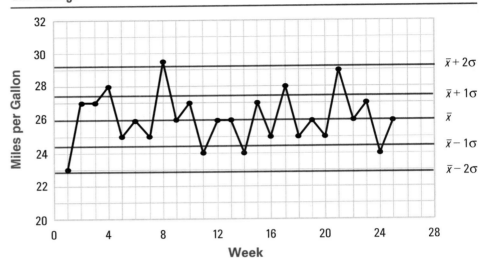

Gas Mileage

b. The mean was 26.06 mpg, and the standard deviation was 1.55. Only during the 8th week was the mileage more than two standard deviations from the mean. We would expect such an event to happen about once out of 25 weeks. $\left(5\% = \frac{1}{25}\right)$

c. Yes, the histogram has about the right shape. See below. The distribution is relatively symmetric. 68% of the data are within one standard deviation of the mean, and only one value is more than two standard deviations from the mean. The mean and the median are approximately the same.

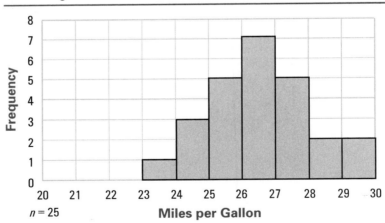

Gas Mileage

d. Fuel consumption seems to be in control. None of the tests is violated.

e. Responses will vary. Since something seems to be wrong with the car, it must be getting lower gas mileage. For example, one reading of below 21.32 mpg would fail Test 1. Four out of five points less than 24.48 mpg (Test 6) or two out of three consecutive points less than 22.9 mpg (Test 5) would also be indicators that the gas mileage was not behaving normally.

2. Suppose you kept track of the gas mileage for your car over a 25-week span. You recorded the data as follows:

Gas Mileage

Week	Miles per Gallon	Week	Miles per Gallon
Feb 7	23	May 9	24
Feb 14	27	May 16	27
Feb 21	27	May 23	25
Feb 28	28	May 30	28
Mar 7	25	June 6	25
Mar 14	26	June 13	26
Mar 21	25	June 20	25
Mar 28	29.5	June 27	29
Apr 4	26	July 4	26
Apr 11	27	July 11	27
Apr 18	24	July 18	24
Apr 25	26	July 25	26
May 2	26		

a. Make a run chart for your gas mileage. What does it tell you about the consistency of your gas mileage?

b. Find the mean and standard deviation. Draw horizontal lines on the run chart representing the mean and one and two standard deviations from the mean. Was your mileage unusual for any week in that time period?

c. To use the eight out-of-control tests, the data must be approximately normally distributed. Does that appear to be the case here? Explain.

d. Would you say fuel consumption of your car is in control? If not, which test is violated?

e. Five weeks after July 25, you discovered that something seemed to be wrong with your car, affecting your gas mileage. Write down two different sets of mileage data for those five weeks that would indicate you had a problem. Explain the test you were using and how it would apply to your data. Use any test only once.

3. In each of the following run charts, the mean is 10 and the standard deviation is 1.

   a. On a copy of each chart, draw in the mean and the interval one, two, and three standard deviations away from the mean.

   b. If possible, locate the next point in each plot so the system is declared out of control by one of the tests. Indicate which test would apply. Use Test 1 no more than once.

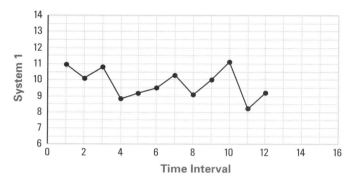

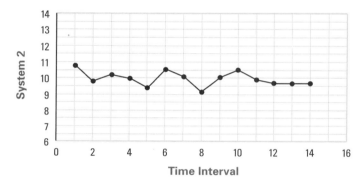

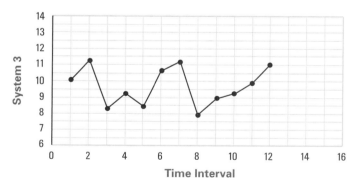

3. **See Teaching Master 153.**

   a. In each plot, a line should be drawn at the mean 10, one standard deviation from the mean at 9 and 11, two standard deviations from the mean at 8 and 12, and three standard deviations from the mean at 7 and 13.

   b. System 1 will be declared out of control by Test 1 if the next value is less than 7 or greater than 13.

   System 2 will be declared out of control by Test 7 if the next value is between 9 and 11, within one standard deviation of the mean.

   System 3 will be declared out of control by Test 3 if the next point is larger than 11.

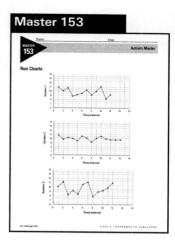

Master 153

Unit 5

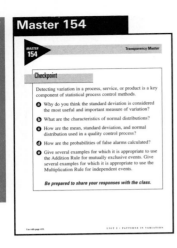

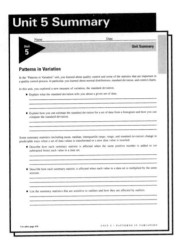

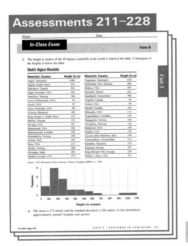

3. c. The probabilities that the next point will set off a false alarm are as follows:

System 1: 0.003 (0.3% of the values will be more than three standard deviations from the mean.)

System 2: 0.68 (68% of the values are within one standard deviation of the mean.)

System 3: 0.16 (16% of the values will be more than one standard deviation above the mean.)

SHARE AND SUMMARIZE full-class discussion

Checkpoint

See Teaching Master 154.

ⓐ Responses may vary. The usefulness of the standard deviation largely depends on its relationship to the normal distribution. Students might discuss the relationship of the standard deviation to the normal curve, the fact that the quality control process is dependent on normal distributions and the standard deviation, and the fact that there are nice theorems, such as the Central Limit Theorem (Extending Task 1 on page 399), that involve the standard deviation.

ⓑ The normal distribution is bell-shaped and symmetrical. The domain is the set of all real numbers. The high point (maximum) occurs at the mean. Some students may have noted that the bends in the graph (inflection points) occur one standard deviation above and below the mean. About 68% of the values lie within one standard deviation of the mean, 95% within two standard deviations, and 99.7% within three standard deviations.

ⓒ The mean and standard deviation are used to determine the "zones." Six of the eight tests are based on the probability that a set of observations from a process that is in control will fall in various zones. These probabilities apply only if the observations are normally distributed.

ⓓ The probabilities of false alarms are calculated by assuming the process is in control and then finding the probability that the next set of observations will give an out-of-control signal by that test.

ⓔ Responses will vary. For the Addition Rule for mutually exclusive events, students' examples should describe events that cannot both happen on the same trial, and related questions should ask for the probability that one or the other or both events occur. For the Multiplication Rule for independent events, students' examples should describe events that are independent, and related questions should ask for the probability that both events occur.

APPLY individual task

▶On Your Own

See Unit 5 Summary Masters.

Responses will vary. Above all, preparation of this unit summary should be something that is useful to the individual student. You may wish to have students use the unit summary masters for "Patterns in Variation" to help them organize the information.

See Assessment Resources pages 211–228.

c. Assuming each system on the previous page is under control, what is the probability that the next observation will set off a false alarm? Show how you found your answers.

Checkpoint

Detecting variation in a process, service, or product is a key component of statistical process control methods.

ⓐ Why do you think the standard deviation is considered the most useful and important measure of variation?

ⓑ What are the characteristics of normal distributions?

ⓒ How are the mean, standard deviation, and normal distribution used in a quality control process?

ⓓ How are the probabilities of false alarms calculated?

ⓔ Give several examples for which it is appropriate to use the Addition Rule for mutually exclusive events. Give several examples for which it is appropriate to use the Multiplication Rule for independent events.

Be prepared to share your responses with the class.

On Your Own

Write, in outline form, a summary of the important mathematical concepts and methods developed in this unit. Organize your summary so that it can be used in future units and courses.

LESSON 4 • LOOKING BACK   **419**

Looking Back, Looking Ahead

▶ Reflecting on Mathematical Content

In this unit, students have learned one way that industry uses statistical methods to maintain the quality of products and services. Control charts are widespread in companies that are serious about providing a product that fits their customers' specifications and expectations. Other methods used in industry include surveys of customer satisfaction and preferences (which students studied in "Modeling Public Opinion") and acceptance sampling (which students may elect to study in Course 4, Unit 5, "Binomial Distributions and Statistical Inference").

By this point in the *Contemporary Mathematics in Context* curriculum, your students have learned a great deal about statistics and probability. Among the big ideas studied were centers (mean and median), measures of variation (mean absolute deviation, standard deviation, interquartile range), and shapes of distributions. Interpretation of graphical displays, including stem-and-leaf plots, histograms, box plots, and scatterplots, was emphasized. Other topics studied included correlation and least-squares regression, sample surveys and confidence intervals, simulation, the geometric distribution, the Multiplication and Addition Rules of probability, the normal distribution, and control charts. All of this knowledge will be useful to students in their science labs, in social science courses, and in interpreting the reports of surveys and experiments that they hear about and read daily in the media.

Students who have completed Course 3 are exceptionally well-prepared to take Advanced Placement Statistics. The AP Statistics syllabus includes all of the topics listed above except control charts and the mean absolute deviation. If your high school offers that course, *Contemporary Mathematics in Context* (*CMIC*) students should be able to complete it in one semester. Students planning to attend college (and do well on college placement tests) should continue their study of mathematics with Course 4 in order to extend and automate their symbolic skills. Students are strongly encouraged to study AP Statistics following Course 4 or to enroll in both Course 4 and AP Statistics.

The probability and statistics strand of *CMIC* concludes with Course 4, Unit 5, "Binomial Distributions and Statistical Inference." This unit extends student understanding of the binomial distribution, including its exact construction and how the normal approximation to the binomial distribution is used in statistical inference to test a single proportion and to compare two treatments in an experiment.

Unit 5 Assessment

Notes continued from page T346

d A box plot helps you visualize the spread of the data by locating the quartiles of the data. A longer box means that the spread of the middle 50% of the data (that is, the IQR) is larger. A longer box does not mean that more than half the data values are between the first and third quartiles. In a similar manner, a long whisker means that the upper or lower quarter of the data has a large spread. Some technology, such as the TI-83 calculator, has a box plot option that displays outliers.

Variability is shown in a histogram by how spread out the bars are along the x-axis.

A stem-and-leaf plot shows variability in much the same way as a histogram, except it is displayed vertically and the individual data values are still available for inspection.

Notes continued from page T348

4. **e.** $SD = \sqrt{\frac{\Sigma(x-\mu)^2}{n}}$

   Many calculators have two kinds of standard deviation: σ and s. (Sometimes s is denoted σ_{n-1}.) The standard deviation we are computing in Lesson 1 is σ. This is the standard deviation of a population. In Lesson 2, students will also compute s, the standard deviation used for a sample. The only difference between the two formulas is that the divisor is n for σ and $n-1$ for s:

   $$\sigma = \sqrt{\frac{\Sigma(x-\mu)^2}{n}}$$

   $$s = \sqrt{\frac{\Sigma(x-\mu)^2}{n-1}}$$

   For Lesson 1, your students should use σ from their calculators. For more information on s and σ, see the student text page 364 and the corresponding teacher's notes.

5. **a.** Results will depend on the measurements.

   b. Groups with more spread or with outliers will generally have larger standard deviations.

6. **a.** If we just add the deviations, the sum will be 0. Also, squaring deviations has the effect of adding very large amounts to the sum when there are outliers.

   b. This makes the standard deviation a type of average. We are finding the mean squared distance and then taking the square root.

   c. Intuitively, without the square root, the resulting number (called the *variance*) seems much too large to be a typical distance from the mean for these perimeter measurements. Taking the square root gives the standard deviation the same units as the original data. The perimeter was measured in millimeters; the standard deviation will be in millimeters.

   d. Millimeter. The original unit of measure was millimeter. Subtracting the mean from each data value kept the unit as millimeter. Squaring the differences changed the unit to square millimeter. Dividing by n kept the unit as square millimeter. Taking the square root returned the unit to millimeter.

   e. Formulas that have involved the sum of squared differences are sum of squared error (SSE), correlation coefficient, and distance formula.

Teaching Notes *continued*

Notes continued
from page T371

In this investigation, students should use the table on page 373, which gives more accurate values and values for other numbers of standard deviations from the mean. For example, using this table, we find that 0.9972 − 0.0228 = 0.9744 or 97.44% of the values lie within two standard deviations of the mean. Students should be comfortable both with the rule of thumb and with the table and may give answers using either. Thus, in cases for which $z = \pm 1$, $z = \pm 2$, and $z = \pm 3$, answers may vary slightly.

Reflecting

Notes continued
from page T378

1. Students may include the following. The distributions in "Modeling Public Opinion" were approximately normal. Students may also include binomial distributions, such as in Investigation 1 of Lesson 3 in that unit.

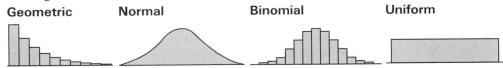

| Geometric | Normal | Binomial | Uniform |

2. Students might suggest grades, data from a science experiment, or data from a psychology experiment. If they look through their other texts, they might find several examples.

Notes continued
from page T379

2. From Activity 6 on page 374, we know that children's IQ scores are approximately normally distributed with $\mu = 100$ and $\sigma = 15$.

   a. From the table on page 373, you expect the proportion of children who have IQs of 145, or three standard deviations above the mean, to be about $1 - 0.9987$ or 0.0013. There are about $\frac{750,000}{13}$ or 57,692 ninth graders in the LAUSD. Notice that $0.0013(57,692) \approx 75$ students. Thus, the 61 looks about right, *except* that not all children with IQs above 145 are tested. Furthermore, many or most of those who are tested probably don't choose to go to a magnet school. Also, there are other similar magnets for ninth graders! Our assumptions don't account for this many highly gifted ninth graders in one school.

   b. You expect about 2.5% of children to have IQs of 130 or above. But $0.025(2,830) = 70.75$. There are far more gifted students than you would expect at this high school. Perhaps there are other ways to be classified as gifted, or perhaps this is a high school that the gifted children choose to attend.

Unit 5

**Notes continued
from page T381**

3. d. Again, the best way to tell is to look at the histogram below. The distribution of scores could well be normal if there were a few more to fill it out.

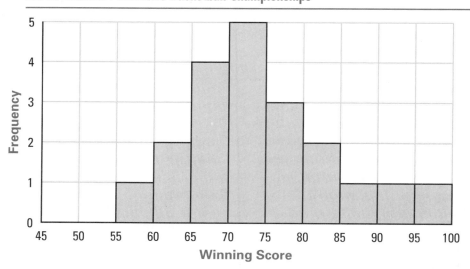

NCAA Division I Women's Basketball Championships

e. The mean, 73.9, is slightly higher than the mean for the men, and the standard deviation is 10.7, somewhat less. This may be because the women's championships began in 1982 after the winning scores had gone up and stabilized.

4. a. For $\mu = 0$ and $\sigma = 1$, $f(x) = \frac{1}{\sqrt{2\pi}} e^{-\frac{x^2}{2}}$. Note that the domain seems to be from about -3.5 to 3.5, but in reality, the curve approaches 0 asymptotically, never reaching it, as x increases or decreases.

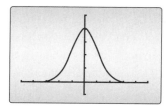

```
WINDOW
 Xmin =-5
 Xmax =5
 Xscl =1
 Ymin =-.1
 Ymax =.5
 Yscl =.1
 Xres =1
```

b. The area under the curve represents the probability that an event will occur. Since the sum of all the probabilities is 1, the entire area must be 1.

c. If you change the mean, the curve will be shifted right or left on the horizontal axis. If you decrease the standard deviation, the curve will become narrower. If you increase the standard deviation, the curve will become wider.

Teaching Notes *continued*

Notes continued from page T401

3. h. For only five years from 1971 through 1998 has the maximum ozone reading been above the median and never once from 1986 through 1998. It is extremely unlikely that this could have happened by chance. You should be convinced that the ozone levels are below what they were in earlier years. However, you have to be very careful here in your reasoning. The probability you computed in Part g is the same as asking, "If I flip a coin, what is the probability that the first thirteen flips are heads?" This is a quite different question than, "If I flip a coin several hundred times, what is the probability I get a string of 13 heads somewhere in the string?" The probability of the second event is much higher than the probability of the first event.

Notes continued from page T402

EXPLORE small-group investigation

INVESTIGATION 3 False Alarms

If you observe a process long enough, eventually one of the eight tests will signal that the process is out of control, even if the process has been in control the entire time. Eventually, the rare events signaled by the tests will occur. In this investigation, students compute the probability that, when monitoring a process in control, an out-of-control signal will be given on the next set of observations by a particular test. Such an out-of-control signal for a process that is in control is called a *false alarm*.

In order to find the probability of a false alarm, students must use the Multiplication Rule for Independent Events. You may want to review the Multiplication Rule before students start these activities. You might do this by recalling examples from prior units of study. (What is the probability of a 6 on one roll of a die? What is the probability of 6s occurring on each of two rolls?) Or you might want to use the context at hand. (What is the probability of a measurement being in Zone A if the process is in control? What is the probability of two consecutive measurements being in Zone A?)

Unit 6 ▶ Families of Functions

UNIT OVERVIEW "Families of Functions" is the final unit in the algebra and functions strand of the *Contemporary Mathematics in Context* three-year core curriculum. The unit completes developments that began in Course 1, where the concepts of variables and functions, along with techniques for modeling quantitative relationships and data patterns, were introduced. In this unit, students are given many opportunities to find symbolic rules that model common data patterns and problem conditions involving quantitative variables and, conversely, to estimate the shapes of graphs and patterns in tables by studying the rules used to generate them. In addition, transformations of basic linear, direct and inverse power, exponential, and trigonometric functions are investigated. The absolute value function is introduced here as students consider translations and vertical and horizontal stretches and compressions.

The unit begins by asking students to think about functions that model patterns in atmospheric change. In Lesson 1, students are asked to identify appropriate models for describing and predicting change in Earth's geology and climate and then to abstract the key mathematical properties of each function family. Students summarize their toolkit of functions, the patterns of variation modeled by each type, and the representation of those patterns in numerical, graphic, and symbolic forms. This toolkit review focuses on linear, quadratic, exponential, power (direct and inverse), and periodic functions. The square root and absolute value functions are added to this toolkit as the unit progresses.

With the repertoire of basic function models clearly summarized, the unit moves to extensions of those function rules for data patterns whose graphs are reflections, translations, and stretches or compressions of familiar forms. Two major sections of the unit lead students to discover techniques for building "customized" function rules. For various given basic functions $f(x)$, students will find rules for $f(x) \pm a, f(x \pm a), af(x),$ and $f(ax)$ and also for combinations of these transformations. Then, they will encounter application situations that require transforming the basic forms and generalizing their findings from specific cases.

Families of Functions

Unit 6

Unit 6

421

Unit 6 Objectives

■ To describe the table and graph patterns expected in linear, direct power, inverse power, exponential, sine, cosine, absolute value, and square root models, given the corresponding algebraic rules in function form

■ To identify a function as a variation of a basic family of functions

■ To recognize how the patterns in graphs, tables, and rules of functions relate to the functions' transformed graphs, tables, and rules

■ To write function rules which are reflections across the *x*-axis, translations, or stretches (or combinations of these transformations) of basic functions

■ To apply all of the transformations above as they relate to real-world situations

See Teaching Masters 155a–155d for Maintenance tasks that students can work on after Lesson 1.

Unit 6 Planning Guide

Lesson Objectives	MORE Assignments	Suggested Pacing	Materials
Lesson 1 *Function Models Revisited* • To model and answer questions about contexts using linear, exponential, power, and trigonometric functions • To describe the table and graph patterns expected for linear, exponential, power, trigonometric, and square root functions from the symbolic forms	**after page 428** Students can begin Modeling Task 1 or 2 from p. 434. **after page 430** Students can begin Modeling Task 3 or 4 from p. 434. **page 434** **Modeling:** 1 or 2, 3, and 4* **Organizing:** 1 and 2 **Reflecting:** 2, and 3 or 4* **Extending:** 1 and choice of one*	8 days	• Teaching Resources 156–160 • Assessment Resources 229–234 • *Optional:* RAP Book Exercise Set 16
Lesson 2 *Customizing Models 1: Reflections and Vertical Transformations* • To recognize how the graph and table of $f(x)$ relate to the graph and table of $f(x) + a$ • To recognize how the graph and table of $f(x)$ relate to the graph and table of $-f(x)$ • To recognize how the graph and table of $f(x)$ relate to the graph and table of $af(x)$ • To reason with the transformations above as they relate to real-world situations	**after page 446** Students can begin Modeling Task 2 or 3 or Extending Task 3 from p. 453. **after page 449** Students can begin Extending Task 4 from p. 453. **page 453** **Modeling:** 2 or 3, and 5* **Organizing:** 2, 4, and 5 **Reflecting:** 2, 3, or 4* **Extending:** Choose one*	4 days	• Teaching Resources 155a–155d, 161–165 • Assessment Resources 235–240 • *Optional:* RAP Book Exercise Set 17
Lesson 3 *Customizing Models 2: Horizontal Transformations* • To recognize how the graph and table of $f(x)$ relate to the graph and table of $f(x + a)$ • To recognize how the graph and table of $f(x)$ relate to the graph and table of $f(ax)$ • To reason with the transformations above as they relate to real-world situations	**after page 466** Students can begin Modeling Task 5 or Reflecting Task 5 from p. 469. **page 469** **Modeling:** 5 and choice of one* **Organizing:** 2 and 4 **Reflecting:** 3 and 5 **Extending:** 3 or 5*	4 days	• Teaching Resources 166–170 • Assessment Resources 241–246 • *Optional:* RAP Book Exercise Set 18
Lesson 4 *Looking Back* • To review the major objectives of the unit		3 days (includes testing)	• Teaching Resources 171–172b • Unit Summary Master • Assessment Resources 247–263 • *Optional:* RAP Book Practice Set 9

When choice is indicated, it is important to leave the choice to the student.
Note: *It is best if Organizing tasks are discussed as a whole class after they have been assigned as homework.*

Unit 6

Lesson 1 **Function Models Revisited**

One of the most important and controversial problems in earth and space science today is measuring, understanding, and predicting causes of global warming. There is concern that the average annual temperature of Earth appears to have been increasing over the past century. Many scientists believe the increase is probably caused by greenhouse gases that reduce the radiation of energy from Earth's surface into space. The graphs below show two key patterns of atmospheric change over time.

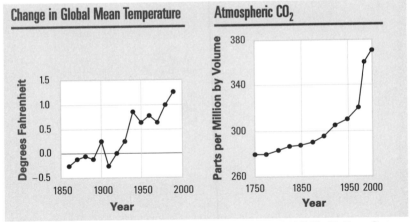

From "A Greenhouse Tool Kit" in *The Washington Post* 11/12/97. Copright © 1997, The Washington Post. Reprinted with permission.

The challenge for scientists is deciding how current trends in greenhouse gas amounts and world temperature change should be projected into the future. Different projections imply that different actions are needed, each with important consequences for industry, agriculture, and personal lifestyles.

Lesson 1 Function Models Revisited

LESSON OVERVIEW In this lesson, students revisit function models that they have studied up to this point in the *Contemporary Mathematics in Context* curriculum. Students investigate contexts which lead to linear, exponential, power, and trigonometric models. Quadratic and square root functions are also revisited. Students formalize their thinking about functions with the language of horizontal and vertical asymptotes and describe changes in function tables and graphs that result from changing parameters in symbolic rules. When students complete this lesson, they should have an organized functions toolkit to include in their Mathematics Toolkit. These functions, along with the absolute value function, are then customized or transformed in Lessons 2 and 3.

Lesson Objectives

- To model and answer questions about contexts using linear, exponential, power, and trigonometric functions
- To describe the table and graph patterns expected for linear, exponential, power, trigonometric, and square root functions from the symbolic form

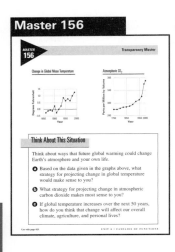

LAUNCH full-class discussion

Think About This Situation

See Teaching Master 156.

ⓐ The graph looks like it might be linear, but it is not clearly so. Some students may want to try an exponential model. Use the data to determine a model, and then use the model to make predictions of future changes.

ⓑ These data look exponential. Students might suggest fitting an exponential model and using that model to make predictions about future changes in atmospheric carbon dioxide levels.

ⓒ The effects that global warming will have partially depend on the degree of change that occurs. If it is very small, the effects will be minimal, but even small rises in temperature might have pronounced effects. Responses may vary; for example, warming trends would possibly affect where people live. Areas that are now very close to sea level might be underwater even with slight warming trends. More water might mean more flooding and cause agricultural losses for many countries. Governments might put legislation into effect to support efforts to curb the increase of carbon dioxide, which might cause taxes to be increased. A warmer and more moist environment might aid the growth of harmful bacteria, causing more disease.

EXPLORE small-group investigation

INVESTIGATION 1▶ Modeling Atmospheric Change

The activities in this investigation prompt students to review and compare linear, exponential, power, and quadratic models. In Activity 1, students set up a family of linear functions, each of which has the same *y*-intercept but a different slope. The effects of these slopes on predicting future temperatures are examined. In Activity 2, students write linear functions to enable them to answer questions about the concentration of CO_2 in the atmosphere. Students should be very familiar with these Course 1 concepts; they were extensively reviewed in the "Multiple-Variable Models" unit at the beginning of Course 3. Activities 3 and 4 review exponential growth and decay, and Activities 5 and 6 review direct and inverse power models and the concepts of perimeter, area, and volume.

You might want to have on hand some cubes, a cylinder or other nonrectangular prism, and a globe or balls of various sizes for demonstration purposes in Activity 5. See the notes for that activity, page T426.

Because no new concepts are introduced in this investigation, you will want to judge how much time you will give to this review. From the "Think About This Situation" discussion, you will have some assessment of your students' retention of the connections among the symbolic, tabular, and graphic representations of these models. You may choose to assign one activity to each group and let groups review and present the activities to the rest of the class, or you may decide that your students need to do all of these activities.

In the first two courses of *Contemporary Mathematics in Context*, you investigated several important **families of functions** that are useful in describing and predicting patterns of change, some of which are similar to those you considered in the "Think About This Situation" above. The members of each family have closely related patterns in tables, graphs, and symbolic rules. In this unit, you will review the properties of each function family and investigate ways to modify the basic function rules to model more complex situations.

INVESTIGATION 1 ▶ Modeling Atmospheric Change

As different scientists have studied the historical records of temperature and carbon dioxide data, they've proposed different scenarios for the future of global warming. Each is based on certain assumptions about the best models for patterns of change.

1. Data giving Earth's surface temperatures are collected from several sources: over 10,000 land-based weather stations, weather balloons sent up regularly by several hundred of those stations, ships and fixed buoys in the ocean, and orbiting satellites. These data are combined to estimate Earth's annual average temperature, which is currently 60°F. The rate at which that average Earth temperature is changing is contro-versial. Many scientists believe it is rising, but estimates vary from about 0.05°F to 0.15°F per decade.

LESSON 1 • FUNCTION MODELS REVISITED   **423**

a. Write rules for function models that predict the annual average temperature x decades from now for three different rate-of-increase estimates: 0.05, 0.10, and 0.15 degree per decade. Draw sketches of the various models on the same coordinate system.

b. Write equations or inequalities whose solutions would answer the following questions in the cases of low (0.05° per decade) and high (0.15° per decade) rate-of-change estimates. In your group, discuss how the results could be determined using function tables and graphs and by manipulation of the symbolic expressions in each rule. Then individually answer the questions, in both the low-estimate and the high-estimate cases, using the method that seems most effective.

■ What will the average Earth temperature be 50 years from now?

■ When will the average Earth temperature reach 61°F?

■ How long will the average Earth temperature remain below 62°F?

2. Perhaps the most well-known theory for global warming is that the increase of atmospheric carbon dioxide (CO_2), methane, nitrous oxide, and chlorofluoro-carbon gases is responsible. Roughly 60% of the increase in these gases is from carbon dioxide. The mass of CO_2 in the atmosphere is commonly measured in billions of tons or *gigatons* (abbreviated Gt). Estimates in 2000 suggested that Earth's atmosphere contained about 750 Gt of CO_2, with another 3 Gt added each year. Atmospheric carbon dioxide is increasing because human activities send more CO_2 into the atmosphere than natural biological processes remove. For example, the burning of fossil fuels sends 5 to 6 Gt of CO_2 into Earth's atmosphere every year.

a. Write a function rule to estimate atmospheric CO_2 at any time x years after 2000.

b. Use the model from Part a to answer these questions:

■ What level of atmospheric CO_2 can we expect in the year 2020?

■ When can we expect atmospheric CO_2 to reach 800 Gt?

c. Suppose that when the atmospheric CO_2 reaches 800 Gt, we find a way to reduce human emissions and increase biological processes that extract CO_2 from the atmosphere.

■ What rate of change would be required to bring atmospheric CO_2 back to 2000 levels in 20 years?

■ What function would predict atmospheric CO_2 levels x years after the time at which corrective action began?

As students work on this investigation, be sure to ask them about how the *y* values are changing for the different models. If you discovered in the "Think About This Situation" discussion that students were saying "exponential" and thinking "x^2," you might want to provide a simple example, such as $y = x^2$, in tabular form to remind them that multiplicative growth is unique to exponential functions.

1. **a.** $f(x) = 60 + 0.05x$
$f(x) = 60 + 0.10x$
$f(x) = 60 + 0.15x$
x represents the number of decades from now.

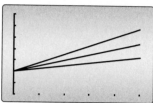

b. The answers to the questions can be determined by using the trace function to examine the graphs, by looking at the tables for the appropriate values of x or $f(x)$, or by using symbolic reasoning. When using symbolic reasoning, the general approach is to isolate the term containing the variable and then divide by the coefficient of the variable.

Using $f(x) = 60 + 0.05x$
■ $f(5) = 60 + 0.05(5)$
   $f(5) = 60.25°$
■ $61 = 60 + 0.05x$
   $x = 20$
   200 years
■ $62 > 60 + 0.05x$
   $40 > x$
   400 years

Using $f(x) = 60 + 0.15x$
■ $f(5) = 60 + 0.15(5)$
   $f(5) = 60.75°$
■ $61 = 60 + 0.15x$
   $x ≈ 6.7$
   67 years
■ $62 > 60 + 0.15x$
   $13.33 > x$
   approximately 133 years

2. **a.** $f(x) = 750 + 3x$; x represents the number of years after 2000.

b. ■ $750 + 3(20) = 810$ Gt of CO_2 in 2020
   ■ $750 + 3x = 800$
   $x ≈ 16.67$
   We can expect the carbon dioxide level to reach 800 between 16 and 17 years after 2000, which is sometime during 2016.

c. ■ To decrease the carbon dioxide by 50 Gt over a 20-year time period, the average annual reduction must be $\frac{50}{20}$ or 2.5 Gt per year.
   ■ The linear function that would model the level of atmospheric CO_2 under these conditions is $f(x) = 800 - 2.5x$.

Unit 6

3. a. $\frac{3}{750} = 0.004$ or 0.4% increase for 2000.

  b. $f(x) = 750(1.004)^x$ where x represents the number of years after 2000.

  c. The exponential model is in Y_1 and the linear model in Y_2 in the tables and graphs below. Comparing the two models, we can see that the predictions based on the linear model show less carbon dioxide than those based on the exponential model. Responses will vary regarding which model is better. Perhaps the fact that population growth rates tend to be exponential and the fact that more people means more use of items that produce carbon dioxide give a stronger case for the exponential model being the better of the two.

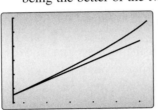

X	Y₁	Y₂
0	750	750
10	780.55	780
20	812.34	810
30	845.42	840
40	879.85	870
50	915.69	900
60	952.98	930

Y₂ ▤ 750+3X

X	Y₁	Y₂
70	991.79	960
80	1032.2	990
90	1074.2	1020
100	1118	1050
110	1163.5	1080
120	1210.9	1110
130	1260.2	1140

Y₁ ▤ 750(1.004)^X

4. a. 4.94 nanograms after 1 century

  4.88 nanograms after 2 centuries

  The function $f(x) = 5(0.988)^x$ will give the amount of carbon-14 that would be expected to be present after x centuries.

  b. Students may use the graph, the tables of values, or symbolic reasoning to find that the half-life of carbon-14 is approximately 5,740 years (actually 5,730 years).

  c. Again, students should be encouraged to use whatever method they choose. If there were 3 nanograms, then the wood would be approximately 4,230 years old. If there was only 1 nanogram, then it would be about 13,300 years old.

3. From the graph of atmospheric CO_2 reproduced at right, it looks as if, over the last 250 years, the rate of increase has not been constant. Suppose that the 2000 increase of 3 Gt per year is expressed as a percent and that future increases occur at that same percent rate.

Atmospheric CO₂

a. What is the 2000 percent rate of increase?

b. Write a function rule to estimate atmospheric carbon dioxide x years after 2000, assuming growth from 750 Gt at a constant percent rate.

c. Compare estimates about the growth of atmospheric CO_2 over the next few decades using the model in Part b to your estimates using the model in Activity 2, which is based on different assumptions. Explain reasons why you believe one or the other model is better.

It has been estimated that in the 10,000 years since the end of the last ice age, the annual average temperature of Earth has increased by about 9°F and atmospheric carbon dioxide has increased by at least 50%. Scientists arrived at such estimates by analyzing material that has been trapped deep in very old glaciers and on the floors of lakes and oceans for thousands of years.

One of the interesting problems in such work is estimating the age of deposits that are uncovered by core drilling. A common technique is called *carbon dating*. Carbon occurs in all living matter in several different forms. The most common forms (carbon-12 and carbon-13) are chemically stable; the other form, carbon-14, is radioactive and decays at a rate of 1.2% per century. By measuring the proportion of carbon-14 in a scientific sample and comparing that figure to the proportion in living matter, it is possible to estimate the time when the matter in the sample stopped growing. Despite the very small amounts of carbon-14 involved (less than 0.000000001% of total carbon in living matter), modern instruments can make the required measurements.

4. Suppose that drilling into what was once a lake bottom produces a piece of wood which, according to its mass, would have contained 5 nanograms (5 billionths of a gram) of carbon-14 when the wood was alive. Use the fact that this radioactive carbon decays continuously at a rate of about 1.2% per century to analyze the sample.

a. How much of that carbon-14 would be expected to remain 1 century later? 2 centuries later? x centuries later?

b. Estimate the half-life of carbon-14.

c. What age estimate would make sense if the sample actually contained 3 nanograms of carbon-14? If it contained only 1 nanogram?

Glaciers sometimes hold clues to the past.

One of the ominous and spectacular predictions about global warming is that the melting of polar ice caps and expansion of ocean water will cause sea levels to rise and flood cities along all ocean shores. One estimate predicts a 1-meter rise in sea levels by the year 2100, a change that would flood large parts of low countries like the Netherlands and Bangladesh.

Estimates of such a rise in the sea level depend on measurements of glacier volumes and ocean surface areas. Earth is approximately a sphere, and oceans cover approximately 70% of Earth's surface. The Greenland and Antarctic ice sheets cover nearly 6 million square miles and contain nearly 7 million cubic miles of ice, but that water is only 2% of all water on the planet.

5. In making estimates of the size of Earth (and other spherical planets as well), it's useful to have formulas showing the circumference, surface area, and volume of a sphere as functions of the diameter or radius. Sometimes it's useful to modify those relationships to show the radius or diameter required to give specified circumference, surface area, or volume.

a. Which of the following function rules will give circumference as a function of radius r? Which will give area? Volume? What clues can you use to make the correct match, even if you don't remember the specific formulas?

- $f(r) = 4\pi r^2$
- $g(r) = \frac{4}{3}\pi r^3$
- $h(r) = 2\pi r$

b. What patterns would you expect in graphs of the functions giving circumference, surface area, and volume of a sphere?

c. Earth is not a perfect sphere, but nearly so, with average radius of about 4,000 miles. What is the approximate surface area of Earth's oceans? What volume of water would be required to raise the level of those oceans by 3 feet? (Assume raising the level would not change the surface area of the ocean significantly.)

d. What rise in ocean levels would be caused by the total melting of the Greenland and Antarctic ice caps? (Again, assume the surface area of the oceans would not change.)

e. Earth is only the fifth largest of the planets in the solar system. The largest planet, Jupiter, has a radius roughly 11 times the radius of Earth. The radius of Mars is roughly half that of Earth. Based on these facts, how would you expect the circumference, surface area, and volume of Jupiter and of Mars to compare to the corresponding measures of Earth? Compare your answers and analysis methods to those of another group. Resolve any differences.

Your students might need a review of concepts associated with perimeter, area, and volume before working on Activity 5. Construct a rectangular prism with some cubes, and ask how the perimeter of the base, the total surface area, and the volume can be computed. Ask your students to give units of measure with their answers. Then continue with the following questions: "How would the height change if we knew that the volume was doubled but the base remained unchanged? What is the height if the length and width are 3 units and 5 units, respectively, and the volume is 75 cubic units? What is the base area of a prism that has an irregular-shaped base, a height of 6 units, and a volume of 42 cubic units?"

When it is clear that students differentiate among the various measures, you can ask for and record general formulas for a rectangular prism ($P_{base} = 2L + 2W$, $A_{base} = LW$, $V = LWH$). Then, tell students that they are going to use what they understand about perimeter, area, and volume to make sensible guesses about formulas for these measures as they relate to spheres. Together, read over the introductory information and Activity 5. Ask for initial estimates of the volume required to raise ocean levels by 3 feet or how much the circumference of Earth would change if the radius were changed by 3 feet. You might want to provide three choices for each. Student guesses are likely to be far too low for the question about raising the water level and far too high for the question about increasing the radius.

5. **a.** The function $h(r) = 2\pi r$ gives circumference of a sphere.

     The function $f(r) = 4\pi r^2$ gives surface area of a sphere.

     The function $g(r) = \frac{4}{3}\pi r^3$ gives volume of a sphere.

     By examining the degree of the formula, students should be able to determine which measurement it will give: Circumference is linear or first degree, surface area is second degree, and volume is third degree.

   b. Students should do more than use the words *linear*, *quadratic*, and *cubic* in describing the patterns in the graphs. The graph of $C = 2\pi r$ will show a linear relationship between C and r, with a slope of 2π and $(0, 0)$ for the y-intercept. The graph of $A = 4\pi r^2$ will show a quadratic pattern, with the curve rising steeply at an increasing rate in the first quadrant and the vertex at $(0, 0)$. (The curve has reflection symmetry across the y-axis, although students may focus on the practical domain rather than the theoretical one.) The graph of $V = \frac{4}{3}\pi r^3$ will rise even more steeply than the area function as r increases. (The curve has rotation symmetry about the origin.)

   c. $f(r) = 4\pi(4,000)^2 \approx 201,061,930$ square miles, so the surface area of Earth is approximately 200,000,000 square miles. Since 70% of Earth's surface is water, the approximate surface area of the oceans is $(0.7)(200,000,000)$ or approximately 140,000,000 square miles.

      To calculate the volume of any prism, we need to know the base area and height. We can think of the surface area of the ocean, 140,000,000 square miles, as the base of an irregular prism and calculate the volume created by using 3 feet or $\frac{3}{5,280}$ miles as the height. $V = \left(\frac{3}{5,280}\right)140,000,000$ or about 80,000 cubic miles.

   d. Again, we can think of the ocean surface area as the base of an irregular prism. Since this melting would add 7,000,000 cubic miles of water to the oceans, to find rise in ocean level we need to solve $\frac{x}{5,280}(140,000,000) = 7,000,000$. Solving for x gives a rise of 264 feet.

See additional Teaching Notes on page T485C.

Unit 6

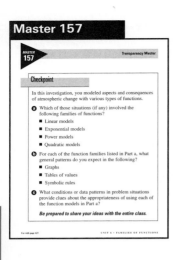

6. **a.** As the bodies move farther apart, the gravitational force decreases. As one or both of the bodies increase in mass, the gravitational force increases.

b. $F = k\left(\frac{m_1 m_2}{d^2}\right)$

c. If the distance is doubled, the gravitational force is divided by 4. If the distance is tripled, the gravitational force is divided by 9.

SHARE AND SUMMARIZE   full-class discussion

Checkpoint

See Teaching Master 157.

ⓐ ■ Linear models were used in modeling (*year, average annual temperature*) data, (*year, atmospheric concentration of CO$_2$*) data, and (*radius, circumference of a sphere*) data.

■ Exponential models were used in modeling (*year, atmospheric concentration of CO$_2$*) data and (*year, amount of carbon-14 remaining*) data.

■ Direct power models were used to model (*radius, surface area of a sphere*) data and (*radius, volume of a sphere*) data. An inverse power model was used to determine the gravitational force between two attracting masses at different distances.

■ The (*radius, surface area of a sphere*) model is quadratic.

ⓑ **Linear models**

■ The graph will be a line.

■ The *y* values in the table will have constant differences for constant increases in the *x* values.

■ The symbolic rule is of the form $f(x) = a + bx$.

Exponential models

■ The graph will be a curve asymptotic to the *x*-axis. For exponential growth, graphs will approach 0 as *x* gets large negatively and will increase at an increasing rate as *x* increases. For exponential decay, as *x* increases, the graph approaches the *x*-axis at a decreasing rate.

■ The *y* values will differ by a constant factor for constant differences in the *x* values.

■ The symbolic form is $f(x) = a(b^x)$, $b > 0$, $b \neq 1$. If *b* is between 0 and 1, then the equation models an exponential decay situation. If *b* is greater than 1, then it is a model of exponential growth.

Power models

■ For even-degree direct power models, the graph will be a parabola (or ∪-shaped) and be symmetric across the *y*-axis. For odd-degree direct power models, the graph will have a $\curvearrowright$ shape and have 180°-rotational symmetry about the origin. The graph of an inverse power model will be asymptotic to both the *x*-axis and the *y*-axis. If *n* is even, the graph will be either entirely above or entirely below the *x*-axis. If *n* is odd, the graph will be in quadrants 1 and 3 or quadrants 2 and 4.

See additional Teaching Notes on page T485C.

6. The gravitational force that holds all of us anchored to Earth's surface diminishes as one moves up into the atmosphere. In general, the gravitational force of attraction between two masses is directly proportional to the product of the masses and inversely proportional to the square of the distance between their centers.

  a. What does the above description of gravitational force suggest will happen as the distance between two planetary bodies increases? As one or both of the bodies increase in mass?

  b. Which of the following expressions matches the given information about the force between masses m_1 and m_2 located at a distance d apart?

  ■ $F = k(m_1 m_2 - d^2)$

  ■ $F = k\left(\dfrac{m_1 m_2}{d^2}\right)$

  ■ $F = k\left(\dfrac{m_1 m_2}{d^2}\right)^2$

  c. If the distance between two attracting masses is doubled, how will the gravitational force of attraction between those bodies change? What if the distance is tripled?

Checkpoint

In this investigation, you modeled aspects and consequences of atmospheric change with various types of functions.

ⓐ Which of those situations (if any) involved the following families of functions?

  ■ Linear models

  ■ Exponential models

  ■ Power models

  ■ Quadratic models

ⓑ For each of the function families listed in Part a, what general patterns do you expect in the following?

  ■ Graphs

  ■ Tables of values

  ■ Symbolic rules

ⓒ What conditions or data patterns in problem situations provide clues about the appropriateness of using each of the function models in Part a?

Be prepared to share your ideas with the entire class.

LESSON 1 • FUNCTION MODELS REVISITED   **427**

On Your Own

Think back over previous units and courses and consider the variety of problem situations that you modeled with function rules. Which involved mathematical relations similar to those that you've just used to model patterns of change in global temperature, atmospheric CO_2, and decay of carbon-14? Which involved mathematical relations similar to those used to model patterns of Earth sea levels, planetary size, and gravity? Organize your responses by families of functions.

INVESTIGATION 2 Modeling Periodic Change

Increasing carbon dioxide in the atmosphere has been suggested as a leading cause for the recent observed increase in Earth temperatures. If such global

warming continues, polar and glacial ice may melt and ocean waters may expand, causing the oceans to rise. However, not all changes in Earth's climate and geography are strictly increasing. Some important variables are **periodic**: They change in regular patterns that repeat over constant intervals of time.

1. Suppose you lived near the Atlantic Ocean or a tidal bay and tracked the depth of the water on a retaining wall every three hours. If you began recording data at high tide of five feet, the data might yield a pattern like the one shown in the plot below.

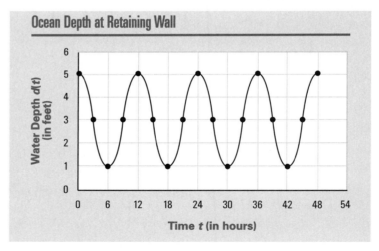

Ocean Depth at Retaining Wall

▶On Your Own

Responses may vary. As examples of linear models, students may mention the relationships between weight and stretch for the bungee apparatus or between ticket price and income (or other cost-per-item relationships). Students might mention population growth in the United States, Brazil, and China as situations that are modeled well by exponential models. The whale population, wolf population, or bacteria populations are other exponential growth situations that students might remember. Exponential decay models were used to analyze decay rates for a variety of medicines and radioactive materials.

As examples of power models, students might recall the "Power Models" unit in which they thought about the proportional size of the balloon figures in a parade. They might also mention the activity in which they examined the relationships between the edge length of a cube and the area of one face, the total surface area, and the volume. As examples of inverse power models, students may recall the relationships between distance and the intensity of sound or light. When thinking about quadratic models, they might think of dropping rocks, diving, kicking or hitting balls, jumping on trampolines, or situations involving profit or income.

MORE

ASSIGNMENT *pp. 434–440*

Students can now begin Modeling Task 1 or 2 from the MORE assignment following Investigation 3.

Unit 6

INVESTIGATION ▶2▶ Modeling Periodic Change

In this investigation, students review some characteristics of trigonometric curves and learn vocabulary useful in describing them. Students have already encountered these functions in the Course 2 unit "Geometric Form and Its Function," but they are likely to remember only that these functions produce a wave shape; they are not likely to have a clear idea about the impact of the parameters in the general form $f(x) = a \sin(bx) + c$. You might want to remind them of the Ferris wheel example for which the function was $f(t) = 30 \sin t + 35$. This will help them recall that the parameters play a specific role in each context. In Lessons 2 and 3, the specific influence of the parameters in transforming the general shape is examined in detail. At this point, students should be able to identify the functions and know how the amplitude and period are reflected in tables, graphs, and symbolic forms of $c(x) = a \cos(bx) + k$ and $s(x) = a \sin(bx) + k$. You may wish to review, as a large group, how to set up a graph for $s(x) = \sin x$ on the calculator and appropriate windows for angles measured in degrees and in radians. Students need to understand that a change in unit does not change the relationship between angle size and value of the sine ratio, but rather the window must be adjusted to see this relationship.

1. a. Ocean Depth at Retaining Wall

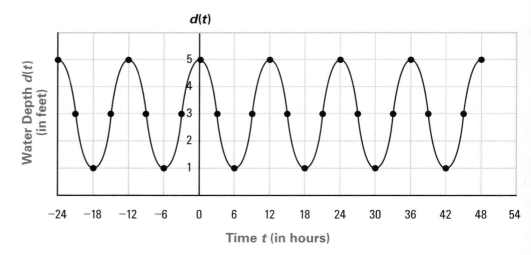

b. The period is approximately 12 hours.

c. The entire graph would be translated up $\frac{4}{12}$ or $\frac{1}{3}$ of a foot.

d. The function $d(t) = 2\cos\left(\frac{\pi}{6}t\right) + 3$ is the correct model for this situation.

e. The new function would be $d(t) = 2\cos\left(\frac{\pi}{6}t\right) + 3.33$ where t is time in hours.

2. Students should focus on the sine function for this activity. Some students may suggest $y = 2\cos\left(\frac{\pi}{6}t - \frac{\pi}{2}\right) + 3$ or another shift of the cosine function for Part c. You should acknowledge that such a shift would work; in fact, students will be performing horizontal shifts in Lesson 3. Then point out that the directions for Part c ask students to use the sine function.

a.

![Graph titled d(t) showing Water Depth d(t) (in feet) on vertical axis from 0 to 5 and Time t (in hours) on horizontal axis from 0 to 48, displaying a sine curve oscillating between 1 and 5 with midline at 3.]

b. The graph has the same general shape but a different period and a different amplitude from the graph of $y = \sin t$. Also, the midline is at $y = 3$ rather than at $y = 0$.

c. $y = 2\sin\left(\frac{\pi}{6}t\right) + 3$

d. The water is four feet deep at 1, 5, 13, 17, 25, 29, 37, and 41 hours.

3. a. $h(t) = 6\sin\left(\frac{\pi}{6}t\right)$, where t is time in seconds.

b. $h(t) = 6\cos\left(\frac{\pi}{6}t\right)$, where t is time in seconds.

c. The function rules use the same parameters, but one uses the sine function and one uses the cosine function.

a. Extend a copy of the graph on the previous page to show the predicted pattern of change for the previous 24 hours.

b. What is the period of this cyclical pattern?

c. Suppose melting of ice caps caused a four-inch rise in ocean levels. How would this change be reflected in the plot of water depths?

d. Which of the following rules models the water depth $d(t)$ in Part a as a function of time beginning at high tide? Assume radian measure for the input variable t.

- $d(t) = 2 \cos t$
- $d(t) = 2 \cos t + 3$
- $d(t) = 2 \cos \left(\frac{\pi}{6} t \right)$
- $d(t) = 2 \cos \left(\frac{\pi}{6} t \right) + 3$

e. Write a rule that models the water depth in Part c as a function of time beginning at high tide.

2. Suppose you began tracking the depth of the water on the retaining wall every three hours, beginning midway between low tide and high tide, as the tide is rising.

a. Make a graph of the expected pattern of change in water depth over the first 48 hours.

b. How is your graph similar to and different from the graph of $y = \sin t$?

c. Write a rule using the sine function that models the water depth in this situation.

d. When is the depth of the water four feet?

3. In modeling the behavior of tides using variations of the cosine and sine functions, you may have informally used the fact that the **period** of each of these functions is 2π and the **amplitude**, $\frac{1}{2} |maximum\ value - minimum\ value|$, of each is 1. Use similar reasoning to model the height of a Ferris wheel rider above the center line of a Ferris wheel that has a 6-meter radius and makes one revolution every 12 seconds. Using the diagram at the right, assume the wheel rotates in the counterclockwise direction.

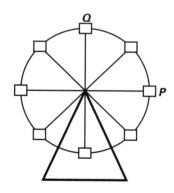

a. Write one rule assuming the rider begins at P.

b. Write another rule assuming the rider begins at Q.

c. How are your function rules in Parts a and b similar, and how are they different?

4. Work with partners to brainstorm a list of other variables in the world around you that change in periodic patterns. Then pick two of the variables and complete the following.

  a. Sketch graphs of each variable and estimate the period and amplitude.

  b. Describe how you would modify the basic cosine or sine function rules to fit the patterns in your graphs.

Checkpoint

In this investigation, you reviewed how to use variations of the trigonometric functions $s(x) = \sin x$ and $c(x) = \cos x$ to model periodic change.

ⓐ What clues in problem situations suggest using the cosine function as the basic building block? What clues suggest using the sine function?

ⓑ Suppose you are modeling a periodic phenomenon using the function $f(x) = a \cos (bx)$.

  ▪ How would you determine the value of a?

  ▪ How would you determine the value of b?

Be prepared to explain your modeling methods to the entire class.

▶ On Your Own

Weather conditions and the interdependence of animal species sometimes produce periodic fluctuations in animal populations. Suppose the rabbit population in the Sleeping Bear Dunes National Forest is at a minimum of approximately 4,000 rabbits in January. By July the population reaches a maximum of about 12,500. It returns to a low of around 4,000 in the following January, completing the annual cycle.

a. Make a plot of the rabbit population for a two-year period, starting in January.

b. What is the amplitude and period of your graph?

c. How is your plot of the rabbit population as a function of time similar to and different from the graph of $c(x) = \cos x$? Of $s(x) = \sin x$?

4. This activity is very open. You will get many examples from different groups. Having large sheets of paper to record these and posting them will be helpful. Variables and sketches will vary and might include some of the following situations, periods, and amplitudes.

Situation	Period	Amplitude
height of tides	12 hours	2–4 feet
fraction of the Moon	30 days	1
hours of sunlight	1 year	depends on location

For the following, consider the distance on an analog clock or watch from the tip of the specified hand to the line passing through 3 o'clock and 9 o'clock.

Situation	Period	Amplitude
second hand on a watch or clock	1 minute	length of second hand
minute hand on a watch or clock	1 hour	length of minute hand
hour hand on a watch or clock	12 hours	length of hour hand

SHARE AND SUMMARIZE   full-class discussion

Checkpoint

See Teaching Master 158.

ⓐ Both the sine and cosine functions model periodic change. If you start measuring a periodic change at its maximum value, it may be easier to try building a model using the cosine function. If the measurement when $x = 0$ is halfway between the maximum and minimum values, then the sine function may be easier to use.

ⓑ ■ The value of a is equal to the amplitude of the graph that models the data. So to find the value of a, evaluate $\frac{1}{2}|maximum\ value - minimum\ value|$.
■ b is related to the period of the data. To find the value of b, evaluate $\frac{2\pi}{period}$.

APPLY   individual task

▶On Your Own

a.

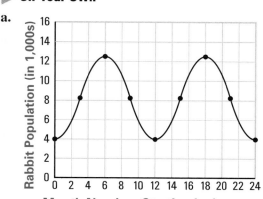

Month Number, Starting in January

b. The amplitude is 4,250 or 4.25 thousand, and the period is 12 months.

c. It is similar to both the cosine and sine functions in that it is periodic. If it were reflected across the line $y = 8.25$, it would be the graph of $y = 4.25 \cos\left(\frac{\pi}{6}x\right) + 8.25$. If it were translated 3 units to the left, it would be the graph of $y = 4.25 \sin\left(\frac{\pi}{6}x\right) + 8.25$.

MORE
ASSIGNMENT   *pp. 434–440*

Students can now begin Modeling Task 3 or 4 from the MORE assignment following Investigation 3.

Unit 6

EXPLORE small-group investigation

INVESTIGATION 3 It's All in the Family

In this investigation, students will carefully organize and formalize their understanding of all function models they have studied. In Activity 1, students' descriptions of patterns should be tied to their specific function examples. They will generalize their descriptions in Activity 2. During the Checkpoint discussion, consider having different groups present different function families. You may wish to design, in collaboration with students, an organized way of presenting the material to the class. Charts that can be created by the groups and put on large sheets of paper might be used to display the work of each group. Students will add new families to this functions toolkit as they progress through the unit.

NOTE: The precision of language required of students in this investigation should vary depending on the students. Those intending to pursue collegiate science courses should be required to be very precise with their functions toolkit language.

---

1. **See Teaching Masters 159a–159c.**
   a. See the chart, tables, and graphs on page T432 for Part a. One example from each family is provided below. Note that in Part b, *NOW-NEXT* equations give values of the functions evaluated at consecutive integers. Students need not consider both odd and even exponents for power models at this time. They should be discussed at the Checkpoint Part b.

   Linear Functions
   b. ■ For a 1-unit change in x values, there will be a 0.5-unit change in corresponding $f(x)$ values. The amount of change is equal to the coefficient of the x term in the symbolic rule.
      ■ $NEXT = NOW + 0.5$ (start at 3)
   c. The graph will be a line with y-intercept of 3 and slope of 0.5. In the symbolic rule, these values correspond to the constant term and the coefficient of the x-term, respectively. In the table of values, these can be seen as the $f(x)$ value corresponding to 0 and to the difference between subsequent $f(x)$ values.

   Exponential Functions
   b. ■ The ratio of consecutive $f(x)$ values will be a constant that corresponds to the base of the exponential model, in this case 3. This is seen in the table by noticing that each $f(x)$ value is 3 times the preceding $f(x)$ value.
      ■ $NEXT = NOW \cdot 3$ (start at 5)
   c. The y-intercept of the graph will be the constant by which the exponential term is multiplied. In the table, the y-intercept can be found by finding the $f(x)$ value corresponding to $x = 0$. Since the base is greater than 1, the graph curves upward at an increasing rate. The "steepness" is determined by the base. The base of the exponential equation can be seen in the graph by the tripling of the distance from the x-axis with each consecutive integer value for x. This distance is seen in the table by the tripling of $f(x)$ values for integer increases in x. (If the base were between 0 and 1, the graph would show decreasing $f(x)$ values as the x values increased. The $f(x)$ values would decrease at a decreasing rate.)

See additional Teaching Notes on page T485D.

INVESTIGATION 3 ▶ It's All in the Family

Studying the causes and effects of change in Earth's climate requires modeling and forecasting change in many variables. The functions that model relations among those variables and their patterns of change over time are often drawn from several important families that you've studied in earlier work: linear, exponential, power, and periodic. You've probably discovered that, to use those functions as descriptive and predictive models of change, it's important to know well the numeric, graphic, and symbolic patterns that are typical of each type.

The activities in this investigation ask you to construct and then extend an outline of the functions toolkit that you've been building throughout your study of algebra and trigonometry. As you complete this unit and other units in the *Contemporary Mathematics in Context* curriculum, you should add other function families to this toolkit outline.

1. On a copy of the functions toolkit outline on the next page, create your own toolkit by doing the following for each basic type of function.

   a. Give an example of a typical symbolic rule to calculate outputs from given inputs. Describe the domain and range of your sample function.

   b. Provide a table of sample (*input*, *output*) number pairs.

   - Explain how the table pattern can be predicted from the symbolic rule and how the rule can be predicted from the table pattern.

   - If possible, describe the pattern in the output values using a *NOW-NEXT* equation.

   c. Sketch a graph of the function. Explain how the graph pattern can be predicted from the symbolic rule and table pattern and how the rule and table pattern can be predicted from the graph.

2. Looking back at your toolkit of functions, you can see that the general symbolic rule for each function family involves one or more constants *a* and *b*, called **parameters**. For each function family, describe how different values of the parameters match different patterns in tables and graphs.

3. Examine this graph of the inverse power function $f(x) = \frac{1}{x}$.

   a. Note that for large values of *x*, either positive or negative, the graph gets closer and closer to the *x*-axis. Explain why the distance between the graph and the *x*-axis gets closer and closer to zero.

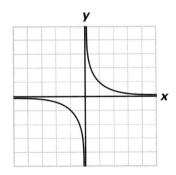

Functions Toolkit

Function Family/Example	Table	Graph
Linear Functions $f(x) = a + bx$ $f(x) = 0.5x + 3$ domain: all real numbers range:		

Linear Functions

$f(x) = a + bx$

$f(x) = 0.5x + 3$

domain: all real numbers

range:

x	f(x)
0	3

Exponential Functions

$f(x) = a(b^x)$, $a \neq 0$,

$b > 1$ or $0 < b < 1$

$f(x) =$

domain:

range:

x	f(x)

Power Functions

Direct: $f(x) = ax^n$, $a \neq 0$, $n > 0$

$f(x) =$

domain:

range:

x	f(x)

Inverse: $g(x) = ax^n$, $a \neq 0$, $n < 0$

$g(x) =$

domain:

range:

x	g(x)

Trigonometric Functions

$s(x) = a \sin(bx)$, $a \neq 0$, $b > 0$

$s(x) =$

domain:

range:

period:

x	s(x)

$c(x) = a \cos(bx)$, $a \neq 0$, $b > 0$

$c(x) =$

domain:

range:

period:

x	c(x)

Functions Toolkit

Function Family/Example	Table			Graph

Linear Functions

$f(x) = a + bx$

$f(x) = 0.5x + 3$

domain: all real numbers

range: all real numbers

x	f(x)
−2	2
−1	2.5
0	3
1	3.5
2	4
3	4.5

Exponential Functions

$f(x) = a(b^x)$, $a \neq 0$, $b > 1$ or

$0 < b < 1$

$f(x) = 5(3^x)$

domain: all real numbers

range: all positive numbers

x	f(x)
−2	$\frac{5}{9}$
−1	$\frac{5}{3}$
0	5
1	15
2	45
3	135

Power Functions

Direct: $f(x) = ax^n$, $a \neq 0$, $n > 0$

  $f(x) = 3x^2$

domain: all real numbers

range: $f(x) \geq 0$

x	f(x)
−2	12
−1	3
0	0
1	3
2	12
3	27

Inverse: $g(x) = ax^n$, $a \neq 0$, $n < 0$

  $g(x) = 2x^{-1} = \frac{2}{x}$

domain: all real numbers except 0

range: all real numbers except 0

x	g(x)
−2	−1
−1	−2
0	undefined
1	2
2	1
3	$\frac{2}{3}$

Trigonometric Functions

$s(x) = a \sin(bx)$, $a \neq 0$, $b > 0$

$s(x) = 3 \sin x$

domain: all real numbers

range: $-3 \leq s(x) \leq 3$

period: 2π

$c(x) = a \cos(bx)$, $a \neq 0$, $b > 0$

$c(x) = 3 \cos x$

domain: all real numbers

range: $-3 \leq c(x) \leq 3$

period: 2π

x	s(x)	c(x)
0	0	3
$\frac{\pi}{4}$	2.12	2.12
$\frac{\pi}{2}$	3	0
$\frac{3\pi}{4}$	2.12	−2.12
π	0	−3
$\frac{3\pi}{2}$	−3	0
2π	0	3

Unit 6

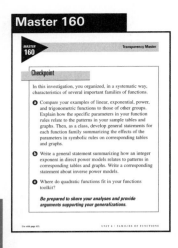

CONSTRUCTING A MATH TOOLKIT: Students should include their functions toolkits in their Math Toolkits. You may wish to ask students to provide specific examples of a quadratic function and both odd and even power functions. After the "On Your Own" tasks, students should include the square root function in their Math Tookits.

EXPLORE *continued*

3. **b.** The solution to Part a explains how the *x*-axis is an asymptote. Similarly, the *y*-axis is an asymptote since the value of $\frac{1}{x}$ gets very large, either positive or negative, as *x* approaches 0. Also, since $\frac{1}{x}$ never equals 0, the graph has no points on the *y*-axis.

   c. Inverse power functions all have the *x*- and *y*-axes as asymptotes. Direct power functions have no asymptotes.

   d. Exponential functions have the *x*-axis as a horizontal asymptote (the positive *x*-axis when $0 < b < 1$; the negative *x*-axis if $b > 1$).

   e. If a problem situation has one variable that gets arbitrarily close to a given number as *x* increases or decreases, then there is likely to be an asymptote at that number.

SHARE AND SUMMARIZE full-class discussion

Checkpoint

See Teaching Master 160.

ⓐ At this point, make sure that all students have complete general statements for each family of functions and the effects of parameters in their functions toolkit.

ⓑ Make sure students know the differences in the patterns for even and odd exponents for direct and inverse power models, as described in Activity 2, page T485E.

ⓒ Quadratic functions are direct power functions of degree 2 that have been translated horizontally or vertically. Quadratic polynomials should be added to students' function toolkits. There are functions of the form $f(x) = ax^2 + bx + c$, where $a \neq 0$. So direct power functions of degree 2 are also quadratric polynomials.

Additional Practice

In order for students to practice identifying function family patterns, you may wish to do the following activity: Have each group write 8 challenges in the form of 2 rules, 2 tables, 2 graphs, and 2 problem situations on index cards. Collect the cards and redistribute them among the groups. Have each group tape its cards to the function family charts that the cards match.

APPLY individual task

On Your Own

a. $f(x) = \sqrt{x}$

domain: $x \geq 0$

range: $f(x) \geq 0$

x	f(x)
0	0
1	1
2	1.414
4	2
9	3

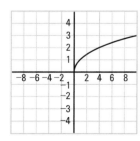

b. Problem contexts will vary. Any context that involves the distance formula or the lengths of sides of a right triangle would be appropriate for the use of the square root function. Another context that students might suggest is finding the time it takes for an object to fall a given distance using the rule $d(t) = -16t^2$.

b. The graph of $f(x) = \frac{1}{x}$ is said to have the x-axis as a **horizontal asymptote**. This graph also has a **vertical asymptote**, which is the y-axis. Explain why this is the case.

c. Describe the asymptotes of the family of power functions.

d. What other function families have graphs with *asymptotic behavior*? What are the asymptotes?

e. What conditions in problem situations suggest function models with one or more asymptotes?

Checkpoint

In this investigation, you organized, in a systematic way, characteristics of several important families of functions.

ⓐ Compare your examples of linear, exponential, power, and trigonometric functions to those of other groups. Explain how the specific parameters in your function rules relate to the patterns in your sample tables and graphs. Then, as a class, develop general statements for each function family summarizing the effects of the parameters in symbolic rules on corresponding tables and graphs.

ⓑ Write a general statement summarizing how an integer exponent in direct power models relates to patterns in corresponding tables and graphs. Write a corresponding statement about inverse power models.

ⓒ Where do quadratic functions fit in your functions toolkit?

Be prepared to share your analyses and provide arguments supporting your generalizations.

On Your Own

In Course 2 of *Contemporary Mathematics in Context*, you explored the **square root function** $f(x) = \sqrt{x}$, where $x \geq 0$.

a. Include this function model in your toolkit. Supply a sample table of (*input*, *output*) pairs, a graph, and information on the domain and range.

b. Describe at least two specific problem contexts that you think are good illustrative examples of this function model.

MORE

Modeling • Organizing • Reflecting • Extending

Modeling

1. Many variables are involved in operating a business delivery van. Write function models for the relationships described below. Then use those models to sketch the graphs you would expect in each case. For each function model, write several specific questions that could be answered by use of an equation or inequality and show at least two methods of answering each question.

a. One company calculated that the annual operating cost of its business delivery van was $4,000 for insurance and a part-time driver, plus $0.40 per mile for gas, oil, and maintenance. How does total operating cost depend on number of miles driven x?

b. The company decides to buy a new delivery van for $25,000. The van's resale value decreases at a rate of 20% per year. What is the resale value of the van x years after its purchase?

c. Accounting rules allow the company to recognize the expense from wear and tear by reducing the value of its new van on its records by $2,500 per year. This expense, called *depreciation*, reduces income and thus saves the company money on income taxes. What is the accounting value of the van x years after its purchase?

d. Inflation adds to the operating cost of the van at a rate of about 5% per year. If the total operating cost in 1998 was $8,800, what operating cost would be predicted for a time x years later?

Modeling

MORE
ASSIGNMENT *pp. 434–440*

Modeling: 1 or 2, 3, and 4*
Organizing: 1 and 2
Reflecting: 2, and 3 or 4*
Extending: 1 and choice of one*

When choice is indicated, it is important to leave the choice to the student.
NOTE: *It is best if Organizing tasks are discussed as a whole class after they have been assigned as homework.*

1. Student questions will vary. The questions given are samples of the types students might suggest. These questions can be answered by using tables, graphs, or symbolic rules.

   a. $C(x) = 4,000 + 0.4x$

   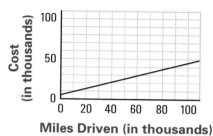

   How much will the annual operating costs be if the van is driven 35,000 miles during the year?

   If the operating expenses for one year are $64,000, how many miles was the van driven?

   b. $V(x) = 25,000(0.8)^x$

   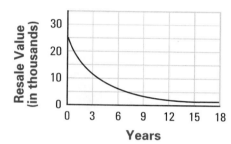

   When will the resale value be $10,000?

   What will the resale value be 5 years after the van is purchased?

   c. $A(x) = 25,000 - 2,500x$

   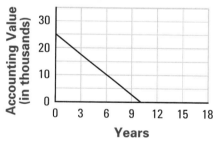

   What is the accounting value of the van after 3 years?

   When will the accounting value of the van equal zero?

   d. $O(x) = 8,800(1.05)^x$

   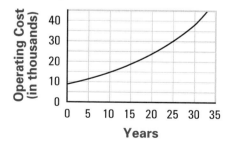

   When will the predicted operating expenses be $10,000?

   What operating cost is estimated for the year 2005?

Unit 6

2. **a.** $V = \pi(2)^2(5) \approx 62.83$ cubic feet

   $V \approx 62.83(7.5) \approx 471.24$ gallons

   b. The greater change comes from changing the radius. If you graph the function representing changes in volume as the radius changes, $V = 5\pi r^2$, and the function representing changes in volume when the height changes, $V = 4\pi h$, you can see that the graph of $V = 5\pi r^2$ rises more quickly as long as you are considering values greater than 1. If $0 < x < 1$, then the linear function increases more quickly.

   c. ■ $10,000 = \pi r^2 h$

   ■ $r = \sqrt{\frac{10,000}{\pi h}} = \frac{100}{\sqrt{\pi h}}$

   $r \approx 12.6$ feet when $h = 20$ feet

   ■ $h = \frac{10,000}{\pi r^2}$

   $h \approx 14.15$ feet when $r = 15$ feet

   d. Increasing the radius or the height causes the other variable to be reduced, but increasing the radius causes a bigger reduction in the height than the reduction in radius caused by an increase in height. This can be seen in the graphs of the two functions. The graph of the height function decreases at a faster rate than the graph of the radius function. Both functions are inverse power functions, so they have graphs that decrease at a decreasing rate and are asymptotic to both the x- and y-axes.

2. Storage containers often are rectangular or cylindrical in shape. The volume V of a cylinder is a function of its radius r and height h. The relationship among these variables is given by the equation $V = \pi r^2 h$. One of the most common uses of cylindrical containers is in tanks for fuel storage at refineries, factories, filling stations, and apartments or houses. Tanks can be designed and built to a variety of specifications.

a. If the design for a home oil tank calls for a radius of 2 feet and a height of 5 feet, what is the volume of that tank in cubic feet? What is the volume in gallons? (There are about 7.5 gallons to a cubic foot.)

b. The functions $V = (\pi r^2)(5)$ and $V = \pi(2^2)h$ show how volume depends on radius when height is fixed at 5 and on height when radius is fixed at 2. Which change in the design will produce the greatest change in volume: increasing or decreasing the radius or the height by some given amount? How is your answer shown in the graphs of the functions?

c. Suppose that you need to design a tank with fixed volume of 10,000 cubic feet (about 75,000 gallons).

■ Write an equation showing the relationship among radius r, height h, and this fixed volume.

■ Solve your equation for r to show how the required radius depends on the choice of height. Use this equation to find the required radius if the height is 20 feet.

■ Solve your original equation for h to show how the required height depends on the choice of radius. Use this equation to find the required height if the radius is 15 feet.

d. Study the relationships in Part c to see how changes in the two design options, height and radius, affect each other. How will increasing the design height of the tank change the required radius? How will increasing the design radius change the required height? What will the graphs of those relations look like?

Unit 6

3. There are many important situations in which variables are related by a function. Here are graphs and descriptions of several such situations. Match the descriptions to the graphs that seem to fit best. Then for each situation, describe the following:

■ The sorts of numerical values you would expect for each variable

■ A reasonable domain and range for each function

■ The function family (if any) that would probably provide a good modeling rule

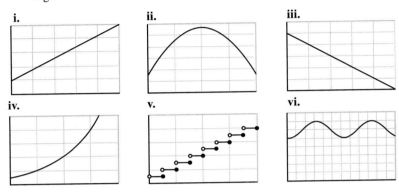

i.   ii.   iii.

iv.   v.   vi.

a. When a football team's punter kicks the ball, the ball's height changes as time passes from kick to catch. What pattern seems likely to relate time and height?

b. The senior class officers at Lincoln High School decided to order and sell souvenir baseball caps with the school insignia and name on them. One supplier said it would charge $100 to create the design and then an additional $4 for each cap made. How would the total cost of the order be related to the number of caps in the order?

c. The number of hours between sunrise and sunset changes throughout the year. What pattern seems likely to relate time and hours of sunlight?

d. In planning a bus trip to Florida for spring break, a travel agent worked on the assumption that each bus would hold at most 40 students. How would the number of buses be related to the number of student customers?

e. When the Lincoln High School sophomore class officers decided to order and sell T-shirts with the names of everyone in their class on the shirts, they checked with a sample of students to see how many would buy a T-shirt at various proposed prices. How would sales be related to price charged?

f. The population of the world has been increasing for as long as records have been available. What pattern of population growth has occurred over that time?

3. Responses will vary. For Part f, students may need to refer to an almanac to get a record of world population. The world population for 2001 is used below.

Description	Graph	Domain	Range	Basic Function Family
a.	ii.	$0 \leq x \leq 4$ seconds	$1 \leq f(x) \leq 55$ feet	Quadratic Polynomial
b.	i.	$0 \leq x \leq 250$ caps	$100 \leq f(x) \leq 1,100$ dollars	Linear
c.	vi.	$0 \leq x \leq 365$	$10 \leq f(x) \leq 14$	Trigonometric
d.	v.	$0 \leq x \leq 320$ students	$0 \leq f(x) \leq 8$ buses	None
e.	iii.	$0 \leq x \leq 25$ dollars	$0 \leq f(x) \leq 250$ T-shirts	Linear
f.	iv.	$1,600 < x < 2001$	$0 < f(x) < 6,189,614,323$	Exponential

Unit 6

MORE *continued*

4. a. Maximum: 25 feet
   Minimum: 15 feet
   Period: 12 hours
   Amplitude: 5 feet
   b. $d(t) = 5 \cos\left(\frac{\pi}{6}t\right) + 20$, where t is in hours.
5. a. Assuming ocean surface area didn't change significantly during that time, the additional ice held $\frac{600}{5,280}$ (145,000,000) or about 16,500,000 cubic miles. This is over twice (approximately 2.36 times) the current figure.
   b. (145,000,000)(average depth) = 350,000,000
   average depth ≈ 2.414 miles
   If the water (average depth) rose by 1 foot, the amount of additional water would be $145{,}000{,}000 \cdot \frac{1}{5{,}280}$ or about 27,462 cubic miles. This is an increase of $\frac{27{,}462}{350{,}000{,}000}$ or about 0.008%.

Unit 6

4. The following graph shows oscillation of the water depth in a shipping channel of an ocean harbor over two days.

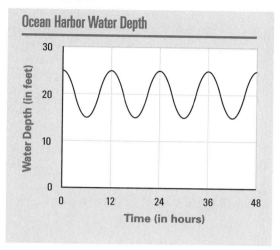

Ocean Harbor Water Depth

a. Based on information in the graph, estimate the maximum and minimum, the period, and the amplitude of periodic change in the water depth of the channel.

b. Write a function rule giving the depth of the channel as a function of time.

5. The surface area of Earth's oceans is about 145 million square miles, and they contain about 350 million cubic miles of water. Use these facts to answer the following questions about the effects of glaciers on ocean sea levels.

a. In the greatest ice age, sea levels were nearly 600 feet lower than they are today. About how much more water could have been contained in the glaciers of that ice age than exists now? How does your answer compare to the current figure of about 7 million cubic miles of glacier-contained water?

b. Sea levels also rise when ocean temperatures rise and cause the saline water in the oceans to expand. What is the average depth of the oceans? What percent expansion of the ocean waters would be required to produce a one-foot rise in sea levels?

Organizing

1. Without using a graphing calculator or computer software, sketch graph patterns that you would expect for each of the following functions. Then use your calculator or computer software to produce each graph and check your symbol sense. Explain how you knew what to expect in those cases for which your sketches were correct, and explain what your errors were in those cases for which your sketches were incorrect.

   a. $f(x) = 5 - 4x$ **b.** $g(t) = 3(2^t)$ **c.** $h(s) = -3s^2$

   d. $j(t) = 0.5 \sin t$ **e.** $k(r) = 2.5(0.4^r)$ **f.** $m(x) = \dfrac{5}{x}$

2. Describe the domain and range for each of the functions in Organizing Task 1, and be prepared to explain how you could determine each answer by examining the symbolic rule.

3. Write *NOW-NEXT* equations that correspond to each of the following function rules:

   a. $f(x) = 3 + 2x$ **b.** $g(x) = 4(1.5^x)$ **c.** $h(x) = -2x + 4.5$

4. Graphs of periodic functions, by definition, have translation symmetry. Reproduced below is the graph (from Investigation 2, Activity 1, page 428) of the cyclic pattern of depth of water in a tidal bay. Also shown is the *midline* of the graph.

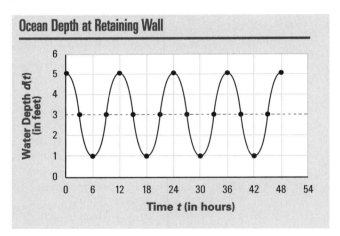

Ocean Depth at Retaining Wall

   a. Assuming the pattern of the graph continues to the left and to the right, what is the magnitude of the translation that maps the curve onto itself?

   b. What other types of symmetry are present in this graph?

   c. How is the amplitude of this function related to the midline?

   d. What is the midline of the graphs of $s(x) = \sin x$ and $c(x) = \cos x$? How is the midline related to the amplitude of each of these functions?

Organizing

1. Shown below are calculator graphs for each of the functions. Be sure students explain any errors or how they know what the graph should look like.

a. 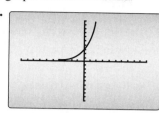 **b.** 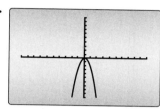 **c.**

d. 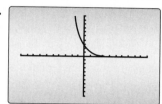 **e.** **f.**

2.

Part	Function	Domain	Range
a.	$f(x) = 5 - 4x$	all real numbers	all real numbers
b.	$g(t) = 3(2^t)$	all real numbers	$g(t) > 0$
c.	$h(s) = -3s^2$	all real numbers	$h(s) \leq 0$
d.	$j(t) = 0.5 \sin t$	all real numbers	$-0.5 \leq j(t) \leq 0.5$
e.	$k(r) = 2.5(0.4^r)$	all real numbers	$k(r) > 0$
f.	$m(x) = \frac{5}{x}$	x is any real number except 0	$m(x) \neq 0$

3. **a.** $NEXT = NOW + 2$, starting with 3
   b. $NEXT = 1.5NOW$, starting with 4
   c. $NEXT = NOW - 2$, starting with 4.5

4. **a.** A translation of magnitude 12 hours in either direction, or $12n$ hours for any integer n, will map the curve onto itself.
   b. The graph has reflection symmetry across any vertical line containing a maximum or minimum point of the graph. It also has glide-reflection symmetry with a glide of $6n$ hours for any odd integer n and reflection across the line $d(t) = 3$.
   c. The amplitude of 2 is equal to the distance from the midline at 3 to the maximum of 5 (or minimum of 1).
   d. The midline of each of the graphs $s(x) = \sin x$ and $c(x) = \cos x$ is the x-axis. The distance from the midline to the maximum (or minimum) is equal to 1, which is the amplitude of each of the graphs.

Unit 6

Reflecting

1. Responses will vary.

2. In many cases, these terms are used with the correct mathematical understanding, but in other cases they are not. If the phrase "growing exponentially" is used, this may simply mean that the growth is rapid. The word "periodic" is often used for something that repeats, but that might not be in the same way that trigonometric functions repeat. When the phrases "directly and inversely" are used, people are often referring to linear relationships that increase as direct relationships and linear relationships that decrease as inverse relationships. These are common misconceptions. Some students will remember that two quantities vary directly if $f(x) = kx$; thus, the function is a line passing through the origin, with either a positive or a negative slope. Two quantities vary inversely if $f(x) = \frac{k}{x}$. A quantity $f(x)$ varies inversely as the square of a quantity x if $f(x) = \frac{k}{x^2}$.

3. **a.** Graphs i, iii, v, and vi are functions. (This assumes that none of graph iii is vertical.)

   b. Graph i looks as though it belongs to the family of inverse power functions but could belong to the family of exponential functions.

   Graph iii does not belong to any of the basic families.

   Graph v is a graph of a periodic (trigonometric) function.

   Graph vi is a graph of a power function.

4. Function values are always increasing or decreasing for the following families:

   Linear functions

   Exponential functions

   Square root functions

   Odd power functions (direct and inverse)

   Function values increase over some intervals and decrease over others for the following:

   Even power functions (direct and inverse, including quadratic functions)

   Periodic functions, specifically the sine and cosine functions

Reflecting

1. When you think about the various function families, do you think about them *first* in terms of their symbolic rules, their graphs, or their table patterns? Why?

2. News stories that involve consideration of change in some variable over time or the relation between two or more variables often use phrases like "growing exponentially," "periodic," or "directly or inversely related." What do you think people generally mean when they use each of those descriptive terms? How do the common usages relate to the technical mathematical usage?

3. Examine each of the following graphs.

   a. Which show relationships between variables in which *y* is a function of *x*?

   b. For each function, identify, if possible, the function family to which it belongs.

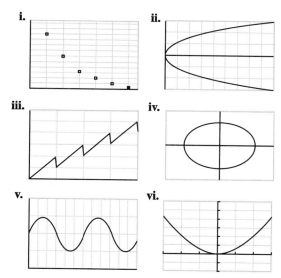

4. Some function families have the property that for the entire domain, function values are always increasing or always decreasing. For other function families, function values increase on some intervals and decrease on others. Sort the function families by these criteria.

Extending

1. In Activity 3 of Investigation 3, page 431, you saw that the graph of the inverse function $f(x) = \frac{1}{x}$ has the x-axis as a horizontal asymptote and the y-axis as a vertical asymptote.

   a. Describe the asymptotic behavior of this variation of the basic inverse function: $g(x) = \frac{2}{x} + 3$.

   b. Make and test a conjecture about the asymptotic behavior of $h(x) = \frac{a}{x} + b$, where $a > 0$ and $b > 0$.

   c. Describe the asymptotic behavior of this variation of the basic inverse function: $j(x) = \frac{5}{x + 2}$.

   d. Make and test a conjecture about the asymptotic behavior of $i(x) = \frac{a}{x + b}$, where $a > 0$ and $b > 0$.

Each of the following displays in Tasks 2 through 5 shows graphs for two functions $f(x)$ and $g(x)$. In each case, the rules for the two functions are closely related to each other. For the pair of given graphs in each task, do the following:

   a. Explain the relation between rules for $f(x)$ and $g(x)$.

   b. Write function rules for $f(x)$ and $g(x)$ that you expect to give graphs with the same basic patterns as shown.

   c. Test your function rules to see how their graphs compare to those that are given. Then explain why the graphs turned out to be the same as or different from what you had expected.

2.
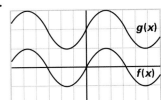

3.
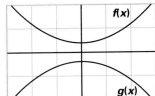

4.
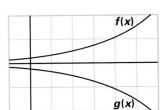

5.
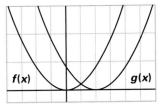

MORE *continued*

Extending

Assessments 229–231

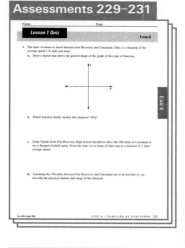

1. a. The graph of $g(x) = \frac{2}{x} + 3$ has a horizontal asymptote of $y = 3$ and the y-axis as a vertical asymptote.

b. The graph of $h(x) = \frac{a}{x} + b$ will have the y-axis as a vertical asymptote and a horizontal asymptote of $y = b$.

c. The graph of the function $g(x) = \frac{5}{x+2}$ has a horizontal asymptote of $y = 0$ and a vertical asymptote of $x = -2$.

d. The function $h(x) = \frac{a}{x+b}$ will have the x-axis as a horizontal asymptote and the line $x = -b$ as a vertical asymptote.

In Tasks 2–5, responses for Parts b and c for each task will depend on the scales that students assume for the graphs. Equations given are sample responses. The important part of these tasks is knowing the patterns and the transformations. The graphs are not expected to be exact. Note that in Part c, students should explain if the examples are different from those they expected.

Assessments 232–234

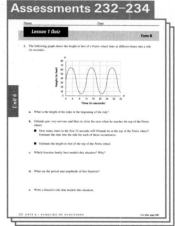

2. a. The rule for $g(x)$ is the rule for $f(x)$ plus a positive constant.

b. $f(x) = \sin x$
$g(x) = \sin x + 2$

c.
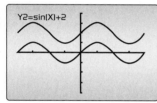

3. a. The rule for $g(x)$ is the opposite or negative of the rule for $f(x)$.

b. $f(x) = 0.5x^2 + 0.4$
$g(x) = -(0.5x^2 + 0.4)$

c.
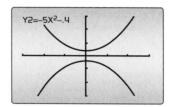

4. a. The rule for $g(x)$ is the opposite or negative of the rule for $f(x)$.

b. $f(x) = (0.25)(1.5)^x$
$g(x) = -(0.25)(1.5)^x$

c.
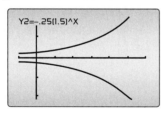

5. a. The rule for $g(x)$ is the rule for $f(x)$ with the domain values adjusted by 2.

b. $f(x) = 0.2x^2$
$g(x) = 0.2(x - 2)^2$

c.
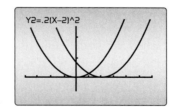

See Assessment Resources, pages 229–234.

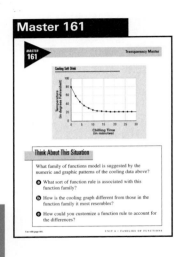

Lesson **2** *Customizing Models 1: Reflections and Vertical Transformations*

LESSON OVERVIEW In this lesson, students focus on how to modify the symbolic rule of a basic function model in order to translate the graph of the function vertically, to reflect the graph across the *x*-axis, and to stretch or shrink the graph vertically.

Lesson Objectives

■ To recognize how the graph and table of *f*(*x*) relate to the graph and table of *f*(*x*) + *a*
■ To recognize how the graph and table of *f*(*x*) relate to the graph and table of −*f*(*x*)
■ To recognize how the graph and table of *f*(*x*) relate to the graph and table of *af*(*x*)
■ To reason with the transformations above as they relate to real-world situations

LAUNCH full-class discussion

Think About This Situation

See Teaching Master 161.

ⓐ Students may suggest an exponential decay model or an inverse power model. You may need to help them recall how the symbolic equations for those two models create the particular characteristics that can help distinguish between their graphs. For example, in $y = 80(0.8)^x$, at $x = 0$, $y = 80(0.8)^0 = 80$. However, for $y = \frac{80}{x}$, there is no solution when $x = 0$, and, thus, there is no *y*-intercept. This discussion might bring out the fact that because there is a *y*-intercept, the inverse power model must be ruled out. Students might also notice that there is a problem with both models because the line that the curve is approaching is not the *x*-axis. See Part b.

ⓑ Again, you may need to help students recall why both exponential and inverse power models have the *x*-axis as an asymptote. In $y = 80(0.8)^x$, as *x* increases by 1, the next value of *y* is 80% of the current value of *y*. This produces smaller and smaller answers without ever getting to zero. And, for $y = \frac{80}{x}$, as *x* increases by 1, the value of the next *y* decreases, but can never reach zero because $\frac{80}{x} = 0$ has no solution. In this case, the curve is similar to an exponential model, but it does not have the *x*-axis as an asymptote. Instead, the asymptote in this case appears to be the line $y = 20$.

ⓒ Students might suggest subtracting 20 from each data value and then fitting an exponential model to the new data and adding 20 to that model. If students have no suggestions, you can leave the question open. They should be able to answer this question by the end of Investigation 1.

Lesson 2

Customizing Models 1: Reflections and Vertical Transformations

If you take a warm soft drink can and place it in a freezer that is at 20° Fahrenheit, the drink will chill in a pattern like the one shown by this graph:

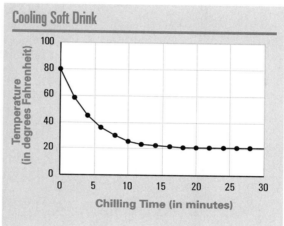

Cooling Soft Drink

Temperature (in degrees Fahrenheit) vs *Chilling Time (in minutes)*

Think About This Situation

What family of functions is suggested by the numeric and graphic patterns of the cooling data above?

a What sort of function rule is associated with this function family?

b How is the cooling graph different from those in the function family it most resembles?

c How could you customize a function rule to account for the differences?

Trial-and-error testing of options or using calculator-based regression methods are effective ways to find models for data patterns. It is also helpful to know some general principles for modifying and combining the rules of basic function families to build new model rules for more complex situations. As you complete the following investigations, look for general methods to build symbolic rules so you can apply those methods in many different situations.

INVESTIGATION 1 ▶ Vertical Translation

The cooling function on the previous page looks a lot like an exponential decay function whose graph had been translated up about 20 units. In this investigation, you will explore connections between the forms of symbolic rules for functions whose graphs are related by *vertical translations*. For each graph, the scale on both coordinate axes is 1.

1. This diagram shows the graph of an important special function called the **absolute value function**. For each input value of x, the output is the distance from x to 0. The rule for the absolute value function can be written $f(x) = |x|$ or, in calculator and computer notation, $f(x) = abs(x)$. For example, $|-3| = 3$ and $|5.4| = 5.4$.

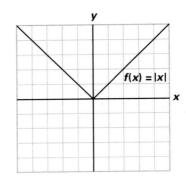

$$f(x) = |x|$$

a. Use the graph to complete a table of sample $(x, f(x))$ pairs.

x	−4	−3	−2	−1	0	1	2	3	4	5
f(x)										

b. Describe in words the rule for finding outputs from the absolute value function.

c. What value would you expect for $f(23.5)$? For $f(-14.7)$?

d. Include the absolute value function in your functions toolkit. Supply information on the domain and range.

INVESTIGATION 1 Vertical Translation

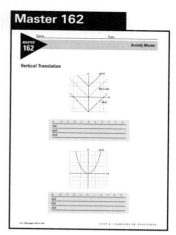

Master 162

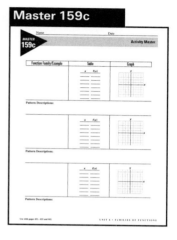

Master 159c

The absolute value function, introduced in this investigation, is used to allow students to explore vertical translations of graphs. Then students consider the symbolic rule for a quadratic function graph that has been translated vertically and extend the patterns they have found to trigonometric functions. In the "On Your Own" at the end of this investigation, students apply what they have learned to linear, exponential, and power functions.

Since students have not seen an absolute value function before, you may wish to do a brief introduction before Activity 1 or to complete Activity 1 as a large group. You might consider creating a table comparing the heights of a few students to their deviation from the mean height. Write the deviation as an absolute deviation, and ask which student's height was farthest from the mean. (This concept was addressed in Course 1.) *Deviation* = $|height - mean|$. Then you can introduce the formal definition: $|x|$ is the distance from x to zero. (See the introductory paragraph for Activity 1 in the student text.)

As groups discuss these activities, it will be helpful if they use the terms *input*, *output*, and *translation* to describe what they see in the tables and graphs. For example, the inputs remain unchanged, but 3 has been added to each output. Or, the effect of subtracting 4 from each output is to translate the graph of the function down by 4 units. In Lesson 3, students will encounter horizontal translations. They often confuse the symbolic changes that cause these different transformations. If students realize that the constant is being directly added to or subtracted from the output in a vertical translation, it will help them understand horizontal translations in Lesson 3.

1. See Teaching Master 162.

    a.

x	−4	−3	−2	−1	0	1	2	3	4	5
f(x)	4	3	2	1	0	1	2	3	4	5

    b. If x is positive or zero, the output will always be the given number; if x is negative, the output will be the opposite of the given number.

    c. $f(23.5) = 23.5$
        $f(-14.7) = 14.7$

    d. **See Teaching Master 159c.**
        Students should include their table of values, a graph, and a description of the graph of the function in their function families toolkit. The domain of the absolute value function is all real numbers, and the range is all nonnegative real numbers.

CONSTRUCTING A MATH TOOLKIT: See Activity 1 Part d.

Unit 6

EXPLORE *continued*

2. a.

x	−4	−3	−2	−1	0	1	2	3	4	5
$g(x)$	7	6	5	4	3	4	5	6	7	8

   b. $g(23.5) = 26.5$, $g(-14.7) = 17.7$

   c. $g(x) = |x| + 3$

3. $h(x) = |x| - 4$

4. The graph of $g(x)$ is the same shape as the graph of $f(x)$. In fact, it is the graph of $f(x)$ translated up c units. The graph of $h(x)$ is the same shape as the graph of $f(x)$, translated down c units.

   Students' arguments will vary. Arguments should focus on the fact that adding a positive number to each y value of $f(x)$ raises all the y values of $g(x)$ a constant amount.

2. Consider what variation of the absolute value function rule might produce a rule for the function $g(x)$ with the graph shown here. (Assume that the graph continues in the pattern shown.)

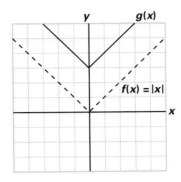

a. Use the graph to complete a table of sample $(x, g(x))$ pairs.

x	−4	−3	−2	−1	0	1	2	3	4	5
g(x)										

b. What value would you expect for $g(23.5)$? For $g(-14.7)$?

c. What rule would produce a graph and table for the function $g(x)$? Test and, if necessary, modify your conjecture.

3. Find a variation of the absolute value function that will produce a rule for the function $h(x)$ with the graph shown below. (Again, assume that the graph continues in the pattern shown.) Compare your rule to the rules found by other groups. Resolve any differences.

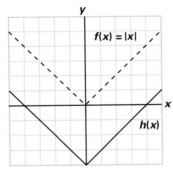

4. In general, if c is a positive number, how are the graphs of $f(x) = |x|$ and $g(x) = |x| + c$ related? How are the graphs of $f(x) = |x|$ and $h(x) = |x| - c$ related? Provide evidence or an argument that supports your conjectures.

5. The diagram below shows a graph of the function $s(x) = 0.5x^2$.

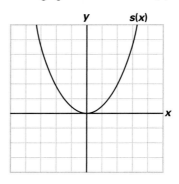

a. Complete a table of sample $(x, s(x))$ pairs.

x	−4	−3	−2	−1	0	1	2	3	4
s(x)									

b. Consider the function $t(x) = 0.5x^2 + 2$. Without using your calculator, do the following:

■ Sketch graphs of $t(x)$ and the function $s(x) = 0.5x^2$ on the same set of coordinate axes. If possible, use different color pens or pencils.

■ Complete a table like the one below.

x	−4	−3	−2	−1	0	1	2	3	4
t(x)									

c. Sketch a graph of $u(x) = 0.5x^2 - 3$ on the same coordinate axes you used in Part b. Then, without your calculator, complete a table like the one below.

x	−4	−3	−2	−1	0	1	2	3	4
u(x)									

6. In general, if c is a positive number, how are the graphs of $f(x) = x^2$ and $g(x) = x^2 + c$ related? How are the graphs of $f(x) = x^2$ and $g(x) = x^2 - c$ related? Explain your reasoning.

7. Draw a careful sketch of the function $c(x) = \cos x$ for $-2\pi \le x \le 2\pi$. Use *critical points* such as intercepts, maximums, and minimums. Then on the same coordinate axes, draw sketches of $f(x) = \cos x + 2$ and $g(x) = \cos x - 1$. Compare your sketches to those of other group members.

5. a.

x	−4	−3	−2	−1	0	1	2	3	4
s(x)	8	4.5	2	0.5	0	0.5	2	4.5	8

b. ■

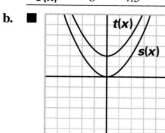

■

x	−4	−3	−2	−1	0	1	2	3	4
$t(x) = 0.5x^2 + 2$	10	6.5	4	2.5	2	2.5	4	6.5	10

c.

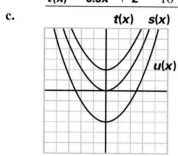

x	−4	−3	−2	−1	0	1	2	3	4
$u(x) = 0.5x^2 − 3$	5	1.5	−1	−2.5	−3	−2.5	−1	1.5	5

6. The graph of $g(x) = x^2 + c$ is the graph of $f(x) = x^2$ translated up c units. The graph of $g(x) = x^2 − c$ is the graph of $f(x) = x^2$ translated down c units.

Students' explanations will vary. Explanations should focus on the fact that adding a positive number to each y value of $f(x)$ raises all the y values of $g(x)$ a constant amount.

7.

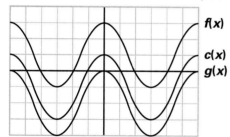

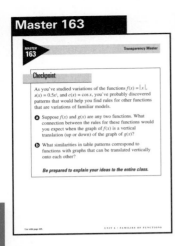

Checkpoint

See Teaching Master 163.

ⓐ The rules will differ by a constant: $f(x) = g(x) \pm k$, $k > 0$.

ⓑ In the tables, if the corresponding function values differ by a constant, then one function is a vertical translation of the other.

Before students begin the "On Your Own," you might want to help them generalize more. Although the Checkpoint refers to any function, students are probably thinking only of the examples they have seen so far. You might sketch one or more of the following graphs:

■ $f(x) = 2^x$　　　■ $g(x) = \dfrac{1}{x}$　　　■ $k(x)$, a function that cannot be defined easily with a familiar model

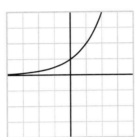
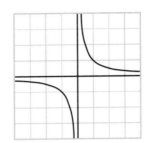
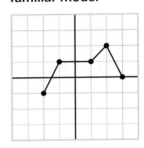

Then ask students to sketch translations, such as $y = f(x) + 1$, $y = g(x) - 3$, and $y = k(x) - 4$.

CONSTRUCTING A MATH TOOLKIT: Students should include the absolute value function in their function families toolkit. Students should also describe how tables and symbolic rules are related for functions that have graphs that are vertical translations of each other.

APPLY　individual task

▶On Your Own

a. $g(x) = x + 2$
　　$h(x) = x - 3$

b. The lower graph is $i(x)$. The upper function is $j(x)$, where $j(x) = 8(0.8)^x + 6$.

Checkpoint

As you've studied variations of the functions $f(x) = |x|$, $s(x) = 0.5x^2$, and $c(x) = \cos x$, you've probably discovered patterns that can help you find rules for other functions that are variations of familiar models.

ⓐ Suppose $f(x)$ and $g(x)$ are any two functions. What connection between the rules for these functions would you expect when the graph of $f(x)$ is a vertical translation (up or down) of the graph of $g(x)$?

ⓑ What similarities in table patterns correspond to functions with graphs that can be translated vertically onto each other?

Be prepared to explain your ideas to the entire class.

On Your Own

Check your understanding of connections among graphs, tables, and symbolic rules of related functions.

a. The diagram at the right shows graphs of three functions, one of which is the basic linear model with rule $f(x) = x$. The scale on both axes is 1. What are the rules for the other two functions, $g(x)$ and $h(x)$? (Remember to assume that the graphs continue in the same pattern shown.)

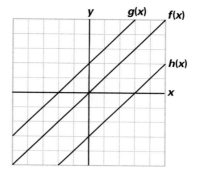

b. The next diagram shows graphs of the function $i(x) = 8(0.8)^x$ and another function $j(x)$. Which graph is $i(x)$, and what rule would match the graph pattern of $j(x)$?

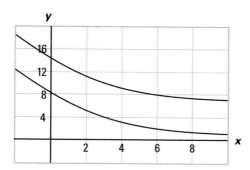

Unit 6

c. The table that follows shows a sample of (*input*, *output*) pairs for the function $c(x) = x^3$ and another function $d(x)$.

x	−3	−2	−1	0	1	2	3	4
c(x)	−27	−8	−1	0	1	8	27	64
d(x)	−32	−13	−6	−5	−4	3	22	59

■ How are the graphs of $c(x)$ and $d(x)$ related to each other?

■ What rule matches the given $(x, d(x))$ values?

INVESTIGATION 2 ▸ Reflection across the *x*-axis

In many situations, you'll find data patterns that look like graphs of familiar functions that have been reflected across the *x*-axis. That observation often makes it easy to find symbolic rules for the new relation.

1. Study the pairs of function graphs and tables shown below and find the missing symbolic rule in each case.

a. $f(x) = 0.8x$

$g(x) = ?$

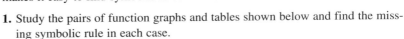

X	Y₁	Y₂
−3	−2.4	2.4
−2	−1.6	1.6
−1	−.8	.8
0	0	0
1	.8	−.8
2	1.6	−1.6
3	2.4	−2.4

X= −3

b. $h(x) = 0.5x^2$

$i(x) = ?$

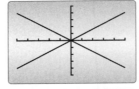

X	Y₁	Y₂
−3	4.5	−4.5
−2	2	−2
−1	.5	−.5
0	0	0
1	.5	−.5
2	2	−2
3	4.5	−4.5

X= −3

c. $j(x) = \dfrac{1}{x}$

$k(x) = ?$

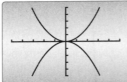

X	Y₁	Y₂
0	ERROR	ERROR
1	1	−1
2	.5	−.5
3	.3333	−.3333
4	.25	−.25
5	.2	−.2
6	.1667	−.1667

X= 0

d. $s(x) = \sin x$

$t(x) = ?$

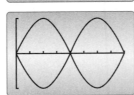

X	Y₁	Y₂
0	0	0
.7854	.70711	−.7071
1.5708	1	−1
2.3562	.70711	−.7071
3.1416	0	0
3.927	−.7071	.70711
4.7124	−1	1

X= 0

c. ■ The graph of $d(x)$ will be a translation of the graph of $c(x)$ down 5 units.
■ $d(x) = x^3 - 5$

EXPLORE small-group investigation

INVESTIGATION 2 Reflection across the *x*-axis

MORE
ASSIGNMENT *pp. 453–461*

Students can now begin Modeling Task 2 or 3 or Extending Task 3 from the MORE assignment following Investigation 3.

In this investigation, students explore reflections across the *x*-axis for familiar functions. Absolute value models, quadratic models, inverse models, exponential models, and trigonometric models are all included in this investigation.

1. a. $g(x) = -0.8x$
   b. $i(x) = -0.5x^2$
   c. $k(x) = -\frac{1}{x}$
   d. $t(x) = -\sin x$

Unit 6

2. It may be helpful to have a class discussion about Parts a and b before students complete Part c.

a. $g(x) = -|x| + 3$

2. The next graph shows the way an ice cream bar warms up when set out in a hot summer sun. The basic shape probably looks a bit familiar but not exactly like one of the basic function types you've encountered before.

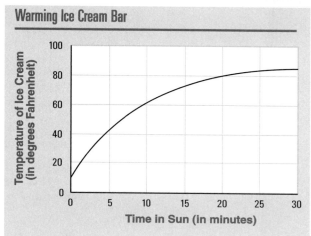

To construct a function rule matching this graph pattern, it might help to solve some related problems first, combining strategies you have studied thus far.

a. In the following diagram, the rule for one function is $f(x) = |x|$. The scale on both coordinate axes is 1. What rule gives the indicated graph of $g(x)$?

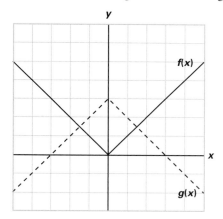

Unit 6

b. In the next diagram, the rule for one function is $h(x) = 0.2x^2$. The scale on both coordinate axes is 1. What rule would give the indicated graph of the function $i(x)$?

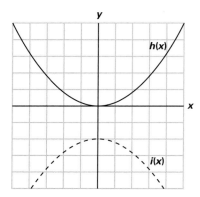

c. Now construct a function rule to match the "ice cream warming" function graphed at the beginning of this activity. As a hint to get you started, try building your function rule as a variation of $f(x) = 80(0.9^x)$.

3. Write a rule for a function whose graph is the graph of $c(x) = \cos x$ reflected across the x-axis and translated up 1 unit. How does the amplitude and period of this new function compare to those of $c(x) = \cos x$? Why does this make sense?

Checkpoint

As you've studied rules and graphs of the functions in this investigation, you've probably discovered some ways to build more variations on the basic linear, power, exponential, absolute value, and trigonometric models. What connection between the rules for two functions $f(x)$ and $g(x)$ would you expect:

ⓐ when the graph of $f(x)$ is a vertical translation of the graph of $g(x)$?

ⓑ when the graph of $g(x)$ is a reflection across the x-axis of the graph of $f(x)$?

ⓒ when the graphs of the two functions are related by a combination of reflection across the x-axis and then vertical translation (up or down)?

Be prepared to explain your ideas to the entire class.

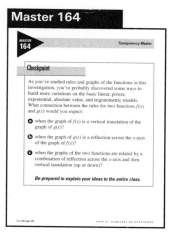

2. b. $i(x) = -0.2x^2 - 2$

c. $g(x) = -80(0.9)^x + 90$

The graph can be obtained by first reflecting the graph of $f(x) = 80(0.9)^x$ across the x-axis and then translating that result up 90 units.

3. $f(x) = -\cos x + 1$

The amplitude and period of $f(x)$ are the same as those for $c(x)$. This is the case because reflections and translations do not change the shape of a graph.

SHARE AND SUMMARIZE full-class discussion

Checkpoint

See Teaching Master 164.

ⓐ If the graph of $f(x)$ is a vertical translation of the graph of $g(x)$, then $f(x) = g(x) + k$ for some number k.

ⓑ If the graph of $g(x)$ is a reflection across the x-axis of the graph of $f(x)$, then $g(x) = -f(x)$.

ⓒ If $f(x)$ and $g(x)$ are related by a combination of reflection across the x-axis and a vertical translation, then $f(x) = -g(x) + k$ for some number k.

In this investigation, students have probably naturally reflected functions before translating. You may wish to ask them if they can reverse the order: translate and then reflect. Many students will say that the reverse order does in fact give the same result. If you ask them to show you graphically what a specific translation followed by a specific reflection would look like, you will probably find that your students are not reflecting the curve across the x-axis. Students should be able to see symbolically and graphically that reflecting $f(x) = |x|$ across the x-axis and then translating up 3 units is *not* the same as translating up 3 units and then reflecting across the x-axis. Ask students if $-|x| + 3$ is equal to $-(|x| - 3)$. It may help them if you also ask what the second expression means in terms of a translation and reflection across the x-axis.

JOURNAL ENTRY: The graphing calculator language is very compatible with the transformations students are learning about here. You can take advantage of this compatability. For example:

Enter $Y_1 = x^5 - 4x^3$.

Enter $Y_2 = -Y_1$. Predict how Y_1 and Y_2 will be related. Check.

Enter $Y_3 = Y_1 + 4$. Predict how Y_3 and Y_1 will be related. Check.

Enter $Y_4 = -Y_1 + 4$. Predict how Y_4 and Y_2 will be related. How are Y_4 and Y_1 related? Check.

Enter $Y_5 = -(Y_1 + 4)$. Predict how Y_5 and Y_1 will be related and how Y_3 and Y_5 will be related. Check.

Make sketches for each in your Math Toolkit, and label them appropriately.

▶On Your Own

a. As x increases from -4 to 0, $f(x)$ decreases at an increasing rate. As x increases from 0 to 4, the value of the function decreases at a decreasing rate. You can predict this pattern from the function rule alone by considering that as you increase the denominator of a fraction, the value of that fraction decreases.

b. Student sketches should be similar to those shown below. Scales on all axes are 1.

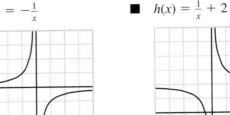

■ $g(x) = -\dfrac{1}{x}$ ■ $h(x) = \dfrac{1}{x} + 2$ ■ $i(x) = 3 - \dfrac{1}{x}$

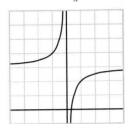

EXPLORE small-group investigation

INVESTIGATION 3 ▶ Vertical Stretching and Shrinking

In this investigation, students explore vertical stretching and shrinking through explorations involving the sine and cosine functions. Students then extend this concept to $f(x) = a|x|$ and $g(x) = ax^2$. Students also investigate the effects of $a > 1$, $0 < a < 1$, and $a < 0$ on the graphs of these functions. Then in the MORE tasks, students will apply these transformations to additional function types.

In the Course 2 unit "Geometric Form and Its Function," students made models that permitted them to use the basic definition of the sine of an angle (the ratio of the lengths of the opposite side and the hypotenuse in a right triangle) to estimate sines of angles. You may wish to review this process by referring to a circle and having students find sine values for various angle measures, such as $\sin 20°$, $\sin 30°$, $\sin 150°$, and $\sin 225°$. By sharing the workload among groups, a table can be created quickly and a graph can be sketched. The same approach can be used, changing degrees to radians and repeating the effort, to illustrate that the pattern does not change, just the scale on the x-axis. The scale on the x-axis is often a source of confusion for students. Reviewing the scale issues and basic shape of the graph first may save time in the long run. Be sure students select the appropriate mode on the calculator. When graphing trigonometric functions, a standard trigonometric scale can be selected. (For the TI-82 and TI-83, ZOOM 7:ZTRIG will select such a scale for the x values.) The window may need to be adjusted, depending upon the transformation for a given function.

MORE

ASSIGNMENT   *pp. 453–461*

Students can now begin Extending Task 4 from the MORE assignment following Investigation 3.

Unit 6

> **On Your Own**

The calculator display below shows a graph of $f(x) = \frac{1}{x}$ for $-4 \le x \le 4$.

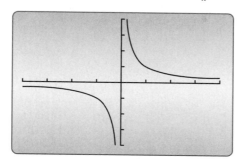

a. Describe the pattern of change in $f(x)$ values as x increases from -4 to 4, and explain how that overall pattern could be predicted from studying the function rule alone, without specific calculations.

b. Without using a graphing calculator, sketch the general pattern of the graphs you'd expect for the following functions.

- $g(x) = -\frac{1}{x}$
- $h(x) = \frac{1}{x} + 2$
- $i(x) = 3 - \frac{1}{x}$

INVESTIGATION 3 ▶ Vertical Stretching and Shrinking

In many important problems, the key variables change in periodic patterns as time passes. For example, the pendulum on a grandfather clock swings from right to left and back again. The depth of water in an ocean harbor rises and falls as tides move in and out. As you have previously seen, the trigonometric functions $s(x) = \sin x$ and $c(x) = \cos x$ are the basic tools for modeling many periodic variables, since they give graphs that oscillate up and down in repeating patterns.

To model different patterns of periodic change, you need variations of the basic sine and cosine rules. For example, recall that the basic sine and cosine functions oscillate between $y = -1$ and $y = 1$, but a pendulum might swing through a range that is 5 inches left and right of vertical. The depth of water in an ocean harbor might vary from 15 to 20 feet as time passes. The electricity in a standard AC circuit oscillates between -150 and $+150$ volts. In order to model these situations, you will have to *stretch* the basic trigonometric graphs.

1. The two diagrams below show graphs for two variations of $s(x) = \sin x$. In each case, the scale on both axes is 1. The graphs were produced using radian measure for the input variable x.

   How could you adapt the basic sine function rule to model the patterns in these graphs? Compare your customized function rules to those of other groups.

a.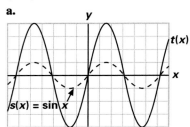

b.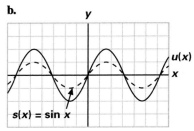

2. The next diagram shows a slightly different variation of the graph of the basic sine function.

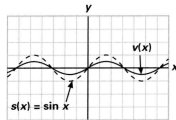

   a. How would you describe the relationship between the two graphs?

   b. Find a variation of the basic sine function that will give a rule for the function $v(x)$.

3. Now, use your calculator to compare graphs and tables of values for these functions:

   ■ $c(x) = \cos x$ ■ $d(x) = 5 \cos x$ ■ $e(x) = 0.5 \cos x$ ■ $f(x) = 5 \cos x - 2$

   a. How is the graph of $d(x)$ similar to and different from the graph of $c(x)$ for $-2\pi \le x \le 2\pi$? How is $e(x)$ similar and different? How is $f(x)$ similar and different?

   b. Produce tables of the four functions for $0 \le x \le 2\pi$, and describe ways that the table for $d(x)$ is similar to and different from the table for $c(x)$. Then compare the tables for $e(x)$ and $f(x)$ to the table for $c(x)$.

4. Look back at your work in Activities 1 through 3 and think about general patterns you found in Investigation 2.

   a. How does a vertical stretch or a vertical translation affect the amplitude of a periodic graph? How does each affect the period?

1. Students have just studied transformations by adding a constant or multiplying by −1, so some students may try something similar here, even though that is not logical. It is important to resist telling them too much. They will soon discover which transformation gives the desired effect. Once they have established that multiplying the sine value is appropriate, you can ask them to explain what happened in the transformed tables and graphs. The vocabulary they develop will help them to make sense of the transformation. The factor stretches the curve (but leaves the zeroes unchanged), or it multiplies the outputs. Students have seen this effect in Course 2, when they used a scale factor to multiply both coordinates of a point. This time we are multiplying just the y-coordinate: $(x, y) \rightarrow (x, ay)$.

   a. $t(x) = 4 \sin x$

   b. $u(x) = 2 \sin x$

2. a. The two graphs have the same zeroes, and the minimum and maximum values occur at the same values of x. However, each $v(x)$ value is one-half the corresponding $s(x)$ value.

   b. $v(x) = \frac{1}{2} \sin x$

3. $c(x) = \cos x$ $\qquad$ $d(x) = 5 \cos x$ $\qquad$ $e(x) = 0.5 \cos x$ $\qquad$ $f(x) = 5 \cos x - 2$

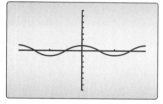 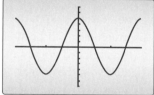 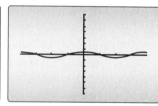 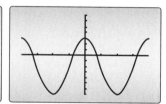

   a. The graphs of $c(x)$, $d(x)$, and $e(x)$ have the same zeroes, and the minimum and maximum values for the functions occur at the same values of x. For each x value, $d(x)$ is 5 times the value of $c(x)$ and $e(x)$ is $\frac{1}{2}$ of $c(x)$. In other words, the graph of $d(x)$ is stretched by a factor of 5, and the graph of $e(x)$ is shrunk by a factor of $\frac{1}{2}$.

   The graph of $f(x)$ does not have the same zeroes, but the minimum and maximum values of the functions occur at the same values of x.

   All four graphs have the same period, 2π or $360°$.

   b. **Students have been directed to produce tables for $0 \leq x \leq 2\pi$. You might suggest using step sizes of 0.25π so that students will see the zeroes.**

$c(x)$ $\qquad\qquad\qquad$ $d(x)$ $\qquad\qquad\qquad$ $e(x)$ $\qquad\qquad\qquad$ $f(x)$

X	Y1
0	1
.7854	.70711
1.5708	0
2.3562	−.7071
3.1416	−1
3.927	−.7071
4.7124	0

Y1 ▤ cos(X)

X	Y1
0	5
.7854	3.5355
1.5708	0
2.3562	−3.536
3.1416	−5
3.927	−3.536
4.7124	0

Y1 ▤ 5cos(X)

X	Y1
0	.5
.7854	.35355
1.5708	0
2.3562	−.3536
3.1416	−.5
3.927	−.3536
4.7124	0

Y1 ▤ 0.5cos(X)

X	Y1
0	3
.7854	1.5355
1.5708	−2
2.3562	−5.536
3.1416	−7
3.927	−5.536
4.7124	−2

Y1 ▤ 5cos(X)−2

See additional Teaching Notes on page T485E.

4. **b.** The amplitude of each graph is *a*, and the period is 2π. The period is 2π since each graph will have maximums and minimums occurring at the same *x* value as the corresponding basic function, and the period of both $c(x) = \cos x$ and $s(x) = \sin x$ is 2π. However, the maximum and minimum values are multiplied by *a*; thus, the amplitude is multiplied by *a*.

   c. ■ The stretch is applied first since the algebraic order of operations tells us to multiply before adding. So cos *x* is first multiplied by *a*, and then *b* is added to that result.

   ■ The graph would not be the same. One way to determine this is to think about what the equation would look like if the order of transformation were reversed. In general, it would be $f(x) = a[\cos x + b]$ if the translation were to be done before the vertical stretch. But this equation is equivalent to $f(x) = a \cos x + ab$. So this equation is really a vertical translation of *ab* units rather than *b* units.

5. **a.** $f(x) = \cos x + 3$, for the dashed graph
        $g(x) = 0.5 \cos x + 3$, for the solid graph

   b. $j(x) = \sin x - 2$, for the dashed graph
        $h(x) = 2 \sin x - 2$, for the solid graph

6. **a.** In order to build a complete model, you would need to know when high and low tides occur to determine the period.

   b. It is reasonable to assume that the period would be 12 hours. Since the overall change in depth is 4 feet, the basic graph needs to be stretched by a factor of 2. Also, since the "middle" *y* value is 18, the stretched graph needs to be translated up 18 units. So the function equation and graph would be either

   $$z(x) = 2 \sin\left(\tfrac{\pi}{6}x\right) + 18 \qquad\qquad \text{or} \qquad\qquad z(x) = 2 \cos\left(\tfrac{\pi}{6}x\right) + 18.$$

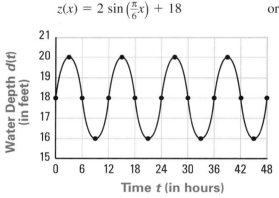

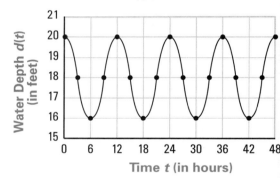

   c. This is an opportunity for students to check their assumptions and to see that both sine and cosine can be used to model this situation.

7. **a.** If $a > 1$, the graph of $h(x) = a\lvert x \rvert$ is "narrower" than the graph of $f(x) = \lvert x \rvert$. If $0 < a < 1$, the graph of $h(x)$ is more "spread out" or flatter than the graph of $f(x)$. If $a < 0$, then $h(x)$ is the reflection of $y = \lvert a \rvert f(x)$ across the *x*-axis. The relations show up in the tables in the following manner:

   ■ If $a > 1$, then $h(x) > f(x)$ for all values of *x*, except $x = 0$.
   ■ If $0 < a < 1$, then $h(x) < f(x)$ for all values of *x*, except $x = 0$.
   ■ If $a < 0$, then $h(x) < 0 < f(x)$ for all values of *x*, except $x = 0$.

   b. The same relationships will hold for these functions. In general, the graphs of variations on the two functions $f(x) = \lvert x \rvert$ and $g(x) = x^2$ are related to their associated functions in the same way.

See additional Teaching Notes on page T485E.

b. What can you say about the amplitude and period of $f(x) = a \sin x + b$ and $g(x) = a \cos x + b$? Why does this make sense?

c. The graph of $gx = a \cos x + b$ involves a vertical stretch and translation of the graph of the basic function $c(x) = \cos x$.

- Which transformation is applied first, the stretch or the translation? How do you know?

- Would you get the same graph if you reversed the order of the transformations of the given graph? Explain.

5. Find variations of the basic sine or cosine function rules that model these four graph patterns. The scale on each coordinate axis is 1.

a.

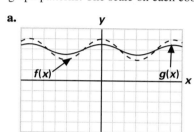

b.

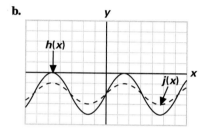

6. Now, combine what you have noticed about variations of $s(x) = \sin x$ and $c(x) = \cos x$ to build a model for depth of water in an ocean harbor, rising and falling between a maximum of 20 feet and a minimum of 16 feet.

a. What additional information about the behavior of tides would you need to know to refine your model?

b. Make an assumption about this information and then produce a graph of a possible function model. Write a symbolic rule that matches your graph.

c. Compare your function model to those of other groups. Resolve any differences.

7. In Investigations 1 and 2, you explored the connection between the symbolic rules and the position and shape of graphs for variations of $f(x) = |x|$ and $g(x) = x^2$. Study tables and graphs of several functions with rules in the form $y = a|x|$ and $y = ax^2$ with various values of a.

a. How are the graphs of $f(x) = |x|$ and $h(x) = a|x|$ related by shape and position, if $a > 1$? If $0 < a < 1$? If $a < 0$? How do those relations show up in tables of the basic function and the variations?

b. Do the relationships that you discovered in Part a also apply to the functions $g(x) = x^2$ and $k(x) = ax^2$? Explain your reasoning.

c. Determine if the relationships that you discovered in Part a also apply to the functions $u(x) = x$ and $v(x) = ax$.

d. Do the relationships that you discovered in Part a also apply to the functions $e(x) = b^x$ and $h(x) = a(b^x)$ for $b > 1$? For $0 < b < 1$?

Checkpoint

As in the case of vertical translations and reflections across the *x*-axis, you may have discovered that vertically stretching or shrinking graphs is related to the form of symbolic rules and patterns in tables of values.

a What connection between rules for functions $h(x)$ and $k(x)$ would you expect when the graph of one is found by vertically stretching or shrinking the other?

b What table patterns correspond to vertically stretching and shrinking graphs?

c What connection between rules for functions $f(x)$ and $g(x)$ would you expect when the graph of one is vertically stretched (shrunk) and then translated vertically?

Be prepared to explain your findings to the entire class.

On Your Own

The following graph again shows the function $y = \sin x$. The scale on each coordinate axis is 1.

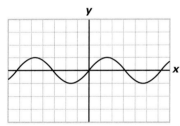

What variations of the basic sine function rule model the patterns in the graphs below?

a.

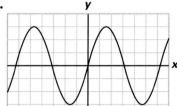

b.

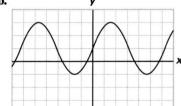

Checkpoint

See Teaching Master 165.

ⓐ You would expect $h(x)$ to be the product of some constant times $k(x)$.

ⓑ The x-intercepts or the zeroes of the function remain the same. The intervals of increasing and decreasing values remain the same. The maximum and minimum values occur at the same x values. The values of the maximums and minimums are multiplied by the stretch (or shrink) factor.

ⓒ You would expect $g(x) = af(x) + b$.

CONSTRUCTING A MATH TOOLKIT: After the Checkpoint, students should summarize the general effects of a stretch factor on a function. By drawing specific functions, students can record examples of this type of transformation, along with its impact on zeroes, maxima, and minima. Two examples that you might give students follow.

■ $f(x) = x^2 - x$

■ $g(x)$, a function that cannot be defined easily with a familiar model

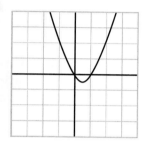   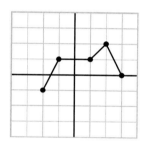

Suggest that students draw sketches of $y = 5f(x)$, $y = -5g(x)$, $y = 0.5f(x)$, and $y = 2g(x)$.

APPLY   individual task

▶On Your Own

a. $f(x) = 3 \sin x$

b. $g(x) = 2 \sin x + 1$

APPLY *continued*

c. ■ The graph of the basic sine function is stretched vertically 30 units and shifted up 35 units. $h(0) = 35$ and $\sin (0) = 0$ indicate that $h(x)$ may be obtained through a vertical translation of 35 units (since there is no horizontal translation). Also, since there is a difference of 60 units in the maximum and minimum heights, the graph of $y = \sin x$ must also have been stretched vertically by 30 units. The table of values of $h(x)$ can be obtained by multiplying the functional values of the sine function by 30 and then adding 35.

■ The 30 tells us that the radius of the Ferris wheel is 30 feet. The 35 tells us that the position marked by the asterisk (*) is 35 feet off the ground. Since the radius is 30 feet, the lowest point of the wheel is 5 feet off the ground.

MORE   independent assignment

Modeling

1. a. $f(x) = 99 + 24.5x$

b. $f(x) = 49.95 + 24.5x$

The graph of the new cost function would be parallel to the original function but 49.05 units below the graph of the original function.

c. $f(x) = 99 + 19.95x$

The graph of this cost function would not be parallel to either the original function or the second function. The slope of this function is less than the slopes of the other two graphs. However, this function has the same initial value, or y-intercept, as the original equation. It does not have the same y-intercept as the second function.

MORE

ASSIGNMENT   *pp. 453–461*

Modeling: 2 or 3, and 5*
Organizing: 2, 4, and 5
Reflecting: 2, 3, or 4*
Extending: Choose one*

When choice is indicated, it is important to leave the choice to the student.
NOTE: *It is best if Organizing tasks are discussed as a whole class after they have been assigned as homework.*

Unit 6

c. In Unit 3, "Symbol Sense and Algebraic Reasoning," you studied the function $h(t) = 30 \sin t + 35$ giving the height of a Ferris wheel rider at any time t during a ride.

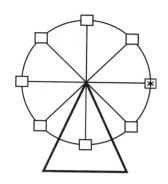

- How does the graph of this function relate to the graph of the basic sine function? How does that relation appear in a table of values for the two functions?

- What do the numbers 30 and 35 tell about the Ferris wheel and a rider's height at various times during the ride?

MORE
Modeling • Organizing • Reflecting • Extending

Modeling

1. Home security systems are a big business in many urban areas. One such service offers a package that costs $99 for installation and $24.50 per month for monitoring.

a. What rule gives the total cost of using that service for x months?

b. How would that rule change if the installation charge was reduced to $49.95? How would the graph of this new cost function be related to the graph of the rule for the original offer?

c. How would the cost function rule change if the monthly fee was reduced to $19.95 (but the installation charge remained $99)? How would the graph of that new cost function be related to the graphs of the rules for the original offer and the modification in Part b?

Unit 6

2. Consider again the cooling graph from the lesson introduction, page 441, reproduced here:

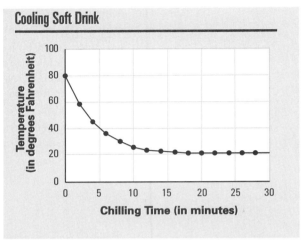

Cooling Soft Drink

a. Complete the following data table with estimates for a function $g(t)$ that has the same shape as this cooling curve but asymptotically approaches the t-axis rather than the line $y = 20$.

t	0	2	4	6	8	10	12	14	16	18	20	22
$g(t)$												

b. Use a statistical curve-fitting tool or other analysis to find an exponential function rule that fits $g(t)$.

c. Use your rule for $g(t)$ to write a rule for $f(t)$ that models the actual soft drink temperature data in the graph.

3. The Jefferson High School marching band is so good that it gets invited to perform all over the country. The band members often have to find ways to raise money for their trips. On one occasion, the director proposed selling tickets for a raffle, with the prize being an all-expense-paid trip for two to Walt Disney World®.

2. **a.** The temperature values for this table can be obtained by subtracting 20 from *y* values estimated from the graph. There may be slight variation in students' estimates from the graph.

t	0	2	4	6	8	10	12	14	16	18	20	22
$g(t)$	60	38	25	16	10	6	4	3	2	1	1	0

b. **You may want to caution students about using function values of 0 when they are trying to fit an exponential model, as in this case. They will not be able to use points of the form (*t*, 0) because decreasing exponential functions only approach, but never reach, the *t*-axis. Students might omit the last data value.**

Student equations will vary somewhat based upon the values in the table in Part a. The equation $g(t) = 57(0.8)^t$ models the values given, with the last data value omitted.

c. $f(t) = 57(0.8)^t + 20$

Unit 6

3. **a.** $S(p) = -75p + 1,500$

    b. $I(p) = (-75p + 1,500)p$

    The maximum income, \$7,500, is earned when p is 10.

    c. $N(p) = (-75p + 1,500)p - 1,500$

    This graph is a translation of $I(p)$ down 1,500 units. The process for determining the maximum point will be identical to finding the maximum point for $I(p)$, and the maximum point for $N(p)$ will occur at the same value of p. This should make sense because when a graph is translated up or down, the actual minimum and maximum values will change, but the p coordinate of the maximum or minimum points will not change.

4. **a.**

    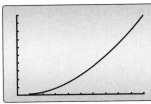 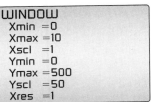

    As time passes (increases), the speed of the object increases.

    b. $h(t) = 200 - 4.9t^2$

    The graphs of $h(t)$ and $d(t)$ are related by reflection and translation. If you reflect $h(t)$ across the t-axis and then shift it up 200 units, it corresponds to $d(t)$. The curve $h(t)$ can be modified to represent objects at different heights by simply changing the number 200 to correspond to the drop height.

    c. Remind students that they are to use symbolic reasoning and not the graph to solve this problem. Solving $0 = 200 - 4.9t^2$ for t, we get that t is about 6.39 seconds. In a table of $d(t)$, find t when $d(t) = 200$. To find the time using a graph of $d(t)$, find the t value for which $d(t) = 200$. In a table of $h(t)$, find t when $h(t)$ is 0. In a graph of $h(t)$, find the t value of the t-intercept.

    d. Distance fallen: $d(t) = \frac{4.9t^2}{6}$ or $d(t) = 0.817t^2$

    Height of fallen object dropped from 200 meters: $h(t) = 200 - \frac{4.9t^2}{6}$ or $h(t) = 200 - 0.817t^2$

    The Moon-based functions are basically the same shape as Earth-based ones, but they are wider.

a. Some students surveyed their classes to estimate how many raffle tickets would be sold at various prices. Based on their sampling, they estimated the following relations between ticket price and ticket sales:

Raffle Prospects

Ticket Price	$1	$5	$10
Number of Tickets Sold	1,425	1,125	750

Find a rule for a linear function $S(p)$ that models the pattern in these data relating predicted ticket sales to ticket price p.

b. Use the result of Part a to write a rule for the function $I(p)$ that gives predicted income from raffle ticket sales. Find the maximum income predicted.

c. The raffle-prize trip will cost $1,500. Write a rule for the function $N(p)$ that gives net income or profit from the raffle. Explain how the graph of this function is related to the graph of the income function and how you can find the ticket price leading to maximum profit without further calculation.

4. In many problems, you've worked with the quadratic relationship between time and distance traveled for objects dropped from high places. For action near Earth's surface, the function rule $d(t) = 4.9t^2$ gives the distance in meters that an object has fallen t seconds after being dropped.

a. Graph $d(t)$ and explain what the shape of that graph says about the change in speed of the falling object as time passes.

b. Use the rule for distance to write a rule for the function $h(t)$ giving the height of the object t seconds after it has been dropped from a tower that is 200 meters high. Explain how the graphs of $h(t)$ and $d(t)$ are related to each other and how the rule could be modified to fit different drop heights.

c. Use symbolic reasoning to find the time when the object in Part b will reach the ground. Explain how that point could also be located on graphs and in tables of values of $d(t)$ and $h(t)$.

d. The coefficient 4.9 is determined by the gravity of our planet, Earth. Gravitational force near the surface of the Moon is only about one-sixth of the force on Earth. So in any time period, objects falling toward the Moon's surface move only one-sixth the distance that they would move if falling toward Earth's surface.

Assuming an object is dropped from a height of 200 meters above the Moon's surface, write rules for the distance fallen by the object and for the height of the object above the Moon's surface. Explain how the graphs of these Moon-based distance and height functions are related to those for Earth-based activity.

Unit 6

5. If the temperature in a restaurant's pizza oven is set at 500°F, it will actually vary above and below that setting as time passes. Suppose the actual temperature, after the oven is heated, is a function of time in minutes with rule $t(x) = 10 \sin x + 500$.

   a. What are the high and low temperatures that will occur in this oven after it has been preheated?

   b. Describe the pattern of the temperature function's graph?

   c. What patterns of variation in temperature of different pizza ovens are predicted by each of the following functions?

   ■ $u(x) = 15 \sin x + 500$

   ■ $v(x) = 10 \sin x + 550$

Organizing

1. Given below are graphs of a function $f(x)$ and four functions whose graphs are closely related to the graph of $f(x)$.

   Graph of $f(x)$:

   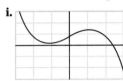

   Related Function Graphs:

   i. 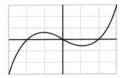   ii.

   iii.   iv.

   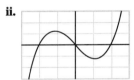
   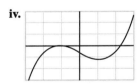

   Match each graph to the function rule below that best fits it, and explain the reasoning that supports each match. Make your matches without using a calculator.

   a. $g(x) = -f(x)$

   b. $h(x) = f(x) - 3$

   c. $j(x) = 2f(x)$

   d. $k(x) = 4 - f(x)$

5. a. The low temperature is 490° and the high temperature is 510°F.

b. The temperature rises to 510°F, then falls to 490°F, and then goes back up again in about 6.28 minutes.

c. ■ The temperatures will now vary between 485°F and 515°F. Changing the "10" to "15" increases the range of temperatures.

■ The temperatures will now vary between 540°F and 560°F. Changing the "500" to "550" changes the range of the function.

Organizing

1. a. Graph iii matches this equation. The negative in front of $f(x)$ indicates a reflection across the x-axis.

b. Graph iv matches this equation. The graph of $h(x)$ will be a vertical translation of the graph of $f(x)$. Since no other graph is a vertical translation, we can assume that the scale on the x-axis is 5.

c. Graph ii matches this equation. The zeroes must be the same as those for $f(x)$, and each y value should be twice the y value for $f(x)$.

d. Graph i matches this equation. Reflecting the graph of $f(x)$ across the x-axis and then translating it up 4 units will produce Graph i. Since no other graph indicates a reflection across the x-axis and a vertical translation, we can assume the scale on the x-axis is 5.

Unit 6

2. **a.** $f(x) = |x|$

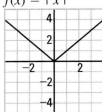

$g(x) = |x| + 2$

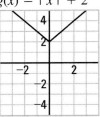

$h(x) = -|x|$

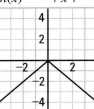

$k(x) = 0.5|x|$

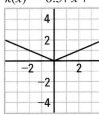

$m(x) = -2|x| - 3$

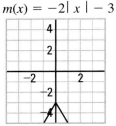

b. $f(x) = x^2$

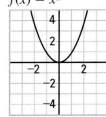

$g(x) = x^2 + 2$

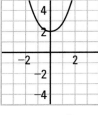

$h(x) = -x^2$

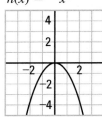

$k(x) = 0.5x^2$

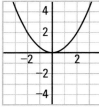

$m(x) = -2x^2 - 3$

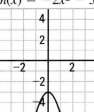

c. $f(x) = \cos x$

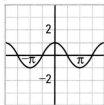

$g(x) = \cos x + 2$

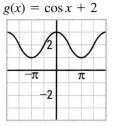

$h(x) = -(\cos x)$

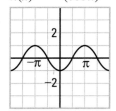

$k(x) = 0.5 \cos x$

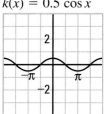

$m(x) = -2(\cos x) - 3$

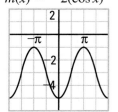

See additional Teaching Notes on page T485F.

Unit 6

2. For each of the functions in Parts a through d below, use what you know about the relationships between function rules and geometric transformations of graphs to sketch graphs of the following:

■ $f(x)$

■ $f(x) + 2$

■ $-f(x)$

■ $0.5f(x)$

■ $-2f(x) - 3$

Sketch the graphs without using your calculator. Check your ideas and then, with another color pen or pencil, note any corrections needed.

a. $f(x) = |x|$

b. $f(x) = x^2$

c. $f(x) = \cos x$

d. $f(x) = 1.5^x$

3. The rule for the original function in Organizing Task 1, page 456, was $f(x) = x^3 - 4x$.

a. Write rules for the related functions $g(x)$, $h(x)$, $j(x)$, and $k(x)$ whose graphs were given in Task 1. Use what you know about equivalence of algebraic expressions to write each rule in two different symbolic forms, one of which is the standard polynomial form.

b. Check your ideas with a graphing calculator or computer software. Make notes of errors and make any needed corrections.

4. Shown below is the graph of the square root function, $f(x) = \sqrt{x}$, for $0 \le x \le 20$.

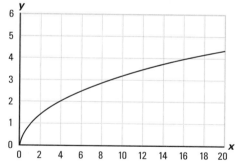

Sketch graphs of the following variations of the square root function, and then check your ideas. With another color pen or pencil, note any needed corrections.

a. $g(x) = 3\sqrt{x}$ b. $h(x) = 0.5\sqrt{x}$ c. $j(x) = -\sqrt{x}$

d. $k(x) = \sqrt{x} + 5$ e. $m(x) = -\sqrt{x} + 5$ f. $n(x) = 2\sqrt{x} + 2$

5. The graph at the right is a parabola with *x*-intercepts at –2 and 3.

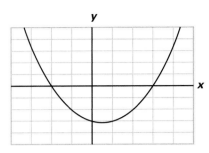

a. Write two different but equivalent symbolic rules, one in factored form and the other in standard polynomial form, for a quadratic function $f(x)$ that has the given graph. Use symbolic reasoning to prove the two forms are equivalent.

b. Without using your calculator, sketch graphs of the following related functions. Explain why the zeroes and maximum or minimum points on their graphs will be the same as or different from those for $f(x)$.

■ $g(x) = -f(x)$

■ $h(x) = 15f(x)$

■ $j(x) = f(x) + 5$

■ $k(x) = -4f(x)$

Reflecting

1. Which of the following functions will have graphs that are *congruent* to the graph of $f(x)$? Explain your reasoning.

a. $g(x) = -f(x)$ **b.** $h(x) = f(x) + c$

c. $j(x) = cf(x)$, with $|c| \neq 1$ **d.** $k(x) = -f(x) + c$

2. Below are graphs of functions with rules formed by modifying basic exponential, power (both direct and inverse), and periodic function rules. In each case, identify as specifically as possible the basic function family that you would use in constructing a rule to match the given graph. Then, also explain the type of transformations that would probably be needed: translation, reflection, stretch or shrink, or some combination of these.

a.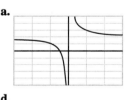

b.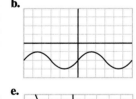

c.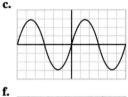

d.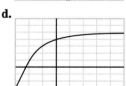

e.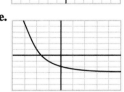

f.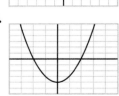

5. a. $f(x) = (x + 2)(x - 3)$
$f(x) = x^2 - x - 6$
These two forms are equivalent because $(x + 2)(x - 3) = x(x - 3) + 2(x - 3) = x^2 - 3x + 2x - 6 = x^2 - x - 6$.

b. ■ $g(x) = -f(x)$
The zeroes do not change because they are on the reflection line. The maximum is the opposite of the minimum of $f(x)$.

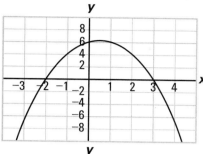

■ $h(x) = 15f(x)$
This is a vertical stretch, so the zeroes will not change and the minimum will occur at the same x value. The minimum value will be multiplied by 15.

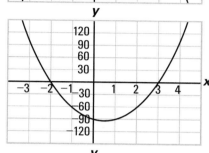

■ $j(x) = f(x) + 5$
The zeroes will change because $j(x)$ is a vertical translation of $f(x)$ up 5 units. The minimum will still occur at $x = 0.5$. The minimum value will be increased by 5 units.

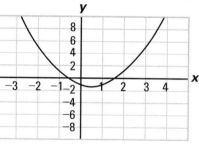

■ $k(x) = -4f(x)$
The zeroes are not affected by the indicated reflection and vertical stretch. The minimum will change to a maximum and be multiplied by -4. It will occur at the same x value.

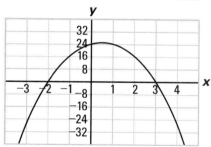

Reflecting

1. a. The graphs will be congruent. Reflection does not change size or shape.
  b. The graphs will be congruent because $h(x)$ is just a translation of $f(x)$.
  c. The graphs will not be congruent since $j(x)$ is a vertical stretch of $f(x)$.
  d. The graphs will be congruent since $k(x)$ can be obtained by first reflecting $f(x)$ across the x-axis and then translating it. Neither of these transformations will change the size or shape of $f(x)$.

See additional Teaching Notes on page T485G.

Unit 6

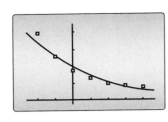

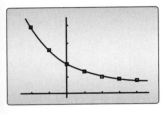

3. a. The exponential regression equation is $y = 9.83(0.76)^x$. See the graph at the left.

    The model found using exponential regression does not seem to be very accurate since points on the end are above the curve and points in the middle are below the curve. They should notice, however, that the end points are farther and farther away from the calculated model. The quadratic regression equation is $y = 0.58x^2 - 3.62x + 9.53$, but neither the quadratic nor the exponential function is the best model.

    b. From the given model, students know that the function is an exponential model that has been translated up 3 units. However, the calculator fits the exponential regression equation without considering translation.

    c. If the data seem to approach a lower limit of 3 instead of 0, as you would expect with an exponential model, you can translate all of the data down 3 units, forcing them to approach 0. Then use your new data to calculate an exponential model. After getting the exponential model, add 3 to translate the model up 3 units. As you see at the left, this method works well. The regression equation will be $y = 6(0.6)^x$, and the curve appears to go through the given data points.

4. Students may be encouraged to give specific examples for this problem in order to support their conjectures. They should determine that zeroes of a function are not changed when the graph is reflected or stretched vertically, but zeroes are changed when the graph is translated vertically. Students can explore this observation graphically, but they can also reason about the question symbolically. For example, if you multiply $f(x) = (x + 2)(x - 3)$ by any stretch factor, the function will still be equal to zero when x is -2 or 3. However, if you think about a vertical translation of a very simple function, such as $f(x) = x$, you can see that if you add any nonzero value to the function, the line will no longer pass through the origin and the zero of the function will change.

5. a. In the graph shown below, $a = 99$ and $b = 0.85$.

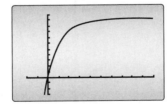

```
WINDOW
 Xmin =-10
 Xmax =50
 Xscl =5
 Ymin =-30
 Ymax =110
 Yscl =10
 Xres =1
```

    The shape of the graph is the same as the shape of an exponential decay graph that has been reflected across the x-axis (and then translated up).

    b. This news-spread model is based upon the exponential decay function with equation $f(x) = 99(0.85)^x$.

    c. If the graph of $f(x) = 99(0.85)^x$ is reflected across the x-axis and then translated up 100 units, it will coincide with the graph of $K(t)$.

    d. The pattern of the graph seems reasonable because you expect rapid spread or growth initially, but then as more and more people have heard the story, the growth rate is going to decrease.

3. The statistical curve-fitting routines of calculators and computer software help in many situations in which you need to find a function rule that matches a data pattern. In fact, those routines will almost always give "an answer" when you enter some data. However, there are times when the technology-produced models are not very useful.

a. Make a scatterplot of the following data and use an exponential curve-fitting routine to produce a model for the pattern in the data. Then, compare a graph of the indicated function model to the data plot.

x	−2	−1	0	1	2	3	4
y	19.7	13	9	6.6	5.2	4.3	3.8

b. The (x, y) data used in Part a were actually generated using $y = 6(0.6^x) + 3$. How does that fact help explain the poor fit of the calculator's exponential model to the actual data?

c. What sort of adjustment could you have made in finding a good function model for the data if you knew that the pattern was tending to a lower limit of $y = 3$? Test your idea and see how well it works.

4. In one class that was working on problems involving transformations of graphs and their associated function rules, a student conjectured that zeroes of any function are not changed when the graph is reflected across the x-axis, vertically translated, or stretched vertically. Do you agree with this conjecture? Explain your reasoning.

5. When a major news event occurs, such as a coming hurricane, a plane crash, or a spectacular crime, word about the event spreads rapidly through the media and by word of mouth. Models for predicting the rate of news spread often use the general form $K(t) = 100 - a(b^t)$, where t represents time since the event occurred, a and b are numbers that can be estimated from previous experience with spread of news, and $K(t)$ is the percent of the population who know the news after t hours.

a. If $a = 99$ and $b = 0.85$, what is the shape of the graph of $K(t)$?

b. What familiar function type is the basis of this news-spread model?

c. What geometric transformations would convert the basic graph type into the graph of the new function $K(t)$?

d. Why does the pattern of this function graph seem reasonable for the situation being modeled?

LESSON 2 • REFLECTIONS AND VERTICAL TRANSFORMATIONS   459

Extending

1. Rules of familiar functions can be modified to produce new functions that model graphs or data patterns that are vertical translations, reflections, or stretches of both the basic functions (linear, exponential, power, and trigonometric) and special functions such as the absolute value or square root functions. Below are rules for functions based on a general function, $f(x)$. Try to predict what geometric transformations of the graph of $f(x)$ will give the graphs for the new functions. Then explore each pattern with several specific basic functions for $f(x)$ to test your predictions. Record any general patterns that you believe will hold for any $f(x)$.

   a. $g(x) = f(x + 5)$

   b. $h(x) = f(-x)$

   c. $j(x) = f(5x)$

   d. $k(x) = f(0.5x)$

   e. $m(x) = f(x - 5)$

2. Rules for basic linear and exponential models can be expressed in "$y = \dots$" form or in *NOW-NEXT* form. However, customizing linear and exponential patterns to fit more complex situations changes things a bit.

   a. What *NOW-NEXT* equation matches the linear function $f(x) = a + bx$? How, if at all, will that equation change if the function needs to be modified to fit a graph that is

   ■ translated up or down by some number c?

   ■ reflected across the x-axis?

   ■ stretched vertically by a factor k?

   b. What *NOW-NEXT* equation matches the exponential function with rule $f(x) = a(b^x)$? How, if at all, will that equation change if the function needs to be modified to fit a graph that is

   ■ translated up or down by some number c?

   ■ reflected across the x-axis?

   ■ stretched vertically by a factor k?

3. When a shoe company launches a new model, it has certain startup costs for design and advertising. Then, it has production costs for each pair of shoes that is made. When the planning department of Start Line Shoes estimated costs of a proposed new model bearing a popular athlete's name, it reported that the average cost per pair of shoes would depend on the number made, with the equation $C(x) = 29 + \frac{25{,}000{,}000}{x}$.

   a. Describe the asymptotic behavior of the graph of $C(x)$.

   b. What connection is there between the graph of $C(x)$ and one of the basic function types you reviewed in this unit?

Extending

1. Encourage students to look at specific examples until they can see a pattern in each case.
   a. Horizontal translation 5 units to the left
   b. Reflection across the *y*-axis
   c. Horizontal shrink by a factor of $\frac{1}{5}$
   d. Horizontal stretch by a factor of 2
   e. Horizontal translation 5 units to the right

2. a. *NEXT* = *NOW* + *b*, starting with *a*
      ■ Only the starting value will change. The new starting value will be *a* ± *c*.
      ■ *NEXT* = *NOW* − *b*, starting with −*a*
      ■ *NEXT* = *NOW* + *kb*, starting with *ka*
   b. *NEXT* = *NOW* · *b*, starting with *a*
      ■ *NEXT* = (*NOW* − *c*) · *b* + *c*, starting with *a* + *c*
      ■ *NEXT* = *NOW* · *b*, starting with −*a*
      ■ *NEXT* = *NOW* · *b*, starting with *ka*

3. a. The graph of *C*(*x*) has the *y*-axis as a vertical asymptote and the line *y* = 29 as a horizontal asymptote. As *x* gets closer to 0, the value of *C*(*x*) grows without bound. As *x* gets large, $\frac{25{,}000{,}000}{x}$ gets close to 0, so the value of *C*(*x*) gets closer to 29.
   b. This is an inverse power model translated up 29 units.

Unit 6

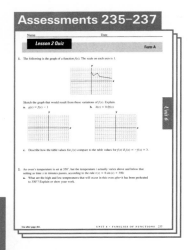
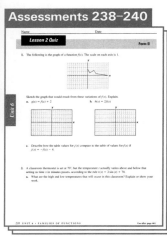
MORE *continued*

4. **a.** $f(x) = 100 - 3x$

$f(x) = 0$ when $x = 33\frac{1}{3}$

According to this particular model, oil reserves would run out in the year 2003.

b. $NEXT = NOW \cdot 1.05$, starting at 3

Year	Amount Used	Year	Amount Used	Year	Amount Used
1970	3	1984	5.9398	1998	11.7604
1971	3.15	1985	6.2368	1999	12.3484
1972	3.3075	1986	6.5486	2000	12.9658
1973	3.4729	1987	6.8761	2001	13.6141
1974	3.6465	1988	7.2199	2002	14.2948
1975	3.8288	1989	7.5809	2003	15.0096
1976	4.0203	1990	7.9599	2004	15.7600
1977	4.2213	1991	8.3579	2005	16.5480
1978	4.4324	1992	8.7758	2006	17.3754
1979	4.6540	1993	9.2146	2007	18.2442
1980	4.8867	1994	9.6753	2008	19.1564
1981	5.1310	1995	10.1591	2009	20.1143
1982	5.3876	1996	10.6670	2010	21.1200
1983	5.6569	1997	11.2004		

c. Students will have to use two sets of *NOW-NEXT* equations.

For consumption: $NEXT_c = 1.05 \cdot NOW_c$, starting at 3.

For supply: $NEXT_s = NOW_s - LAST_c$, starting at 100, where $LAST_c$ is last year's consumption.

Another way to write the equation showing how remaining oil supplies will decline as time passes is to use the sequence or recursive mode of a graphing calculator. (On a TI-82 or TI-83, students must select **Seq** in the **MODE** menu. Have students learn about this operation by reading the manual.) Let $u(n)$ represent the increase of oil consumption and $v(n)$ represent remaining oil supplies over time.

$u_n = 1.05u_{n-1}$, where $u_0 = 3$

$v_n = v_{n-1} - u_{n-1}$, where $v_0 = 100$

n	u(n)	v(n)
0	3	100
1	3.15	97
2	3.3075	93.85
3	3.4729	90.543
4	3.6465	87.07
5	3.8288	83.423
6	4.0203	79.594

n=0

n	u(n)	v(n)
7	4.2213	75.574
8	4.4324	71.353
9	4.654	66.92
10	4.8867	62.266
11	5.131	57.38
12	5.3876	52.249
13	5.6569	46.861

n=13

n	u(n)	v(n)
14	5.9398	41.204
15	6.2368	35.264
16	6.5486	29.028
17	6.8761	22.479
18	7.2199	15.603
19	7.5809	8.383
20	7.9599	.80214

n=20

n	u(n)	v(n)
21	8.3579	-7.158
22	8.7758	-15.52
23	9.2146	-24.29
24	9.6753	-33.51
25	10.159	-43.18
26	10.667	-53.34
27	11.2	-64.01

n=27

n	u(n)	v(n)
28	11.76	-75.21
29	12.348	-86.97
30	12.966	-99.32
31	13.614	-112.3
32	14.295	-125.9
33	15.01	-140.2
34	15.76	-155.2

n=34

n	u(n)	v(n)
35	16.548	-171
36	17.375	-187.5
37	18.244	-204.9
38	19.156	-223.1
39	20.114	-242.3
	21.12	-262.4

n=40

See additional Teaching Notes on page T485G.

Unit 6

4. One limitation on the growth of atmospheric CO_2 is the finite supply of fossil fuels like coal, oil, and gas that produce greenhouse gases when burned. However, modeling of both supply and consumption of those resources is not a simple matter.

a. Around 1970, estimates placed the world's proven oil reserves at 100 billion tons, with annual extraction of about 3 billion tons. If that rate of extraction held constant over many years, what function would predict world oil reserves x years after 1970? When would that model predict supplies to run out?

b. The growing world population and industrial development will actually increase usage each year. Suppose that those factors produce a 5% increase in annual usage each year. Use this assumption to write a *NOW-NEXT* equation showing how annual consumption will increase as years pass. Then use your equation to produce a table of annual consumption estimates for the 40 years from 1970 to 2010.

c. Use the assumptions of Part b to write a *NOW-NEXT* equation showing how the remaining world oil supplies $v(x)$ will decline as time passes. Then use your equation to produce a table giving world oil supply estimates for the 40 years from 1970 to 2010.

d. As you know, the world has not depleted its reserves of oil, as the 1970 prediction suggested. What factors do you believe contributed to the fact that world oil reserves have not been completely drained?

Lesson 3

Customizing Models 2: Horizontal Transformations

Many important physical variables, such as ocean tides, positions of the planets in orbit around the sun, and household electrical currents, oscillate in periodic patterns that suggest modeling by the trigonometric functions sine and cosine.

$s(x) = \sin x$

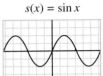

The periods of these basic trigonometric functions are both 2π (approximately 6.28). But ocean tides typically vary, with a period of about 12 hours, and the voltage of standard alternating current electricity has a period of $\frac{1}{60}$ of a second. As you previously have seen, the graphs of the required function models will be similar to sine and cosine, but stretched or squeezed horizontally (and vertically). In this lesson, you will investigate how to write symbolic function rules that correspond to these variations in graph patterns.

$c(x) = \cos x$

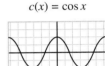

Think About This Situation

What modification of the rules for $s(x) = \sin x$ and $c(x) = \cos x$ might produce functions with graphs that are stretched, squeezed, or shifted like those below? (The scale on each x-axis is 1, and the scale on each y-axis is 0.5.)

a Longer period:

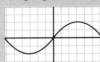

b Shorter period:

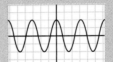

c Shifted; not symmetric about the y-axis or the origin:

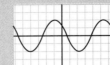

Customizing Models 2: Horizontal Transformations

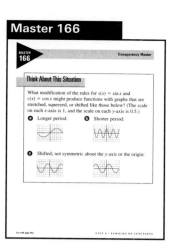

LESSON OVERVIEW In this lesson, students customize various function models as they explore horizontal shifts and horizontal stretching and compression. A variety of functions are used to explore these transformations, including absolute value, quadratic, periodic, exponential, and square root.

Lesson Objectives

■ To recognize how the graph and table of $f(x)$ relate to the graph and table of $f(x + a)$

■ To recognize how the graph and table of $f(x)$ relate to the graph and table of $f(ax)$

■ To reason with the transformations above as they relate to real-world situations

LAUNCH   full-class discussion

Think About This Situation

See Teaching Master 166.

You might encourage your students to experiment using their graphing calculators (set to radian mode) as they try to answer these questions. Students are not expected to know what will produce these graphs. However, they *are* expected to have their curiosity aroused. Simply listen to student conjectures at this time. Resolution on what causes the periodic changes will come later, as students work through this lesson.

ⓐ $f(x) = \sin x$ is altered to become $f(x) = \sin ax$, where a is greater than zero and less than 1.

ⓑ $f(x) = \cos x$ is altered to become $f(x) = \cos ax$, where a is greater than 1.

ⓒ The wording implies that the original function is symmetric about the y-axis, so students may begin with $f(x) = \cos x$ (which is symmetric) and shift the graph by changing the function to $f(x) = \cos(x \pm a)$.

INVESTIGATION 1 Horizontal Shifts

In this investigation, students explore the graphs of horizontal transformations of $f(x) = |x|$ and $f(x) = x^2$ in order to determine the effect of the transformations. This work leads students to the realization that $f(x - a)$, where $a > 0$, is a horizontal shift to the right of $f(x)$, but it may well leave them with the question of why this should be so. It seems counterintuitive. Typically, students will think that $y = f(x - a)$ should be a vertical shift downward or a horizontal shift to the left. Students may have trouble constructing explanations. After giving students time to make and share their own explanations, a full-class discussion may be helpful to clarify or complete student explanations. (See Activity 2 Part d.) Making side-by-side tables seems to help students see that the horizontal transformation affects the inputs first, and through them the output values are affected. Students may make such observations as, "The same output values occur, just later in the table, so the same shape occurs but later (further right) on the x-axis." Some students may focus on the change in the x-intercept. The x-intercept for $f(x) = x^2$ is 0 while the x-intercept for $g(x) = (x - 2)^2$ is 2. Thus, $g(x)$ is a horizontal shift of $f(x)$ to the right 2 units.

x	$f(x) = x^2$		x	$g(x) = (x - 2)^2$
-2	$(-2)^2 = 4$		-2	$(-4)^2 = 16$
-1	$(-1)^2 = 1$		-1	$(-3)^2 = 9$
0	$0^2 = 0$		0	$(-2)^2 = 4$
1	$1^2 = 1$		1	$(-1)^2 = 1$
2	$2^2 = 4$		2	$(0)^2 = 0$
3	$3^2 = 9$		3	$(1)^2 = 1$

It will help with this investigation and the next if students talk about which part of the symbolic representation causes the shape and which part causes the transformation of the shape. In $g(x) = (x - 2)^2$, for example, you might ask how students know this function is going to be a parabola. They will say that the "square" is the relevant characteristic.

You may also ask whether the $(x - 2)$ is done before the squaring or after. This might help your students informally compose transformations. So the symbols for $g(x) = (x - 2)^2$ indicate an input (horizontal) shift of a basic parabola, while $h(x) = x^2 - 2$ indicates that the shape (squaring) is created first, and then the "-2" transformation produces a (vertical) shift of the output values.

1. a.

x	-5	-4	-3	-2	-1	0	1	2	3	4	5
$g(x) = |x + 3|$	2	1	0	1	2	3	4	5	6	7	8
$h(x) = |x - 3|$	8	7	6	5	4	3	2	1	0	1	2

Graph i matches $h(x)$.

Graph ii matches $g(x)$.

b. Students should conjecture and test their ideas with specific functions.

2. a. The rule $g(x) = (x - 2)^2$ matches the graph shown.

INVESTIGATION 1 ▸ Horizontal Shifts

In previous work, you studied several function families with graphs that are symmetric about a vertical line. In the simplest cases, the line of symmetry is the *y*-axis, but there are also some natural ways to modify the rules for those basic functions to produce graphs with other vertical lines of symmetry.

1. The diagram at the right shows the graph of $f(x) = |x|$. The scale on both axes is 1. Consider two variations of the absolute value function:

   $$g(x) = |x + 3|$$
   $$h(x) = |x - 3|$$

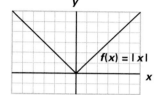

   a. Make and complete copies of the following table of values for these functions. Then match the table and rules for $g(x)$ and $h(x)$ to the given graphs.

x		–5	–4	–3	–2	–1	0	1	2	3	4	5
$g(x) = |x + 3|$												
$h(x) = |x - 3|$												

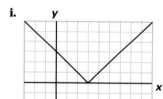
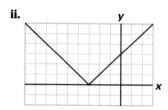

   b. Examine your work in Part a for ideas that could be used to adjust other function rules so they match **horizontal translations** of graphs of other basic functions. Test your ideas with specific functions in your functions toolkit.

2. In this activity, you will explore more complex variations of the familiar function with rule $f(x) = x^2$. In each part, the scale on both axes is 1. Complete Parts a and b without using a graphing calculator or computer software.

   a. Which rule matches the graph below: $g(x) = (x - 2)^2$ or $h(x) = (x + 2)^2$?

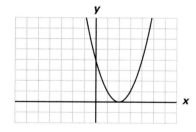

b. Match these rules with the graphs below:

- $f(x) = -x^2 + 4$
- $g(x) = -(x - 4)^2 + 4$
- $h(x) = -(x + 4)^2 + 4$

i. 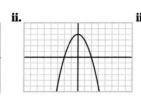 **ii.** 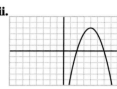 **iii.**

c. Write symbolic rules matching these graphs and check your ideas with a graphing calculator or computer software.

i. 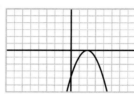 **ii.**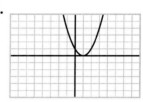

iii. 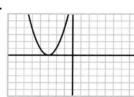 **iv.**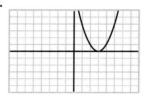

d. Explain why it is reasonable for the graph of $g(x) = (x - 3)^2$ to be positioned 3 units to the right of the graph of $f(x) = x^2$.

3. Use ideas you have from studying the graphs in Activities 1 and 2 to answer these questions about other functions and their graphs.

a. How will the graphs of $g(x) = \cos(x - 2)$ and $h(x) = \cos(x + 2)$ be related to the graph of the basic cosine function $c(x) = \cos x$?

b. How will the graphs of $r(x) = \sin(x + 1)$ and $t(x) = \sin(x - 1)$ be related to the graph of the basic sine function $s(x) = \sin x$?

c. Use the idea of horizontal translation to find a variation of the basic cosine function $c(x) = \cos x$ whose graph coincides with the graph of $s(x) = \sin x$.

d. How do horizontal translations of the graph of a periodic function affect the period? How do they affect the amplitude? Explain your reasoning.

2. b.   **i.** $h(x) = -(x + 4)^2 + 4$

       ii. $f(x) = -x^2 + 4$

      iii. $g(x) = -(x - 4)^2 + 4$

  c.   **i.** $f(x) = -(x - 2)^2$

       ii. $g(x) = (x - 1)^2$

      iii. $h(x) = (x + 3)^2$

      iv. $i(x) = (x - 3)^2$

  d. When $x = 0$, $f(x) = 0$; and when $x = 3$, $g(x) = 0$. This indicates that the vertex of the graph has been shifted 3 units to the right. (See the lesson introduction for another explanation.)

3. a. Based on Activities 1 and 2, $g(x)$ will be shifted 2 units to the right, and $h(x)$ will be shifted 2 units to the left of the graph of $c(x)$.

  b. Following the same pattern, $r(x)$ will be shifted 1 unit to the left, and $t(x)$ will be shifted 1 unit to the right of the graph of $s(x)$.

  c. By graphing the sine and cosine functions, students can see that the graph of the cosine function shifted right $\frac{\pi}{2}$ radians will match the graph of the sine function. Students may use 1.5; this value is close enough for this activity. So the graph of the function $f(x) = \cos(x - 1.5)$ will coincide with the graph of $y = \sin x$. (Some students may respond in degrees, $f(x) = \cos(x - 90)$, rather than radians.)

  d. Horizontal translations, like vertical translations, do not change the shape of the function; therefore the amplitude and period remain the same for a periodic function.

Unit 6

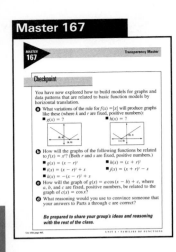

EXPLORE *continued*

4. **a.** Students should check the probabilities.

b. The absolute value function is suggested by the pattern.

c. First think about the graph of a variation of the absolute value function $f(x) = \left|\left(\frac{1}{36}x\right)\right|$ because the slopes of the lines are $\pm\frac{1}{36}$.

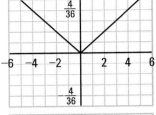

Then, reflect that graph across the x-axis. This function is $f(x) = -\left|\left(\frac{1}{36}x\right)\right|$.

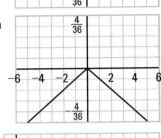

Next translate up $\frac{6}{36}$ and to the right 7 to obtain $f(x) = -\left|\frac{1}{36}(x - 7)\right| + \frac{6}{36}$.

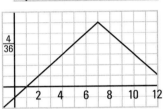

d. If differences exist, students can explain their reasoning to each other or check points for fit to each model. Students may have models that look different but are equivalent.

e. The practical domain is the integers from 2 to 12. The practical range is $\frac{1}{36}, \frac{2}{36}, \frac{3}{36}, \frac{4}{36}, \frac{5}{36}$, and $\frac{6}{36}$.

SHARE AND SUMMARIZE   full-class discussion

Checkpoint

See Teaching Master 167.

ⓐ ■ $g(x) = |x - k|$
■ $h(x) = |x + r|$

ⓑ ■ The graph of $g(x)$ will be the graph of $f(x)$ shifted r units to the right.
■ The graph of $h(x)$ will be the graph of $f(x)$ shifted r units to the left.
■ The graph of $i(x)$ will be the graph of $f(x)$ shifted r units to the right and up s units.
■ The graph of $j(x)$ will be the graph of $f(x)$ shifted r units to the left and down s units.
■ The graph of $k(x)$ will be the graph of $f(x)$ shifted r units to the right, reflected across the x-axis, and then shifted up s units.

ⓒ From $c(x)$, the function $g(x)$ will be shifted right b units, vertically stretched by a factor of a (or compressed if $0 < a < 1$), and translated up c units.

ⓓ Responses may vary. Look for careful explanations for vertical and horizontal translations and reflections. A possible response for horizontal translation is as follows: With the functions $f(x) = |x|$ and $g(x) = x^2$, you can see that if x is replaced by a quantity like $x + 2$ to give $|x + 2|$ and $(x + 2)^2$, the new minimum or maximum value will be shifted 2 units to the left because -2 is the zero for the new function.

CONSTRUCTING A MATH TOOLKIT: Students should add examples of graphical, symbolic, and tabular representations of functions that have been shifted horizontally to their function toolkit.

Unit 6

4. Now combine your strategies for matching function families to data patterns and customizing rules so you can model the following probability situation: Suppose two six-sided dice are rolled and the sum of the dots on the upper faces is computed. The plot at the right shows the probabilities associated with the possible sums.

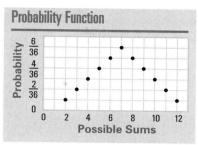

a. Verify that the plot is accurate and accounts for all possibilities. Share the workload among your groupmates.

b. What basic function type is suggested by the pattern in the plot?

c. Use your understanding of graph transformations to build a function rule that models the pattern in the data.

d. Compare your function rule to the rules built by other groups. Resolve any differences.

e. What are the practical domain and range of this function?

Checkpoint

You have now explored how to build models for graphs and data patterns that are related to basic function models by horizontal translation.

ⓐ What variations of the rule for $f(x) = |x|$ will produce graphs like these (where k and r are fixed, positive numbers):

■ $g(x) = ?$ ■ $h(x) = ?$

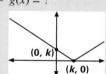 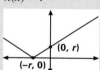

ⓑ How will the graphs of the following functions be related to $f(x) = x^2$? (Both r and s are fixed, positive numbers.)

■ $g(x) = (x - r)^2$ ■ $h(x) = (x + r)^2$

■ $i(x) = (x - r)^2 + s$ ■ $j(x) = (x + r)^2 - s$

■ $k(x) = -(x - r)^2 + s$

ⓒ How will the graph of $g(x) = a \cos (x - b) + c$, where a, b, and c are fixed, positive numbers, be related to the graph of $c(x) = \cos x$?

ⓓ What reasoning would you use to convince someone that your answers to Parts a through c are correct?

Be prepared to share your group's ideas and reasoning with the rest of the class.

▶ **On Your Own**

The following graph shows the function $f(x) = -|x| + 3$.

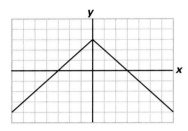

Without using a calculator or computer software, sketch graphs for the following related functions. Then check your ideas with a calculator or computer software, make any needed corrections, and explain your reasoning in the first attempt and in any revisions.

a. $a(x) = -|x - 3| + 3$

b. $b(x) = -|x + 4| + 3$

c. $c(x) = -|x + 4| + 1$

INVESTIGATION 2 Horizontal Stretching and Compression

The connection between vertical and horizontal translation of function graphs and the modification of rules to match those geometric transformations might suggest a strategy for constructing rules for functions with graphs obtained by *horizontal stretching* or *compression* of a familiar graph.

1. The following graphs show two useful variations of the basic sine function. The scale on both axes is 1.

$r(x) = \sin(2x)$ $\qquad\qquad\qquad q(x) = \sin\left(\frac{1}{2}x\right)$

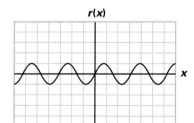 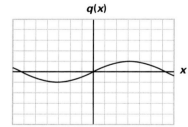

a. Estimate, as accurately as possible, the period of each function.

b. How do the periods of the graphs relate to the period of $s(x) = \sin x$?

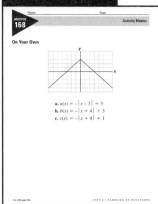
APPLY individual task

▶On Your Own

See Teaching Master 168.

Students' sketches should be similar to the graphs below.

a.

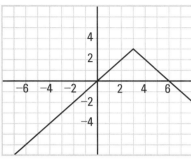

b.

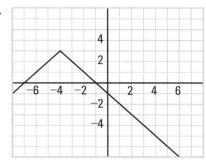

c.

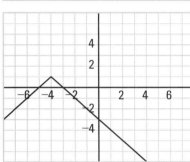

MORE

ASSIGNMENT *pp. 469–479*

Students can now begin Modeling Task 5 or Reflecting Task 5 from the MORE assignment following Investigation 2.

EXPLORE small-group investigation

INVESTIGATION ▶2 Horizontal Stretching and Compression

In this investigation, students examine the transformation that causes the sine and cosine functions to undergo a period change. After the previous investigation of horizontal translations, students may find this new transformation relatively easy to understand. In every activity, the initial transformation (a multiplication) is performed on the input variable before the sine (or cosine) is taken, so no new values for the output variables can occur; the output values occur just at different places, in this case, repeating more or less frequently. Your students should quickly arrive at the conclusion that if $k > 1$, then $y = \sin(kx)$ shows the same outputs repeating more frequently, so the period is shorter than the one for $y = \sin x$. And if $0 < k < 1$, then the period is longer. Students may have more trouble determining the actual period. As you talk to them about this, it will help if you use language like, "When $k = 3$, how many waves does the curve make in the usual 2π radians?" This type of question will help students understand that each wave's length must be a fraction of the usual 2π.

1. a. For $r(x) = \sin(2x)$, the period is just over 3 (exactly π).
    For $q(x) = \sin\left(\frac{1}{2}x\right)$, the period is a little more than 12 (exactly 4π).
  b. The period of $r(x) = \sin(2x)$ is half the period of $s(x) = \sin x$. The period of $q(x) = \sin\left(\frac{1}{2}x\right)$ is twice the period of $s(x) = \sin x$.

2. **a.** ■ The period of $p(x)$ is shorter than the period of $s(x)$.

■ The period of $h(x)$ is longer than the period of $s(x)$.

■ The period of $k(x)$ is shorter than the period of $s(x)$.

b. ■ If $k > 1$, then the period will be shorter than 2π.

■ If $0 < k < 1$, then the period will be longer than 2π.

3. **Encourage students to study Activity 1 to determine a rule for the period of $\sin(kx)$. They may see that the period is $\frac{2\pi}{k}$.**

a. ■ The period of $f(x)$ is $\frac{2}{3}\pi$ or approximately 2.09.

■ The period of $d(x)$ is 6π or approximately 18.85.

■ The period of $e(x)$ is 0.2π or approximately 0.628.

b. The period of $f(x) = \sin(kx)$ is $\frac{2\pi}{k}$.

For each function in Part a: $\frac{2\pi}{3} = \frac{2}{3}\pi$; $\frac{2\pi}{\frac{1}{3}} = 6\pi$; and $\frac{2\pi}{10} = 0.2\pi$.

4. The period of the cosine function behaves in the same way as the period of the sine function. The period of $g(x) = \cos(kx)$ will be $\frac{2\pi}{k}$.

5. **If students use the SinReg for the (*month, temperature*) data, they will obtain the equation $y = 29.75 \sin(0.47x - 1.77) + 46.82$. You might wish to discuss with students which model, the calculator-produced or the context-produced, is best. Even though the calculator-produced equation fits this set of data well, it will not be as helpful for predicting long term. Comparing the two models beyond $x = 12$ shows that the sine regression period is more than 12. This is a good example to use to discuss the importance of using contextual information along with data to write equations.**

a.

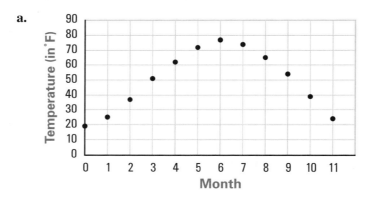

b. It seems that a sine or cosine function best fits the data.

c. The amplitude is approximately $\frac{1}{2}(77 - 19)$ or 29.

d. The period is 12.

e. Responses may vary. (See Part g.) The cosine function can be used with no horizontal shift, but in that case a vertical shift of $19 + 29$ or 48 is evident and the function must be reflected across the x-axis.

2. Now consider other variations on the basic sine function rule.

    a. Which of the following variations of $s(x) = \sin x$ have a period that is longer than the period of $s(x)$, and which have a shorter period than $s(x)$?

       ■ $p(x) = \sin(3x)$

       ■ $h(x) = \sin\left(\frac{1}{5}x\right)$

       ■ $k(x) = \sin(4.5x)$

    b. For the function $p(x) = \sin(kx)$, what positive values of k will produce periodic functions that have

       ■ shorter periods than $s(x) = \sin x$?

       ■ longer periods than $s(x) = \sin x$?

3. The function $s(x) = \sin x$ has a period of 2π (approximately 6.28).

    a. Estimate as accurately as possible the period for the following functions.

       ■ $f(x) = \sin(3x)$

       ■ $d(x) = \sin\left(\frac{1}{3}x\right)$

       ■ $e(x) = \sin(10x)$

    b. In general, how is the period of $f(x) = \sin(kx)$ related to the period of $s(x) = \sin x$? How can this fact be used to explain your answers in Part a?

4. Investigate the periods for variations of the basic cosine function with symbolic rules of the form $g(x) = \cos(kx)$. Write a summary of your findings on the relation between the number k and the period of $g(x) = \cos(kx)$.

5. The following table shows the average monthly Fahrenheit temperatures for Des Moines, Iowa.

Average Temperatures, Des Moines

Month	Jan	Feb	Mar	Apr	May	June	July	Aug	Sept	Oct	Nov	Dec
Temperature	19	25	37	51	62	72	77	74	65	54	39	24

Source: *The World Almanac and Book of Facts 2001*. Mahwah, NJ: World Almanac, 2001.

Botanical Center in Des Moines, Iowa

    a. Plot the (*month*, *temperature*) data using 0 for January, 1 for February, and so on. On the same plot, sketch a graph which fits the data.

    b. What function family best fits the data?

    c. What is the amplitude of the modeling function?

    d. What is the period of the modeling function?

    e. Do the data indicate a horizontal shift from the basic toolkit function for this function's family? Do the data indicate a vertical shift?

f. Write a symbolic rule that gives average monthly temperature as a function of the month.

g. Compare your function rule to the rules of other groups. Resolve any differences.

h. Use your function model to estimate the average monthly temperature for the month of April. Compare the temperature as reported in the table to your estimate.

Checkpoint

In this investigation, you explored modifications of the basic sine and cosine functions to describe variables changing with a variety of periods.

ⓐ How is the graph of a function with rule $f(x) = \sin (kx)$ related to the graph of $s(x) = \sin x$ when $k > 1$? When $0 < k < 1$? How is the situation similar for $g(x) = \cos (kx)$ and $c(x) = \cos x$?

ⓑ How can you construct variations of the basic sine and cosine function rules with period p different from 2π?

ⓒ What reasoning would you use to convince someone that your answers to Parts a and b are correct?

Be prepared to share your group's ideas and reasoning with the entire class.

▶On Your Own

The voltage in standard household alternating current circuits oscillates between −150 and 150 volts with period $\frac{1}{60}$ of a second.

a. What modification of the function $s(x) = \sin x$ will model the periodic variation of voltage in an AC circuit, with x measured in seconds?

b. What geometric transformations of the graph of $s(x) = \sin x$ will give the graph of your answer to Part a?

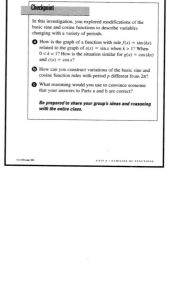

5. **f.** $f(x) = -29 \cos\left(\frac{\pi}{6}x\right) + 48$ (Other rules are also possible. See Part g.)

g. Groups using the sine function will have to shift the graph to the right $\frac{1}{4}$ period. One possibility is $f(x) = 29 \sin\left[\frac{2\pi}{12}(x - 3)\right] + 48 = 29 \sin\left[\frac{\pi}{6}(x - 3)\right] + 48$. The function has a period of 12, so a right shift of $\frac{1}{4}$ period requires subtracting 3 from the input variable x.

h. Either function in Parts f and g gives the April temperature, $f(3)$, as 48°. The table reports 51°.

SHARE AND SUMMARIZE   full-class discussion

Checkpoint

See Teaching Master 169.

ⓐ For $k > 1$, $f(x) = \sin(kx)$ has a period that is less than the period of $f(x) = \sin x$. The new period will be $\frac{2\pi}{k}$. For $0 < k < 1$, $f(x) = \sin(kx)$ has a period that is greater than the period of $f(x) = \sin x$. Again, the new period will be $\frac{2\pi}{k}$. The same patterns hold true for $g(x) = \cos(kx)$. The period will be $\frac{2\pi}{k}$. If $k > 1$, then the period will be less than 2π. If $0 < k < 1$, then the period will be greater than 2π.

ⓑ Variations of the basic sine or cosine function with period p different from 2π will be $\sin\left(\frac{2\pi}{p}x\right)$ or $\cos\left(\frac{2\pi}{p}x\right)$.

ⓒ Using a graphing calculator would definitely be one good strategy. You might also ask students to consider that if you are multiplying by a number greater than 1, you are making the function inputs appear faster. This makes the period shorter. If you are multiplying by a number less than 1 but greater than 0, you are slowing down the appearance of the function inputs, causing a longer period. For example, the normal period for $f(x) = \sin x$ is 2π. This function goes from 0 to 1 as x goes from 0 to $\frac{\pi}{2}$. When you consider $f(x) = \sin 2x$, the function goes from 0 to 1 as x goes from 0 to $\frac{\pi}{4}$.

CONSTRUCTING A MATH TOOLKIT: Students should add examples of graphical, symbolic, and tabular representations of functions that have been compressed and stretched horizontally to their Math Toolkits. You may wish to give students specific functions by rule or graph, such as $f(x) = \cos x$ and $h(x) = x^2$. Then ask students to sketch variations, such as $f(2x)$, $h(x - 3)$, or $h(2(x - 3))$ and describe the transformations in words. (Once students have completed Extending Task 3 or 5, they sketch similar variations to a function defined by a graph such as the one at the right.)

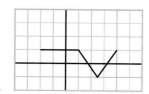

APPLY   individual task

▶ On Your Own

a. Period $= \frac{1}{60}$. This means $f(x) = 150 \sin(120\pi x)$.

b. The geometric transformations that give the graph from Part a are a vertical stretch of 150 and a horizontal shrink by a factor of 120π, giving a new period of $\frac{1}{60}$.

Modeling

1. **a.** Since you want $\sin(kx)$ to have a period of 365 days, $k = \frac{2\pi}{365}$. This means the sine function with period 365 is $f(x) = \sin\left(\frac{2\pi}{365}x\right)$.

    b. $f(x) = 3\sin\left(\frac{2\pi}{365}x\right)$

    c. $f(x) = 3\sin\left[\frac{2\pi}{365}\left(x - \frac{365}{4}\right)\right]$ or $3\sin\left(\frac{2\pi x}{365} - \frac{\pi}{2}\right)$

    d. $f(x) = 3\sin\left[\frac{2\pi}{365}\left(x - \frac{365}{4}\right)\right] + 12$ or $3\sin\left(\frac{2\pi x}{365} - \frac{\pi}{2}\right) + 12$

2. **a.** Any of the following models or their equivalents will work: $f(x) = 2\sin\left(\frac{\pi x}{6}\right) + 20$; $f(x) = 2\cos\left(\frac{\pi x}{6}\right) + 20$; $f(x) = -2\cos\left(\frac{\pi x}{6}\right) + 20$; or $f(x) = -2\sin\left(\frac{\pi x}{6}\right) + 20$.

    b. If the period p is 12 hours, then you know that $k = \frac{\pi}{6}$. Since the water depth changes from 18 to 22 feet, a difference of 4 feet, the amplitude of the function should be 2. In order to have the function move from a minimum value of 18 to a maximum value of 22, you have to add the average of those two numbers, 20, to the function representation.

3. **a.**

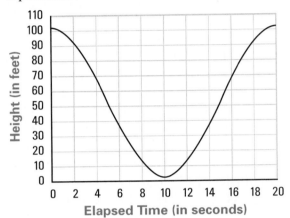

MORE

Modeling • Organizing • Reflecting • Extending

Modeling

1. The number of hours between sunrise and sunset at any location on Earth varies in a predictable pattern with a period of 365 days, not 2π like the basic sine and cosine functions. In the Northern Hemisphere, the shortest days occur very near to the first day of each calendar year.

   a. What modification of the basic sine function will have a period of 365?

   b. What modification of your answer in Part a will have an amplitude of 3, representing the maximum deviation from yearly average sunlight hours in many cities, such as Chicago, Illinois?

   c. What modification of your answer in Part b will shift the graph to the right so the minimum point occurs when $x = 0$, with x measured in days?

   d. What modification of your answer in Part c will represent the fact that the average number of hours of sunlight per day is 12?

2. Suppose that the tides in an ocean harbor cause a change in water depth from 18 to 22 feet from low to high tide, with a period of 12 hours.

   a. Experiment with variations of the rule $y = \sin x$ or $y = \cos x$ to find a function that models this situation.

   b. Explain how the numbers in your symbolic rule are related to the behavior of the tide.

3. Suppose that a Ferris wheel with radius 50 feet makes one complete rotation every 20 seconds and that the ride starts (the last passengers are loaded into their seats) when you are at the top of the ride.

   a. The bottom of the Ferris wheel is 2.5 feet above the ground. Sketch a graph of the relation between elapsed time and your height above the ground during the ride described in this situation.

b. What are the period and amplitude of a function modeling the (*time*, *height*) relation?

c. What geometric transformations of the graph of $c(x) = \cos x$ produce your graph in Part a?

d. What modification of the function $c(x) = \cos x$ models your height above the ground as a function of time?

e. Use your modeling function to predict your height above the ground 24 seconds into the ride.

4. In Activity 5 of Investigation 2, page 467, you saw that the average monthly temperature for a location on Earth varies *sinusoidally* with a period of 12 months. For Phoenix, Arizona, the highest average monthly Fahrenheit temperature is 94° and occurs in July. The lowest average monthly temperature occurs in January and is 54°. (Source: *The World Almanac and Book of Facts 2001*. Mahwah, NJ: World Almanac, 2001.)

Phoenix, Arizona

a. Find a variation of $s(x) = \sin x$ that models the pattern of change in average monthly temperature for Phoenix.

b. Use your modeling rule to predict the average temperature for Phoenix in October.

c. Find a variation of $c(x) = \cos x$ that models the pattern of change in average monthly temperature for Phoenix. What would this model predict for the average monthly temperature for October?

5. In Unit 3, you studied the equation for the height above the road surface of a cable suspended between two 30-foot towers of a 100-foot-long bridge. The minimum height above the road surface was 5 feet in the center.

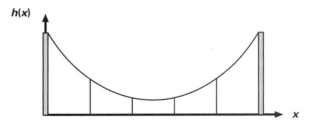

a. Which family of functions is most appropriate to model the height of the suspension cable?

3. **b.** Period: 20 seconds

   Amplitude: 50 feet

   c. The geometric transformations needed are as follows:
   - A horizontal stretch of 0.1π
   - No horizontal translation
   - A vertical stretch of 50
   - A vertical translation up of $2.5 + 50$

   d. $f(x) = 50\cos(0.1\pi x) + 52.5$

   e. The height 24 seconds into the ride would be $f(24)$ or approximately 68.0 feet (the same height as 4 seconds into the ride).

4. **a.** The maximum of $94°$ in July implies that $f(6) = 94$ and the minimum of $54°$ in January implies that $f(0) = 54$, so the amplitude is $\frac{40}{2}$ or 20. A vertical shift of $54 + 20$ or 74 is needed. The period is 12, so $k = \frac{2\pi}{12}$. A shift right of $\frac{1}{4}$ of the period implies that x is replaced by $(x - 3)$. So $f(x) = 20\sin\left[\frac{\pi}{6}(x - 3)\right] + 74$.

   b. October's temperature would be predicted to be $f(9) = 74°$.

   c. If cosine is used to model this situation, we do not need a horizontal shift but rather a reflection across the x-axis. So $f(x) = -20\cos\left(\frac{\pi x}{6}\right) + 74$. For October, $f(9)$ is still $74°$.

5. **This problem might be difficult for students, but it is a worthwhile problem that will give them good insights into transformations. Consider doing this problem in class. Have groups present their solutions to the rest of the class.**

   a. A quadratic function is most appropriate for this model. However, it is possible to fit other families exactly to the three crucial points given in Part b. Note that this is *not* a periodic phenomenon, so the trigonometric functions are not appropriate.

Unit 6

5. **b.** The quadratic equation $f(x) = 0.01x^2 - x + 30$ contains the three points $(0, 30)$, $(50, 5)$, $(100, 30)$.

   c. A horizontal translation left 50 and a vertical translation down 5 give the modified function rule: $f(x) = 0.01(x + 50)^2 - (x + 50) + 25$; $f(-50) = 25$; $f(0) = 0$; $f(50) = 25$.
   The low point of the suspension cable is now at $(0, 0)$ which is also the center of the cable. The distance between the high points is 100 ft. as before. This quadratic function can also model the height of the suspension cable.

   d. $0.01(x + 50)^2 - (x + 50) + 25 = 0.01(x^2 + 100x + 2{,}500) - x - 50 + 25 = 0.01x^2 + x + 25 - x - 25 = 0.01x^2$

6. **a.** The amplitude is only 1, so the amount of sunlight changes by no more than 1 hour from the average length. The deviation is highest on the 181st day (June 30). The minimum daylight (greatest negative deviation) occurs on day 365 (December 31). The daylight is nearest 12 hours on days 88 and 273 (March 29 and September 30).

   b. If we add the deviation function to the 12 hour average daylight, we get $S(x) = 12 + \sin(0.017x - 1.5)$.

   c. For Washington, D.C., $C(x) = 3\sin(0.017x - 1.5)$ gives the variation in sunlight, and $S(x) = 12 + 3\sin(0.017x - 1.5)$ gives the hours of daylight.

b. Use the given information about tower height, bridge length, and the low point of the suspension cable to find an equation to model the height of the suspension cable.

c. Modify your function rule so that the vertex is at (0, 0) instead of (50, 5). Calculate output from this new function rule for $x = -50, 0,$ and 50. Explain what those results tell about the bridge and its suspension cable.

d. Use algebraic reasoning to write the quadratic expression obtained in Part c in equivalent standard polynomial form.

6. All over the world, the number of hours between sunrise and sunset changes in a periodic pattern with the seasons, longer in summer and shorter in winter, with an average of 12 hours that is reached in late March and late September. For regions north of the tropic of Cancer, the deviation from average is a function of the day of the year and the latitude. For a city near the tropic of Cancer, such as Havana, Cuba, the deviation from average is modeled reasonably well by the function $C(x) = \sin(0.017x - 1.5)$, where x is the day of the year using the first of January as day 1. (Source: *The World Almanac and Book of Facts 2001*. Mahwah, NJ: World Almanac, 2001.)

a. Study the function $C(x)$ to find the amplitude of the variation in hours of sunlight in Havana. Find the times of the year when sunlight hours are maximum, minimum, and near the average of 12 hours.

b. Modify the rule for $C(x)$ to give another function $S(x)$ that tells the actual number of hours between sunrise and sunset in Havana on any given day.

c. For cities that are farther north than Havana, the change in hours of sunlight from summer to winter is greater. For example, in Washington, D.C., the longest day is about 15 hours, and the shortest is about 9 hours. What modification of the rule for $C(x)$ will give the variation in hours of sunlight in Washington as a function of the day of the year? What rule will give the actual number of hours of sunlight there on any given day?

LESSON 3 • HORIZONTAL TRANSFORMATIONS   **471**

d. For cities that are even farther north, such as Oslo, Norway, or Stockholm, Sweden (both near 60° north latitude), the longest day has about 18 hours of sunlight, and the shortest has only about 6 hours of sunlight. What rule gives the variation in hours of sunlight in those cities as a function of the day of the year? What rule gives the actual number of hours of sunlight on any given day?

e. For cities in the Southern Hemisphere, such as Rio de Janeiro, Brazil, or Melbourne, Australia, the seasons are the opposite of those in the Northern Hemisphere. For example, Melbourne and Washington, D.C., are about equidistant from the equator, and Melbourne's longest day is the same day as Washington's shortest day. Similarly, Rio de Janeiro and Havana are about equidistant from the equator. Use that information to write rules giving the variation in hours of sunlight for Rio de Janeiro and Melbourne as a function of the day of the year. Then modify those functions to produce rules giving the actual number of hours of sunlight on any given day in the two cities.

Rio de Janeiro

Organizing

1. Consider the absolute value function $A(x) = |x|$. Modify the rule for $A(x)$ to give functions with graphs that have the following properties. Check each answer with a graphing calculator or computer and make any needed corrections. For any errors you make in your first attempt, make notes on how they can be avoided in the future.

a. Minimum point at (3, 0)

b. Minimum point at (–2, 0)

c. Maximum point at (0, 0)

d. Maximum point at (5, 0)

e. Minimum point at (3, –2)

6. **d.** For Stockholm and Oslo, $C(x) = 6 \sin(0.017x - 1.5)$ gives the variation of sunlight in hours, and $S(x) = 12 + 6 \sin(0.017x - 1.5)$ gives the actual number of daylight hours.

   e. $C(x)$ for Rio de Janeiro would be the opposite of the function for Havana, $C(x) = -\sin(0.017x - 1.5)$. Similarly, the function for Melbourne would be $C(x) = -3 \sin(0.017x - 1.5)$. Both of these functions give the longer days in December and January and the shortest day in July. The formulas giving the actual hours of daylight would be $S(x) = 12 - \sin(0.017x - 1.5)$ for Rio de Janeiro and $S(x) = 12 - 3 \sin(0.017x - 1.5)$ for Melbourne.

Organizing

1. **a.** $B(x) = |x - 3|$
   b. $C(x) = |x + 2|$
   c. $D(x) = -|x|$
   d. $E(x) = -|x - 5|$
   e. $F(x) = |x - 3| - 2$

Unit 6

2. **a.** $f(x + 1) = (x + 1)^3 - (x + 1)$
    b. $f(x - 1) = (x - 1)^3 - (x - 1)$
    c. $f(2x) = (2x)^3 - (2x) = 8x^3 - 2x$
    d. $f(\frac{1}{2}x) = (\frac{1}{2}x)^3 - (\frac{1}{2}x) = \frac{1}{8}x^3 - \frac{1}{2}x$

3. **Caution students to pay close attention to the wording of the task.**
    a. $g(x) = f(x + 5) = (x + 5)^2$
    b. $g(x) = f(x - 4) = (x - 4)^2$
    c. $g(x) = f(3x) = 9x^2$
    d. $g(x) = f(\frac{1}{4}x) = \frac{x^2}{16}$
    e. $g(x) = -f(x - 5) = -(x - 5)^2$
    f. $g(x) = f(x - 5) + 3 = (x - 5)^2 + 3$
    g. $g(x) = f(x + 2) + 4 = (x + 2)^2 + 4$
    h. $g(x) = -f(x - h) + k = -(x - h)^2 + k$

4. **a.** The graph of $f(x)$ has been reflected across the x-axis, moved 6 units to the right, and moved up 8 units.
    b. The graph of $h(x)$ has been compressed toward the x-axis by 0.5 and moved down 2 units.
    c. The graph of $c(x)$ has been stretched vertically by a factor of 2.
    d. The graph of $s(x)$ has been stretched vertically by a factor of 3 and moved up 1 unit.
    e. The graph of $u(x)$ has been reflected across the x-axis and moved up 5 units.
    f. The graph of $r(x)$ has been moved to the left 5 units.
    g. The graph of $s(x)$ has been reflected across the x-axis and moved $\frac{\pi}{2}$ units to the right.
    h. The graph of $c(x)$ has been stretched horizontally by a factor of $\frac{4}{\pi}$ and moved down 2 units.

2. The graph of $f(x) = x^3 - x$ with unit scales on the axes is shown at the right. What modifications of the rule for $f(x)$ gives each of the following graphs, in the same window with the same scales?

a.

b.

c.

d.

3. Consider the basic parabola defined by the function $f(x) = x^2$. What function rules will produce graphs related to the graph of $f(x)$ in the following ways?

a. Translated 5 units to the left

b. Translated 4 units to the right

c. Compressed by a factor of 3 toward the y-axis

d. Stretched by a factor of 4 away from the y-axis

e. Vertex at (5, 0) and opening downward

f. Vertex at (5, 3) and opening upward

g. Vertex at (–2, 4) and opening upward

h. Vertex at (h, k) and opening downward

4. Describe how the graph of each function in Column 2 is related to the graph of the corresponding function in Column 1.

	Column 1	Column 2
a.	$f(x) = x^2$	$g(x) = -(x - 6)^2 + 8$
b.	$h(x) = |x|$	$i(x) = 0.5|x| - 2$
c.	$c(x) = \cos x$	$d(x) = 2\cos x$
d.	$s(x) = \sin x$	$t(x) = 3\sin x + 1$
e.	$u(x) = (0.3)^x$	$v(x) = 5 - (0.3)^x$
f.	$r(x) = \sqrt{x}$	$p(x) = \sqrt{x + 5}$
g.	$s(x) = \sin x$	$m(x) = -\sin\left(x - \frac{\pi}{2}\right)$
h.	$c(x) = \cos x$	$n(x) = \cos\left(\frac{\pi}{4}x\right) - 2$

LESSON 3 • HORIZONTAL TRANSFORMATIONS   473

5. Think back to coordinate representations of geometric transformations.

   a. Complete each coordinate rule below.

   - Reflection across the x-axis: $(x, y) \rightarrow (\underline{\quad}, \underline{\quad})$
   - Translation with components (h, k): $(x, y) \rightarrow (\underline{\quad}, \underline{\quad})$
   - Size transformation with center at the origin and scale factor k:
     $(x, y) \rightarrow (\underline{\quad}, \underline{\quad})$

   b. What connections do you see between the coordinate representation of these transformations and the form of algebraic rules for transformed functions?

Reflecting

1. Which transformations of basic function graphs are easiest to predict simply by looking at the symbolic function rules? Which are most difficult to predict?

2. For most students it seems natural to expect that the graph of $g(x) = (x - k)^2$, where $k > 0$, should be congruent to the graph of $f(x) = x^2$ but translated k units to the *left*. As you now know, that isn't what happens; the graph of $g(x)$ is identical to that of $f(x)$ but translated k units to the *right*.

   a. How can you think about this pair of rules and graphs so that the correct relationship makes sense?

   b. How can you adapt your reasoning in Part a to include the case of $h(x) = (x + k)^2$?

3. For many students it seems natural to expect that when $k > 1$, the graph of $g(x) = (kx)^2$ should be similar to the graph of $f(x) = x^2$ but stretched out from the y-axis. As you now know, that isn't what happens; the graph of $g(x)$ is a compression of the graph of $f(x)$ toward the y-axis with a scale factor of $\frac{1}{k}$.

   a. How can you think about this pair of rules and graphs so that the correct relationship makes sense?

   b. How can you adapt your reasoning in Part a to include the case of $h(x) = (kx)^2$ when $0 < k < 1$?

4. In the Southern Hemisphere, the times at which summer and winter occur are reversed relative to the Northern Hemisphere. How would you modify your function rule in Activity 5 of Investigation 2, page 467, so that it models the pattern of change in average monthly temperature for a city in the Southern Hemisphere that geographically corresponds to Des Moines? Will the average monthly temperature in these two cities ever be about the same?

Des Moines, *Iowa*

Puertos Lobos,
Buenos Aires

5. **a.** ■ $(x, y) \rightarrow (x, -y)$

   ■ $(x, y) \rightarrow (x + h, y + k)$

   ■ $(x, y) \rightarrow (kx, ky)$

   b. If in each ordered pair y is replaced with $f(x)$, the algebraic rules for transformed functions can be associated with the y-coordinate of the image. That is, the graph of $g(x) = -f(x)$ is the reflection across the x-axis of the graph of $f(x)$. The graph of $j(x) = f(x) + k$ is a translation up k units of the graph of $f(x)$. The graph of $i(x) = k\left[f\left(\frac{1}{k}x\right)\right]$ is a size transformation of the graph of $f(x)$.

Reflecting

1. Responses may vary. Usually, the easiest to predict is a vertical translation from $f(x)$ to $f(x) + k$. This can be very easily seen in the algebraic rule, as well as in the graph. A reflection across the x-axis from $f(x)$ to $-f(x)$ is similarly easy to predict, and a vertical stretch (compression) from $f(x)$ to $kf(x)$ is also fairly easy to predict. The transformations of $f(x)$ to $f(x + k)$ seem to be the most difficult to predict.

2. **a.** One way to think about this relationship is to think about the location of the vertices of the functions. For $f(x)$ the vertex is at the origin, but with $g(x)$ the vertex is at $(k, 0)$. In other words, the parabola has been moved k units to the right.

   b. Again, think about the location of the vertex of $h(x)$. This would be at $(-k, 0)$, which means that the parabola has been moved k units to the left.

3. **a.** One way to think about this relationship is to recognize that the same y values will be obtained but faster by a factor of $\frac{1}{k}$. For example, the value of $f(1)$ is the same as the value of $g\left(\frac{1}{k}\right)$. Thus, the graph is compressed toward the y-axis, while neither increasing nor decreasing relative maximums and minimums. (See Organizing Task 2.)

   b. If $0 < k < 1$, then the curve will rise more slowly and be wider. Again, thinking of the relationship in terms of the x-axis helps to make sense out of the symbolic form of the transformation.

4. Activity 5, page 467, results in the equation for temperature in Des Moines as $f(x) = -29 \cos\left(\frac{\pi}{6}x\right) + 48$. A corresponding city in the Southern Hemisphere, with comparable temperatures, would have summer and winter reversed. Thus, its temperature function would be $t(x) = 29 \cos\left(\frac{\pi}{6}x\right) + 48$. The two cities will have approximately the same average temperatures in October and April.

Unit 6

5. a.   ■ $(x - 2)^2 + (y - 3)^2 = 25$
   ■ $(x - 2)^2 + (y + 3)^2 = 16$
   ■ $(x + 4)^2 + (y - 5)^2 = 9$
   ■ $(x + 1.5)^2 + (y + 2.9)^2 = 51.84$

b.   When a circle is translated h units to the right or left, the operations work the same as when a function is translated to the right or left. The expression for x is simply replaced with $(x - h)$ or $(x + h)$. However, when the circle is translated up or down, the symbolic expressions are manipulated in a slightly different way compared to moving a function up or down. In order to move a circle up k units, y is replaced with $(y - k)$. In order to move a circle down, y is replaced with $(y + k)$. With a function, you just have to add k to or subtract k from the function output to move the function up or down respectively.

Extending

1.   In the solutions below, models from the calculator are listed before models from algebraic reasoning.

a.   When you try to have the calculator give a quadratic model with just two points, you get an error message. There is an infinite number of quadratics that pass through just two points.
Student rules should be of the following forms:

$$f(x) = a(x - 9)(x - 2) \qquad f(x) = a(x^2 - 11x + 18)$$

b.   Again, there is an infinite number of quadratics that pass through just two points.
Student rules should be of the following forms:

$$f(x) = a(x - 3)(x - 7) \qquad f(x) = a(x^2 - 10x + 21)$$

c.   Minimum point with $y = -8$ means that $(1, -8)$ is the vertex. The three known points are $(-3, 0)$, $(5, 0)$, and $(1, -8)$.

Algebraic reasoning method:

$$f(x) = a(x + 3)(x - 5)$$
$$-8 = a(1 + 3)(1 - 5)$$
$$-8 = a(4)(-4)$$
$$-8 = -16a$$
$$\tfrac{1}{2} = a$$
$$f(x) = \tfrac{1}{2}(x + 3)(x - 5)$$
$$= \tfrac{1}{2}(x^2 - 2x - 15) = \tfrac{1}{2}x^2 - x - \tfrac{15}{2}$$

Curve-fitting method:

$$f(x) = \tfrac{1}{2}x^2 - x - 7.5$$

d.   Maximum point with $y = 168$ means that $(-5, 168)$ is the vertex. The three known points are $(-9, 0)$, $(-1, 0,)$, and $(-5, 168)$.

Algebraic reasoning method:

$$f(x) = a(x + 9)(x + 1)$$
$$168 = a(-5 + 9)(-5 + 1)$$
$$168 = a(4)(-4)$$
$$168 = -16a$$
$$-10.5 = a$$
$$f(x) = -10.5(x + 9)(x + 1)$$
$$= -10.5(x^2 + 10x + 9) = -10.5x^2 - 105x - 94.5$$

Curve-fitting method:

$$f(x) = -10.5x^2 - 105x - 94.5$$

2. a.   Enter the points $(0, 50)$, $(100, 10)$, and $(200, 50)$; then calculate a quadratic model.
The model is $f(x) = 0.004x^2 - 0.8x + 50$.

5. In earlier work, you learned that the points of a circle with radius r and center at the origin have coordinates (x, y) satisfying the equation $x^2 + y^2 = r^2$. In the "Symbol Sense and Algebraic Reasoning" unit, you may have proven that a circle centered at some other point (h, k) has equation $(x - h)^2 + (y - k)^2 = r^2$. (See Extending Task 4 on page 252.)

a. Write the equations of these circles:

- Center $(2, 3)$ and radius 5
- Center $(2, -3)$ and radius 4
- Center $(-4, 5)$ and radius 3
- Center $(-1.5, -2.9)$ and radius 7.2

b. Explain how the connection between equations for circles centered at the origin and equations for circles centered away from the origin is in some ways similar to, and in some ways different from, the connection between rules for functions and rules for related functions with translated graphs.

Extending

1. Find rules for quadratic functions with graphs satisfying the following conditions. In each case, show how one or more correct rules can be obtained by the use of a statistical curve-fitting tool and also by algebraic reasoning alone. If there is more than one correct rule, include all such rules (using parameters such as k or c as needed).

a. Zeroes at $x = 9$ and $x = 2$

b. One zero at $x = 7$ and line of symmetry at $x = 5$

c. Zeroes at $x = -3$ and $x = 5$ and minimum point with $y = -8$

d. Zeroes at $x = -9$ and $x = -1$ and maximum point with $y = 168$

2. Modeling Task 5, page 470, involved finding the equation for the height above the road surface of a suspension cable of a long bridge suspended between two towers. Suppose that the towers are 50 feet high, the bridge road surface is 200 feet long, and the suspension cable has a minimum height at the center, 10 feet above the road.

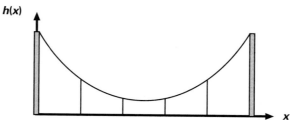

a. How could you use the given information and statistical curve-fitting tools to find the equation of the height of the suspension cable above the bridge?

Unit 6

b. Use the following reasoning to reach the same equation.

 i. Consider first the basic parabola with the *y*-axis as the axis of symmetry. What would its equation be?

 ii. Modify your equation from Part i to get an equation $y = f(x)$ such that $f(100) = f(-100) = 40$.

 iii. Modify the result from Part ii to get an equation $y = g(x)$ with minimum point 10 feet above the *x*-axis and $g(100) = g(-100) = 50$.

 iv. Modify the result from Part iii to get $y = h(x)$ with $h(0) = h(200) = 50$ and $h(100) = 10$.

c. Use algebraic reasoning to prove that the quadratic expression obtained from curve-fitting in Part a is equivalent to the expression obtained from the reasoning outlined in Part b.

3. Shown below is a portion of a graph and a table of sample values for a periodic function $y = f(x)$.

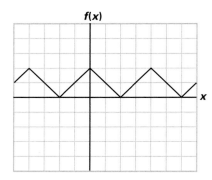

x	f(x)
−4	2
−2	0
0	2
2	0
4	2
6	0

a. What are the domain and range of this function?

b. Explain how a rule for $g(x)$, whose graph is shown below, is related to the rule for $f(x)$ and how tables of sample values for the two functions are related.

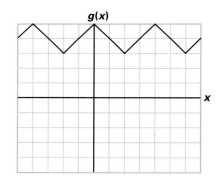

x	g(x)
−4	
−2	
0	
2	
4	
6	

2. b. i. $f(x) = x^2$

    ii. You need to find k for the model $f(x) = kx^2$. $f(100) = 40$, so $k = 0.004$. Thus,
$$f(x) = 0.004x^2.$$

    iii. The function needs to be moved up 10 units, so adding 10 gives
$$f(x) = 0.004x^2 + 10.$$

    iv. The function needs to be translated 100 units to the right:
$$f(x) = 0.004(x - 100)^2 + 10.$$

  c. $f(x) = 0.004(x - 100)^2 + 10$

    $f(x) = 0.004(x^2 - 200x + 10{,}000) + 10$

    $f(x) = 0.004x^2 - 0.8x + 40 + 10$

    $f(x) = 0.004x^2 - 0.8x + 50$

3. a. Domain: real numbers

    Range: $0 \leq y \leq 2$

  b. $g(x) = f(x) + 3$

    For each value of x, the table value for $g(x)$ will be 3 more than the value for $f(x)$.

Unit 6

3. **c.** Two possible rules: $i(x) = f(x + 1)$ or $i(x) = f(x - 3)$

x	−4	−2	0	2	4	6
i(x)	1	1	1	1	1	1

d. $j(x) = 2f(x)$

x	−4	−2	0	2	4	6
j(x)	4	0	4	0	4	0

c. Explain how a rule for $i(x)$, whose graph is shown below, is related to the rule for $f(x)$. Complete a table of sample values for $i(x)$.

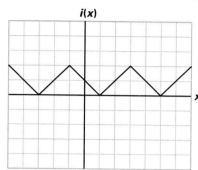

x	i(x)
–4	
–2	
0	
2	
4	
6	

d. Explain how a rule for $j(x)$, whose graph is shown below, is related to the rule for the original function $f(x)$. Complete a table of sample values.

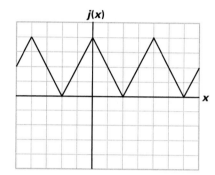

x	j(x)
–4	
–2	
0	
2	
4	
6	

4. In this unit, you have seen how simple geometric transformations of a function graph are connected to corresponding transformations of the function rule. In this task, you will investigate how horizontal shifts are related to the zeroes of quadratic functions and, more generally, to the quadratic formula.

a. First examine each of the following pairs of quadratic functions and their graphs. For each pair of functions, do the following:

■ Write rules for the lines of symmetry.

■ Describe geometrically how the graphs are related.

■ Explain how the zeroes of the two functions are related.

■ Solve $f(x) = 0$ using algebraic reasoning.

i. $g(x) = x^2 - 10x + 16$ $f(x) = x^2 - 9$

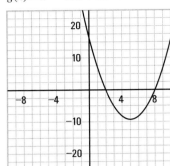 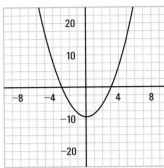

ii. $g(x) = 4x^2 + 24x - 45$ $f(x) = 4x^2 - 81$

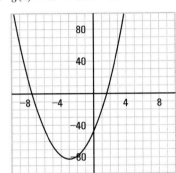 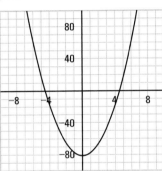

b. Just as you are able to transform the graph of $g(x)$ to the graph of $f(x)$ for each pair of functions above, you can similarly transform the function rule. Consider the function $g(x)$ in Part i above and the related equation:

$$x^2 - 10x + 16 = 0$$

- Define a new variable z by $z = x - 5$. This is a transformation of the variable x to the variable z. Explain how the transformation $z = x - 5$ is related to the axis of symmetry of $g(x)$.

- Solve $z = x - 5$ for x and substitute the resulting expression for each occurrence of x in $x^2 - 10x + 16 = 0$.

- Now use algebraic reasoning to solve your new quadratic for the variable z.

- Finally, use the fact that $z = x - 5$ to find the roots of $x^2 - 10x + 16 = 0$.

c. Use algebraic reasoning similar to what you used in Part b to find the zeroes of $g(x) = 4x^2 + 24x - 45$.

4. a. i. ■ $g(x)$: $x = 5$

$f(x)$: $x = 0$

■ Translate $g(x)$ 5 units to the left to obtain $f(x)$.

■ The zeroes of $f(x)$ are 5 units less than the zeroes of $g(x)$.

■ $x^2 - 9 = 0$

$x^2 = 9$

$x = \pm 3$

ii. ■ $g(x)$: $x = -3$

$f(x)$: $x = 0$

■ Translate $g(x)$ 3 units to the right to obtain $f(x)$.

■ The zeroes of $f(x)$ are 3 units more than the zeroes of $g(x)$.

■ $4x^2 - 81 = 0$

$4x^2 = 81$

$x^2 = \frac{81}{4}$

$x = \pm\frac{9}{2}$

b. ■ Let $z = x - 5$. Then $z = 0$ when $x = 5$, which is the line of symmetry of $g(x)$.

■ $x = z + 5$, so $x^2 - 10x + 16 = 0$ becomes $(z + 5)^2 - 10(z + 5) + 16 = 0$.

■ $z^2 + 10z + 25 - 10z - 50 + 16 = 0$

$z^2 - 9 = 0$

$z = \pm 3$

■ $z = x - 5$ or $x = z + 5 \Rightarrow x = 5 \pm 3$, or $x = 8$ and 2, which are the roots of $x^2 - 10x + 16 = 0$.

c. $g(x) = 4x^2 + 24x - 45$

Let $z = x + 3$ since the line of symmetry of $g(x)$ is $x = -3$. Then $x = z - 3$ and $4x^2 + 24x - 45 = 0$ becomes

$4(z - 3)^2 + 24(z - 3) - 45 = 0$

$4(z^2 - 6z + 9) + 24z - 72 - 45 = 0$

$4z^2 - 24z + 36 + 24z - 72 - 45 = 0$

$4z^2 - 81 = 0$

$4z^2 = 81$

$z^2 = \frac{81}{4}$

$z = \pm\frac{9}{2}$

So, $x = -3 \pm \frac{9}{2}$

$x = -7.5$ or 1.5.

Master 170

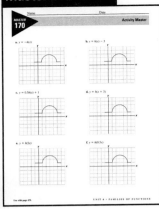

Assessments 241–243

Assessments 244–246

4. **d.** $x = -\dfrac{b}{2a}$ is a line of symmetry for $y = ax^2 + bx + c$.

Let $z = x + \dfrac{b}{2a}$, so $x = z - \dfrac{b}{2a}$. Then $ax^2 + bx + c = 0$ becomes

$$a\left(z - \frac{b}{2a}\right)^2 + b\left(z - \frac{b}{2a}\right) + c = 0$$

$$a\left(z^2 - \frac{2bz}{2a} + \frac{b^2}{4a^2}\right) + bz - \frac{b^2}{2a} + c = 0$$

$$az^2 - bz + \frac{b^2}{4a} + bz - \frac{b^2}{2a} + c = 0$$

$$az^2 - \frac{b^2}{4a} + c = 0$$

$$az^2 = \frac{b^2 - 4ac}{4a}$$

$$z^2 = \frac{b^2 - 4ac}{4a^2}$$

$$z = \pm\sqrt{\frac{b^2 - 4ac}{4a^2}} = \pm\frac{\sqrt{b^2 - 4ac}}{2a}$$

Then $x = z - \dfrac{b}{2a}$ or $x = \dfrac{-b \pm \sqrt{b^2 - 4ac}}{2a}$, which is the solution given by the quadratic formula.

5. **See Teaching Master 170.**

a.

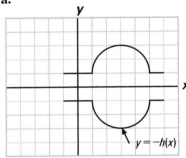

$y = -h(x)$

b.

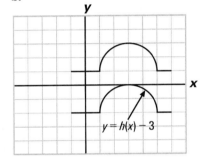

$y = h(x) - 3$

c.

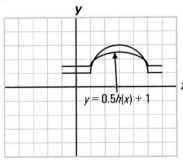

$y = 0.5h(x) + 1$

d.

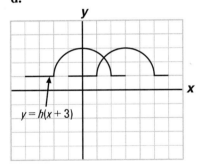

$y = h(x + 3)$

e.

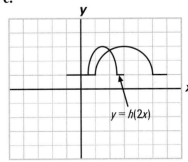

$y = h(2x)$

f.

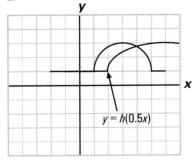

$y = h(0.5x)$

See Assessment Resources pages 241–246.

d. You can use the reasoning in Part c to provide another proof of the quadratic formula. To begin, use the fact that $x = -\frac{b}{2a}$ is the line of symmetry for the parabola $y = ax^2 + bx + c$ to define a new variable $z = x - \left(-\frac{b}{2a}\right)$ or $z = x + \frac{b}{2a}$. So $x = z - \frac{b}{2a}$. Now use what you know about algebraic properties to show that if $ax^2 + bx + c = 0$ and $a \neq 0$, then

$$x = -\frac{b}{2a} \pm \frac{\sqrt{b^2 - 4ac}}{2a}.$$

5. Shown below is a graph of a function $y = h(x)$. The scale on each axis is 1. On copies of this diagram, sketch and label graphs of each related function listed.

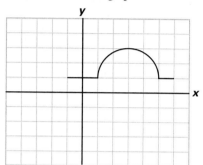

a. $y = -h(x)$

b. $y = h(x) - 3$

c. $y = 0.5h(x) + 1$

d. $y = h(x + 3)$

e. $y = h(2x)$

f. $y = h(0.5x)$

Unit 6

Lesson **4** *Looking Back*

In the investigations of this unit, you have reviewed and extended the range of data table and graph patterns that you can model with function rules. By now, you should be able to recognize patterns of change that are matched well by linear, exponential, power, and periodic functions; by combinations of those function types; and by functions with graphs that are translations, reflections, and stretches or compressions of the basic forms. The activities and tasks in this final lesson will help you consolidate your understanding of function families and their applications.

1. The change from one year, decade, century, or millennium to another seems to prompt people to look back over time to see how things have changed in the past and to make some predictions about the near future. About 1,000 years ago, Earth's human population was about 250 million. One fourth of all those people lived in China. The world's largest city was Cordova, Spain, with a population of  450,000. Half of all children died before the age of five, so the population grew at a rate of only 0.1% per year until modern medicine and improved water and sewage systems emerged in the 1700s. (Source: Making sense of the millennium. 1998. *National Geographic*, January.)

a. What type of function and what specific rule would model the pattern of world population growth described for the period from 1000 to 1700?

b. How does the world population near the turn of the second millennium of about 6 billion compare to what would have happened if growth had continued at the rate of 0.1% from the year 1000 to the year 2000?

c. Assume a world population in the year 2000 of about 6 billion and a growth rate of about 1.7%. What function would predict world population t years later? In particular, what population is predicted for the year 2100 and the end of the next millennium, 3000?

d. How will the graphs of the two functions in Parts a and c be similar, and how will they be different?

e. How do doubling times of world population compare in the cases of 0.1% and 1.7% growth rates?

Lesson 4 *Looking Back*

This Looking Back lesson is in many ways a culmination of algebra concepts developed over the three years of the *Contemporary Mathematics in Context* curriculum.

1. **a.** Exponential, $f(t) = 250(1.001)^t$ in millions

   b. With a growth rate of 0.1%, the current population would be $250(1.001)^{1,000}$ or about 679,000,000 rather than 6,000,000,000. That is a difference of about 5,321,000,000 or almost 9 times as much as predicted.

   c. $f(t) = 6(1.017)^t$ in billions

   For the year 2100, the predicted population is $6(1.017)^{100}$ or approximately 32.378 billion.

   For the year 3000, the predicted population is $6(1.017)^{1,000}$ or approximately 126,000,000 billion.

   d. **If students write their models as given in Parts a and c above, they will need to realize that the units are different (millions or billions).**

   The graphs for the functions in Parts a and c are both exponential models, but the graph for Part c (written as $f(t) = 6,000(1.017)^t$ in millions) is going to start at a much higher value and increase at a faster rate.

   e. With a 0.1% growth rate, the population would double in about 700 years. With a 1.7% growth rate, the population would double in just a bit more than 41 years.

1. f. $d_a(t) = \dfrac{250,000,000(1.001)^t}{57,000,000} = \dfrac{250(1.001)^t}{57}$ people per square mile

$d_c(t) = \dfrac{6,000,000,000(1.017)^t}{57,000,000} = \dfrac{6,000(1.017)^t}{57}$ people per square mile

Both of the density functions are exponential models, which give the population per square mile. These models are very similar to the population models, except that they are divided by 57 million square miles. They are vertical compressions.

g. ■ $f(t) = P_a(10t) = 250(1.001)^{10t}$ in millions

$g(t) = P_c(10t) = 6(1.017)^{10t}$ in billions

■ These functions give the population for every decade rather than for every year. The graphs of the new functions have the same y-intercepts, but they rise much faster. They are horizontal compressions.

h. $p(t) = 6,000 + 100t$ in millions or $p(t) = 6,000,000,000 + 100,000,000t$

i. The graphs of the linear function show constant growth since the line is straight, and the tables show constant growth by constant increments in the output values when the increments in the input values are constant. However, with the exponential model, the graph rises at an increasing rate, and the table of values shows continually larger increments of change from one year to the next.

j. $d(t) = \dfrac{6,000,000,000 + 100,000,000t}{57,000,000} = \dfrac{6,000 + 100t}{57}$

■ This function will have a constant rate of change. The graph will be a straight line, and the table of values will show a constant increment. The y-intercept and the slope of the population model from Part h have been divided by 57,000,000.

■ This population density model is very different from the population density function derived from the percent growth rate assumptions. The initial function values are the same, but after that point the function based on percent growth rate increases much faster than the linear model given in Part j, which has a constant growth rate.

k. Part a: $f(x) = 250(1.001)^x$ in millions

$NEXT = NOW(1.001)$, starting with 250 million

Part c: $f(x) = 6(1.017)^x$ in billions

$NEXT = NOW(1.017)$, starting with 6 billion

Part f: $f(x) = \dfrac{250,000,000(1.001)^x}{57,000,000} = \dfrac{250(1.001)^x}{57}$

$NEXT = NOW(1.001)$, starting with $\dfrac{250 \text{ million}}{57 \text{ million}}$ or approximately 4.39 people per square mile

$f(x) = \dfrac{6,000,000,000(1.017)^x}{57,000,000} = \dfrac{6,000(1.017)^x}{57}$

$NEXT = NOW(1.017)$, starting with $\dfrac{6 \text{ billion}}{57 \text{ million}}$ or approximately 105.3 people per square mile

Part h: $p(t) = 6,000,000,000 + 100,000,000t$

$NEXT = NOW + 100,000,000$, starting with 6 billion

Part j: $d(t) = \dfrac{6,000,000,000 + 100,000,000t}{57,000,000} = \dfrac{6,000 + 100t}{57}$

$NEXT = NOW + \dfrac{100}{57}$, starting with $\dfrac{6 \text{ billion}}{57 \text{ million}}$ or approximately 105.3 people per square mile

Unit 6

f. Earth has a land area of about 57 million square miles (although not all is inhabitable). What functions give population density (people per square mile) as a function of time in the two cases in Parts a and c? How will graphs and tables of the two population density functions be similar to and different from those of the world population functions? (*Caution:* Be careful about units of measure.)

g. If the functions in Parts a and c are denoted by $P_a(t)$ and $P_c(t)$, what information would be given by the functions $f(t) = P_a(10t)$ and $g(t) = P_c(10t)$?

  ■ Write algebraic rules for these new functions.

  ■ How would the graphs of the new functions relate to the graphs of the originals?

h. If you assume that a world population of about 6 billion increases at a constant rate of 100 million people per year, what function would estimate the world population at any time *t* years in the future?

i. How will tables and graphs of the population function described in Part h compare to those of the percent growth rate model in Part c?

j. What is the population density function (people per square mile) associated with the population function described by the information in Part h?

  ■ How will the tables and graphs of that density function compare to those of the population function in Part h?

  ■ How will patterns of this new density function compare to those of the population density function derived from the percent growth rate assumptions of Part c?

k. Which patterns of change in the various questions of this activity can be represented by *NOW-NEXT* equations that describe the change from one time to the next?

2. When the Hale-Bopp comet flew within sight of Earth during 1996 and 1997, there was considerable discussion about the chances that other comets and asteroids might actually enter Earth's atmosphere. Some scientists even made estimates of the damage that would result if such an event did occur. One theory predicts that if an asteroid of only 3 miles in diameter were to

© Copyright 1997 Jerry Lodriguss

land in the middle of the North Atlantic Ocean, it would send a 300-foot tsunami crashing on the shores of the United States and Europe. Fortunately, such events are likely to occur only once in every 10,000,000 years! (Source: Newcott, William R. 1997. The age of comets. *National Geographic*, December, 94–109.)

Assume that the bodies of comets are roughly spherical in shape as you answer the following questions.

a. The sizes of comets and asteroids are usually described by estimates of their radii or diameters, but their visual appearance and the force of a collision would be more directly related to measures of area and volume. For an asteroid with radius measured in miles, what function rules would give the area of the circular disk that we see, the total surface area, and the volume of that asteroid? How would each of those function rules change if the given information was a diameter instead of a radius?

b. Although the tails of comets might be millions of miles long, the core is usually a much smaller body. For example, the core of comet Halley has diameter of less than 10 miles; Earth's diameter is about 8,000 miles. How will the surface area and volume of Earth compare to those of comet Halley? How can you make those comparisons by studying the area and volume formulas and not actually calculating each area and volume?

c. Earth's average density is about 5.5 billion metric tons per cubic kilometer. If other planets or asteroids had the same density, what function rule would give the masses (density × volume) of those bodies as a function of their radii (in kilometers)? How would the graph of this function be related to the volume function in Part a?

d. Comet Hale-Bopp last came near Earth over 4,200 years ago. Because of the gravitational pull of the planet Jupiter, its next return is predicted to occur in 2,400 years. Planets also affect the paths of asteroids. Look back in this unit to find the relationship between the gravitational attraction of two cosmic bodies and the distance between their centers. What does the graph of that relationship look like?

3. For residents of planet Earth, the most important planetary body (other than Earth itself) is the Moon. The visible Moon varies from a small slice to a full disk and then back to a small slice in phases that have names like first quarter, full moon, last quarter, and (when not visible at all) new moon. The full cycle takes roughly 30 days.

a. What function family seems likely to be the best starting point in building a model of the Moon's repeated pattern of phases, if you assume the cycle starts on a full moon?

b. What adjustments to the basic function rule chosen in Part a will give a model with the correct period?

c. What adjustments would give the correct model if you assumed the start of each cycle was the time of a new moon?

2. **a.** **Visible area:** $A(r) = \pi r^2$; $A(d) = \frac{\pi d^2}{4}$. The coefficient using diameter is $\frac{1}{4}$ of the coefficient using radius.
   Total surface area: $S(r) = 4\pi r^2$; $S(d) = \pi d^2$. The coefficient using diameter is $\frac{1}{4}$ of the coefficient using radius.
   Volume: $V(r) = \frac{4}{3}\pi r^3$; $V(d) = \frac{1}{6}\pi d^3$. The coefficient using diameter is $\frac{1}{8}$ of the coefficient using radius.

   b. If the ratio of their diameters is $\frac{8,000}{10} = \frac{800}{1}$, then the ratio of their surface areas is $\left(\frac{800}{1}\right)^2$ or $\frac{640,000}{1}$ and the ratio of their volumes is $\left(\frac{800}{1}\right)^3$ or $\frac{512,000,000}{1}$.
   By examining the formulas for surface area and volume, you can see that when you compare Earth to the comet, all of the constant factors will cancel and you will be left with the ratio of their diameters squared for the surface areas and the ratio of their diameters cubed for the volumes. (Note that the ratio of their diameters is the same as the ratio of their radii.)

   c. The masses of these bodies would be $M(r) = \frac{22}{3}\pi r^3$ in billion metric tons, if we measure r in kilometers.
   The graph of this function is similar to the volume function in Part a, but the curve rises more quickly. The curve has been stretched by a factor of 5.5 billion.

   d. The formula given in Lesson 1 was $F = \frac{km_1m_2}{d^2}$. As the distance between the two cosmic bodies increases, the gravitational force decreases. This is an inverse relationship. The graph looks like a general inverse graph, having the x- and y-axes as asymptotes, and the function decreases as the distance increases.

3. **a.** The periodic (trigonometric) functions are the best starting point.

   b. Multiplying the input variable by $\frac{\pi}{15}$, as in $\cos\left(\frac{\pi}{15}x\right)$ for example, will produce a function with a period of 30 days, if the input variable is measured in days.

   c. Using a cosine model, $c(x) = \frac{1}{2}\cos\left[\frac{\pi}{15}(x - 15)\right] + \frac{1}{2}$, $c(x) = -\frac{1}{2}\cos\left(\frac{\pi}{15}x\right) + \frac{1}{2}$, and $c(x) = \frac{1}{2}\cos\left[\frac{\pi}{15}(x + 15)\right] + \frac{1}{2}$ all start and end at 0 with a maximum of 1 and a minimum of 0. These functions approximate the proportion of the Moon visible on a given day.

Unit 6

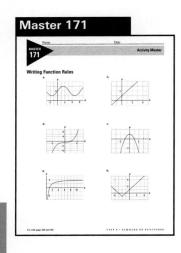

SYNTHESIZE *continued*

4. **a.** Linear
    b. Power
    c. Periodic
    d. Exponential
    e. Power
    f. Trigonometric
    g. Quadratic polynomial
5. **See Teaching Master 171.**
    a. Periodic; $f(x) = \sin x + 2$ (x measured in radians)
    b. Linear; $f(x) = x + 1$
    c. Exponential; $f(x) = (0.5)^x + 2$

Scientists who study the planets and stars of the universe, the climate and geography of Earth, the animals and plants that live on Earth, or the political and economic activity of human beings and their societies often turn to mathematics for models of the patterns and relationships that they find. By now you should know well some of the most useful of those modeling tools (linear, exponential, power, polynomial, and periodic functions) and ways to adjust the basic rules for those functions to match unique conditions.

4. Match the following algebraic rule forms to the corresponding function family.

a. $f(x) = a + bx$ Trigonometric

b. $g(x) = ax^b$ Exponential

c. $h(x) = a \sin(bx) + c$ Power

d. $i(x) = b^x$ Linear

e. $j(x) = \frac{a}{x} + b$ Quadratic polynomial

f. $k(x) = a \cos(x + b)$

g. $m(x) = ax^2 + bx + c$

5. For each of the following graphs and tables, identify the family of functions from which it makes most sense to build a model for the data pattern. Then construct a function model that best fits the pattern. Be prepared to explain the reasoning that led to your choice of a basic function model type and the adjustments needed to make the rule fit the specific pattern of the given table or graph.

a. 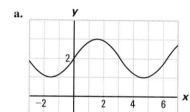   **b.**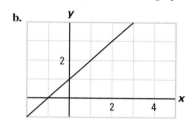

c.

x	−2	−1	0	1	2	3	4
y	6	4	3	2.5	2.25	2.125	2.0625

x	5	6	7	8	9	10	11
y	2.0313	2.0156	2.0078	2.0039	2.0020	2.0010	2.0005

d.

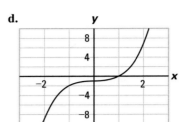

e.

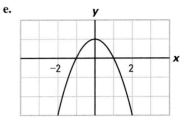

f.

x	−1.571	−0.7854	0	0.7854	1.5708	2.3562	3.1416
y	0	0.7071	1	0.7071	0	−0.7071	−1

x	3.9270	4.7124	5.4978	6.2832	7.0686	7.8540	8.6394
y	−0.7071	0	0.7071	1	0.7071	0	−0.7071

g.

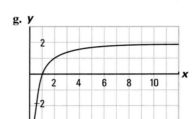

h.

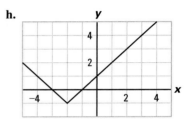

i.

x	−4	−3	−2	−1	0	1	2
y	36	25	16	9	4	1	0

x	3	4	5	6	7	8	9
y	1	4	9	16	25	36	49

6. Draw sketches and find algebraic rules for the functions that meet the following conditions.

a. $f(x)$ has a graph that is a translation 3.5 units upward of the graph of $y = \frac{1}{x}$.

b. $g(x)$ has a graph that is a translation 3.5 units to the right of the graph of $y = \frac{1}{x}$.

c. $h(x)$ has a graph that is a reflection of the graph of $y = \sqrt{x}$ across the x-axis.

d. $i(x)$ has a graph that is a compression with factor of 4 toward the x-axis of the graph of $y = \sin x$.

e. $j(x)$ is periodic with amplitude 5, period $\frac{\pi}{2}$, and $j(0) = 0$.

f. $k(x)$ has a graph that is a reflection of the graph of $y = 1.5^x$ across the x-axis and then translated so that the line $y = 15$ is an asymptote.

5. **d.** Polynomial; $f(x) = x^3 - 1$

e. Polynomial or quadratic; $f(x) = -x^2 + 1$

f. Periodic; $y = \cos x$ or $y = \sin\left(x + \frac{\pi}{2}\right)$

g. Power; $f(x) = -\frac{2}{x} + 2$

h. Absolute value; $f(x) = |x + 2| - 1$

i. Quadratic or polynomial; $f(x) = (x - 2)^2 = x^2 - 4x + 4$

6. **a.** $f(x) = \frac{1}{x} + 3.5$ **b.** $g(x) = \frac{1}{x - 3.5}$ **c.** $h(x) = -\sqrt{x}$

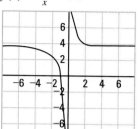 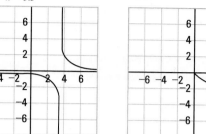

d. $i(x) = 0.25 \sin x$ **e.** $j(x) = 5 \sin(4x)$ **f.** $k(x) = -1.5^x + 15$

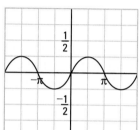 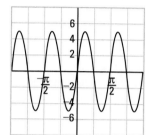 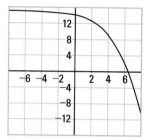

Unit 6

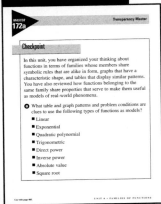

Masters 172a–172b

6. g. $m(x) = \sin(x + 4)$ **h.** $n(x) = -2.5(x - 3) + 4$ **i.** $p(x) = 2(x + 6)^2 + 4$

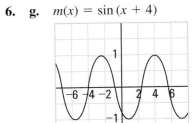 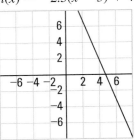

SHARE AND SUMMARIZE   full-class discussion

Checkpoint

See Teaching Masters 172a–172b.

ⓐ ■ Linear functions have graphs that are straight lines, and there is a constant difference in the data table. The primary problem condition is a situation that has a constant rate of change.

■ Exponential functions have graphs that cross the y-axis and approach the x-axis or some line parallel to the x-axis if the curve has been translated. The table values change by a constant factor as the value of x increases. In a problem situation, either growth or decay that occurs at an increasing or decreasing rate indicates that the model is exponential.

■ Graphs for quadratic polynomial functions have a line of symmetry parallel to the y-axis. They also have a maximum or minimum point. The symmetry of the graph can also be found in the table of values. Problem situations like trajectory problems that involve second-degree models use quadratic polynomials.

■ Trigonometric (sine and cosine) functions have graphs that are repeating patterns in a regular cycle. In the table of values, these repeated values will also be seen. Problems that involve situations that are cyclical in nature are most often modeled well by periodic functions.

■ Direct power functions have a U-shaped graph symmetric about the y-axis if the exponent is even. They have an $\int$-shaped graph symmetric about the origin if the exponent is odd. Problem situations involving area or volume could be modeled by direct power functions.

■ Absolute value functions have V-shaped graphs. The patterns of change for each arm of the V are constant. A problem situation in which a quantity increases (decreases) at a constant rate, reaches a maximum (minimum), and then decreases (increases) at a constant rate would be a candidate for an absolute value function.

See additional Teaching Notes on page T485G.

g. $m(x)$ has a graph that is a translation 4 units to the left of the graph of $y = \sin x$.

h. $n(x)$ has a graph that is a translation 3 units to the right of the graph of $y = -2.5x + 4$.

i. $p(x)$ has a graph that is a translation 6 units to the left and 4 units upward of the graph of $y = 2x^2$.

Checkpoint

In this unit, you have organized your thinking about functions in terms of families whose members share symbolic rules that are alike in form, graphs that have a characteristic shape, and tables that display similar patterns. You have also reviewed how functions belonging to the same family share properties that serve to make them useful as models of real-world phenomena.

a What table and graph patterns and problem conditions are clues to use the following types of functions as models?

- Linear
- Exponential
- Quadratic polynomial
- Trigonometric
- Direct power
- Absolute value
- Inverse power
- Square root

b What is the general form of an algebraic rule for each of the above types of functions, and how can the patterns in tables and graphs of specific cases be predicted by inspection of the parameters in those rules?

c How can you adjust the algebraic rules of the basic function types to match graphs that are related to one of the basic function graphs by these transformations?

- Vertical translation
- Vertical stretching or compression
- Horizontal translation
- Horizontal stretching or compression
- Reflection across the x-axis

d How can the sine and cosine function rules be adjusted to give functions with period P and amplitude A?

Be prepared to compare your responses to those of other groups.

On Your Own

Write, in outline form, a summary of the important mathematical concepts and methods developed in this unit. Organize your summary so that it can be used as a quick reference in future units and courses.

Looking Back, Looking Ahead

▶ Reflecting on Mathematical Content

In many ways this unit, "Families of Functions," is the perfect subject for looking both back and ahead in the *Contemporary Mathematics in Context* curriculum. Coming near the end of the material for Course 3, it is a culmination of developments that began in Course 1 with the introduction of the ideas of variables, functions, and modeling of quantitative relationships.

By the end of this unit, the final algebra and functions unit in the three-year core curriculum, students should have a well-developed "function sense" that helps them to interpret function models of many important patterns relating variable quantities. They should also have the technical skills required to create useful models of their own and to explore those models to answer questions involving equations, inequalities, and optimization. With such understanding and skills, students are well prepared as they move ahead to the application of mathematics in other disciplines and as they enter further mathematical studies leading to calculus.

Students studying *Contemporary Mathematics in Context, Course 4* will build on their foundation of understanding about functions. Students may choose to study material that lays the foundation for calculus, with study of rates of change and cumulative change, inverses of functions (particularly the logarithmic function), and composition of functions. This path will extend their study of algebraic analysis of functions and their symbolic forms; expand their skills in formal manipulation of exponents, logarithms, and trigonometric functions; and introduce them to complex numbers. Students who choose the Course 4 path that emphasizes more broadly applicable mathematics will revisit and extend their abilities to analyze quantitative relationships in the context of problem solving with spreadsheets.

By the end of this unit on families of functions, students will have reached a point of consolidation for much earlier work and a bridge to important applications and extensions lying ahead. They will have accomplished a great deal already and be poised for significant growth in the years ahead.

Unit 6 Assessment

Teaching Notes continued

Notes continued from page T426 ▶

5. e.

	Jupiter	Mars
Radius	11 times Earth's	$\frac{1}{2}$ of Earth's
Surface Area	121 times Earth's	$\frac{1}{4}$ of Earth's
Volume	1,331 times Earth's	$\frac{1}{8}$ of Earth's

Students should recall from their study of power models in Course 2 that if the linear measure is increased by a factor of *k*, then the area is increased by a factor of k^2 and the volume is increased by a factor of k^3. In the given formulas, you can see that if you replace *r* with *kr*, then area is increased by a factor of k^2 and volume is increased by a factor of k^3.

Notes continued from page T427 ▶

■ All tables of values for direct power models will contain the origin. For even-degree direct or inverse models, the *y* values for *x* and −*x* will be the same. For odd-degree direct or inverse power models, the *y* values for *x* and −*x* will be opposites.

■ The symbolic form for a direct power model is $f(x) = ax^n$, when *n* is positive, and for an inverse power model is $f(x) = \frac{a}{x^n}$, when *n* is positive.

Quadratic models

■ The graph of a quadratic model will be a parabola. It is symmetric across the vertical line passing through its vertex. Some students may describe a quadratic as a shifted power model with degree 2.

■ The table of values will be "symmetric" about the *x* value of the vertex.

■ The symbolic form of the model is $f(x) = ax^2 + bx + c, a \neq 0$.

ⓒ ■ A situation or data pattern with a constant rate of change indicates that a linear model might be appropriate.

■ A situation or data pattern that indicates change by a constant *factor* is most likely an exponential situation.

■ A situation or data pattern that is increasing at an increasing rate but not by a constant factor may be a situation in which a direct power model is appropriate. An inverse power model may be appropriate in situations or data patterns in which both the *x*- and *y*-axes appear to be asymptotes.

■ If the data pattern or situation indicates symmetry across a vertical line and has a maximum or minimum point, then a quadratic model might be appropriate.

Teaching Notes continued

◀ Notes continued
from page T431

1. **Direct Power Functions**
   b. ■ The $f(x)$ values are symmetric about $x = 0$. The function values are increasing at an increasing rate as $|x|$ increases.
       ■ There is no easy *NOW-NEXT* equation.
   c. Since the exponent of the symbolic equation is even, the graph is U-shaped. Since the coefficient is positive, the graph opens up. The larger the coefficient is, the "steeper" the graph is. The larger the exponent is, the "steeper" the graph is. The fact that the graph is symmetric about the $f(x)$-axis can be seen by the squaring of the x values in the symbolic equation.

   Inverse Power Functions
   b. ■ Since the independent variable x is in the denominator of the symbolic rule, $g(0)$ does not exist, and as x gets large, positively or negatively, $g(x)$ gets small and the graph approaches the x-axis (the asymptote). Also, for x close to 0, $g(x)$ will be large, positively or negatively.
       ■ There is not an obvious *NOW-NEXT* equation.
   c. Since the exponent is a negative odd number and the coefficient is positive, the graph will be in the first and third quadrants. Because the variable is in the denominator, the graph of the function will be asymptotic to the x- and $g(x)$-axes.

   Trigonometric Functions
   b. ■ The table values repeat themselves every 2π (or $360°$). This is the case because these sine and cosine functions are always periodic with period equal to 2π. (Other parameters that affect the period will be considered in Lesson 3.) The maximum and minimum values will be equal to the coefficient of the trigonometric term and the negative of that coefficient.
       ■ There are no obvious *NOW-NEXT* equations.
   c. The graph is periodic because the rule is a trigonometric function. The same periodicity is found in the table of values. The amplitude of the curve is equal to the coefficient of the trigonometric term in the symbolic rule.

2. **Linear Functions: $f(x) = a + bx$**
   The value of a is the $f(x)$-intercept of the graph and is equal to $f(0)$ in the table. The value of b is the slope of the graph and is the constant difference between $f(x)$ values in the table.

   Exponential Functions: $f(x) = a(b^x), a \neq 0, b > 1$ or $0 < b < 1$
   The value of a determines the $f(x)$-intercept of the graph and is equal to $f(0)$ in the table. The value of b determines the steepness of the graph and whether the $f(x)$ values increase or decrease as x increases. If $0 < b < 1$, then the $f(x)$ values will decrease as x increases. If $b > 1$, the $f(x)$ values will increase as x increases.

See additional Teaching Notes on page T485E.

Teaching Notes continued

Notes continued from page T431

2. **Direct Power Functions:** $f(x) = ax^n, a \neq 0, n > 0$
Students may describe even or odd power functions at this time. The Checkpoint Part b discussion should include both types of functions. Even though students have seen power models with noninteger exponents, you may want to suggest that they focus on integer powers to keep this family manageable.

Even n: The value of a determines the "steepness" of the graph and whether it opens up or down. The larger the absolute value of a is, the steeper the graph is. When a is positive, the graph opens up, and when a is negative, the graph opens down.

Odd n: The larger the absolute value of a is, the "steeper" the graph is. If a is positive, the graph will be increasing and located in the first and third quadrants. If a is negative, the graph will be decreasing and located in the second and fourth quadrants.

Inverse Power Functions: $g(x) = ax^n, a \neq 0, n < 0$
The absolute value of a will determine how quickly the graph approaches the axes.

Even n: If a is positive, then the graph will be in the first and second quadrants. If a is negative, then the graph will be in the third and fourth quadrants.

Odd n: If a is positive, then the graph will be in the first and third quadrants. If a is negative, then the graph will be in the second and fourth quadrants.

Trigonometric Functions: $s(x) = a \sin(bx)$ and $c(x) = a \cos(bx), a \neq 0, b > 0$
The value of a determines the amplitude of the function. The value of b adjusts the period from 2π to $\frac{2\pi}{b}$.

3. **a.** As x gets large, either positive or negative, the value of $\frac{1}{x}$ gets very small. Thus, the distance between the graph and the x-axis approaches zero.

Notes continued from page T450

3. **b.** The table for $d(x)$ has values that are 5 times greater than the values of $c(x)$. The zeroes are the same. The table for $e(x)$ has values that are $\frac{1}{2}$ of the values of $c(x)$. The zeroes are the same. The table for $f(x)$ has values that are 2 less than 5 times the values of $c(x)$. The zeroes are not the same. All four tables indicate that all curves are increasing or decreasing over the same intervals.

4. **a.** A translation of a periodic graph does not change either the period or the amplitude of the graph. A vertical stretch of k units multiplies the amplitude of the graph by k but does not change the period of the graph.

Notes continued from page T451

7. **c.** The same general relationships will apply to the rules and graphs of the functions $u(x) = x$ and $v(x) = ax$. If $a > 1$, the graph of $v(x) = ax$ will be steeper or closer to the y-axis than the graph of $u(x)$. If $0 < a < 1$, the graph of $v(x)$ will be flatter than the graph of $u(x)$. If $a < 0$, the graph of $v(x)$ will be the reflection across the x-axis of the graph of $u(x) = |a|x$. However, the inequality relationships in the tables are not the same as those in Part a.

d. The same relationships also hold for exponential growth functions and exponential decay functions.

Teaching Notes *continued*

Notes continued
from page T457

2. d. $f(x) = 1.5^x$

$g(x) = 1.5^x + 2$

$h(x) = -1.5^x$

$k(x) = 0.5(1.5^x)$

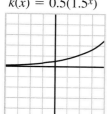

$m(x) = -2(1.5^x) - 3$

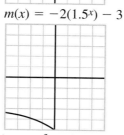

3. a. $g(x) = -f(x) = -(x^3 - 4x) = -x^3 + 4x$

$h(x) = f(x) - 3 = (x^3 - 4x) - 3 = x^3 - 4x - 3$

$j(x) = 2f(x) = 2(x^3 - 4x) = 2x^3 - 8x$

$k(x) = 4 - f(x) = 4 - (x^3 - 4x) = -x^3 + 4x + 4$

b. **This task is one way students can check the accuracy of their symbolic manipulation skills.**

4. a. $g(x) = 3\sqrt{x}$

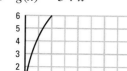

b. $h(x) = 0.5\sqrt{x}$

c. $j(x) = -\sqrt{x}$

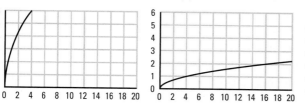

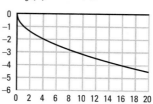

d. $k(x) = \sqrt{x} + 5$

e. $m(x) = -\sqrt{x} + 5$

f. $n(x) = 2\sqrt{x} + 2$

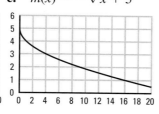

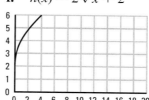

Unit 6

Teaching Notes continued

Notes continued from page T458

2. Answers may vary for this question depending on assumptions made about the original function. For this reason, it is a good idea to have students explain their reasoning.

	Basic Function Family	Transformation
a.	Inverse power function	Vertical translation
b.	Sine function	Vertical translation
c.	Sine function	Vertical stretch
d.	Exponential function	Reflection across x-axis and vertical translation
e.	Exponential function	Vertical translation
f.	Direct power function	Vertical translation

Notes continued from page T461

4. **d.** The world is an extremely complex system, and there are certainly many variables and factors involved in these questions. Student answers will vary but might include some of the following ideas:
   - ■ Population did not increase in the manner predicted in 1970.
   - ■ World oil supplies were actually larger than predicted.
   - ■ Consumption patterns changed: More people used other fuel sources and became more conscious of the need to conserve energy when possible.

See Assessment Resources pages 235–240.

Notes continued from page T485

- ■ Inverse power functions have graphs in which the x- and y-axes are asymptotes. In the table of values, as the absolute value of x gets larger, the value of the function gets closer and closer to zero. A problem situation in which one quantity decreases at a nonconstant rate as another quantity steadily increases might be modeled by an inverse power function.
- ■ Square root functions have graphs that increase in value at a decreasing rate. The function values start rising as x gets larger; then the rate slows down, and the graph flattens out but does not approach a horizontal asymptote. The table of values shows the same pattern as the function values increase, but the increment of change becomes smaller and smaller as x increases.

See additional Teaching Notes on page T485H.

Unit 6

Teaching Notes *continued*

Notes continued from page T485

(b) ■ Linear functions: $f(x) = a + bx$
   If b is positive, the slope of the line is positive. If b is negative, the slope is negative. The y-intercept is a.

■ Exponential functions: $f(x) = a(b^x)$
   The y-intercept is a. If $b > 1$, the model shows exponential growth, and if $0 < b < 1$, the model shows exponential decay.

■ Quadratic polynomial functions: $f(x) = ax^2 + bx + c$
   If $|a| > 1$, the parabola is narrow, and if $|a| < 1$, the parabola is wide. When a is positive, the parabola opens upward, and when a is negative, the parabola opens downward. The parabola is translated horizontally $-\frac{b}{2a}$ units and vertically $\frac{4ac - b^2}{4a}$ units from the origin.

■ Trigonometric functions: $s(x) = a \sin (bx)$ or $c(x) = a \cos (bx)$
   Graph and table values will be between $-a$ and a. The graph is periodic, with period $= \frac{2\pi}{b}$.

■ Direct power functions: $f(x) = ax^n$, $a \neq 0$, n a positive integer. The greater the absolute value of a, the faster the function will increase or decrease.

■ Absolute value functions: $f(x) = a|x|$
   The graph of the absolute value function is a V shape positioned at the origin. The maximum or minimum function value is 0. If $a > 0$ the slope of the left arm is $-a$, and the slope of the right arm is a. If $a < 0$, the slope of the left arm is a and the slope of the right arm is $-a$.

■ Inverse power functions: $f(x) = ax^n$, $a \neq 0$, n is a negative integer
   The greater the absolute value of a, the slower the graph approaches its asymptotes.

■ Square root functions: $f(x) = a\sqrt{x}$
   This function does not have real values for $x < 0$, so in the (x, y) coordinate plane, its graph starts at $(0, 0)$ and then increases gradually at a rate that decreases slightly as x gets larger. The greater the absolute value of a, the faster the function increases.

(c) For any of these functions, $f(x)$, the basic changes are as follows:
   ■ Vertical translation is $f(x) + c$.
   ■ Vertical stretching or compression is $af(x)$.
   ■ Horizontal translation is $f(x + b)$.
   ■ Horizontal stretching or compression is $f(ax)$.
   ■ Reflection across the x-axis is $-f(x)$.

(d) For the sine function $s(x) = \sin x$, the function $g(x) = A \sin \left(\frac{2\pi}{P}x\right)$ will have amplitude A and period P. Similar modifications apply to the cosine function.

APPLY   individual task

▶On Your Own

See Unit 6 Summary Masters.

   Responses will vary. Above all, preparation of this unit summary should be something that is useful to the individual student. You may wish to have students use the unit summary masters for "Families of Functions" to help them organize the information.

See Assessment Resources pages 247–263.

Unit 6

Unit 7 ▶ Discrete Models of Change

UNIT OVERVIEW Although the word "recursion" has not yet been explicitly used in the *Contemporary Mathematics in Context* curriculum, recursion has been a major theme in the curriculum, primarily in terms of work with *NOW-NEXT* equations. Recursion is a fundamental, widely used, and very powerful method for describing sequential change. Using recursion, you can describe the next stage of a sequential process in terms of previous stages.

This unit formalizes the development of recursion while introducing some of its more powerful uses. The major topics covered in this unit are modeling sequential change using recursion, recursive formulas (also called *recurrence relations* or *difference equations*), arithmetic and geometric sequences, arithmetic and geometric sums, finite differences, and function iteration (which implicitly includes function composition). The unit also provides a review of linear, exponential, and polynomial functions.

In a sense, this unit is mainly about recursion equations of the form $A_n = rA_{n-1} + b$. Such recursion equations can be called **combined recursive formulas** because they are a combination of the basic recursion equations that give rise to arithmetic and geometric sequences. (Recursion equations of this form have several different names in discrete mathematics texts. For example, they are also called *affine recurrence relations* or *first-order linear difference equations with constant coefficients*.) In Lesson 1, real-world situations are modeled with combined recursion equations. In Lesson 2, students investigate combined recursion equations with $r = 1$, producing arithmetic sequences. They also investigate geometric sequences, which arise when $b = 0$ in the combined recursion equations. In Lesson 3, the emphasis is on iterating linear functions, which is equivalent to sequentially evaluating combined recursion equations.

Discrete Models of Change

Unit 7

Unit 7

487

Unit 7 Objectives

■ To use iteration and recursion as tools to represent, analyze, and solve problems involving sequential change

■ To formalize and consolidate previous study of *NOW-NEXT* equations, particularly through the use of subscript notation and the introduction of recursive formulas

■ To understand and apply arithmetic and geometric sequences and series

■ To understand and apply the method of finite differences

■ To explore function iteration and, in the process, informally introduce function composition

■ To understand and apply recursive formulas, particularly combined recursive formulas of the form $A_n = rA_{n-1} + b$

■ To review linear, exponential, and polynomial models from a recursive perspective

See Teaching Masters 173a–173e for Maintenance tasks that students can work after Lesson 1.

Unit 7 Planning Guide

Lesson Objectives	MORE Assignments	Suggested Pacing	Materials
Lesson 1 *Modeling Sequential Change Using Recursion* • To use iteration and recursion to model real-world situations involving sequential change • To understand the basic concepts of recursive formulas, particularly for equations of the form $A_n = rA_{n-1} + b$ • To understand the effects of changing certain parameters on the long-term behavior of recursive formulas and the situations they model • To use subscript notation to represent equations that use the words *NOW* and *NEXT* and to take advantage of this notation to analyze recursive formulas more efficiently	**after page 491** Students can begin Modeling Task 3 from p. 494. **page 494** **Modeling:** 3 or 5, and choice of one* **Organizing:** 1 and choice of one* **Reflecting:** Choose one* **Extending:** Choose one*	4 days	• Teaching Resources 174–179 • Assessment Resources 264–269 • *Optional:* RAP Book Exercise Set 19
Lesson 2 *A Discrete View of Function Models* • To understand arithmetic sequences and their connections to linear functions, using recursive formulas, function formulas, and applications • To understand geometric sequences and their connections to exponential functions, using recursive formulas, function formulas, and applications • To understand and apply arithmetic and geometric series (sums of sequences) • To use finite differences tables to find function formulas for certain recursive formulas and to describe the connection between such tables and polynomial functions • To use linear, exponential, and polynomial functions to model discrete situations	**after page 511** Students can begin Modeling Task 1 or 2; Organizing Task 1 or 7; Reflecting Task 1, 2, 4, or 5; or Extending Task 3 from p. 519. **after page 515** Students can begin Modeling Task 3, Organizing Task 5 or 6, Reflecting Task 3, or Extending Task 2 from p. 519. **page 519** **Modeling:** 1 or 2, and 3* **Organizing:** 2, 3, and choice of one* **Reflecting:** Choose one* **Extending:** Choose one*	6 days	• Teaching Resources 173a–173e, 180–183 • Assessment Resources 270–275 • *Optional:* RAP Book Practice Set 10
Lesson 3 *Iterating Functions* • To iterate functions and describe the resulting patterns, the long-term behavior in particular • To describe the connection between function iteration and recursive formulas • To analyze long-term behavior when iterating linear functions, using graphical iteration, numerical iteration, and algebraic methods, including fixed point analysis and connections to slope • To provide an implicit introduction to the composition of functions	**after page 533** Students can begin Organizing Task 4 or 5 or Reflecting Task 1, 4, or 5 from p. 537. **page 537** **Modeling:** 4 and choice of one* **Organizing:** 2 and choice of one* **Reflecting:** 2 and choice of one* **Extending:** Choose one*	5 days	• Teaching Resources 184–187 • Assessment Resources 276–281 • *Optional:* RAP Book Exercise Set 20
Lesson 4 *Looking Back* • To review the major objectives of the unit		2–3 days (includes testing)	• Teaching Resource 188 • Unit Summary Master • Assessment Resources 282–302

*When choice is indicated, it is important to leave the choice to the student.

Note: It is best if Organizing tasks are discussed as a whole class after they have been assigned as homework.

Unit 7

Modeling Sequential Change Using Recursion

We live in a changing world. In previous units, you have used equations, tables, and graphs to investigate linear, exponential, polynomial, and periodic patterns of change. You have used coordinates and matrices to model geometric change in position, size, and shape. In many situations, it is important to also understand **sequential change**, for example, change from year to year. You have already used equations involving the words *NOW* and *NEXT* to describe this type of change. In this unit, you will examine sequential change more fully.

Think About This Situation

Wildlife management has become an increasingly important issue as modern civilization puts greater demands on wildlife habitat. As an example, consider a fishing pond that is stocked with trout from a Department of National Resources hatchery. Suppose you are in charge of managing the trout population in the pond.

a What are some factors to consider in managing the trout population in the pond? List as many factors as you can.

b How could you estimate the current trout population?

c Why would it be useful to be able to predict the year-to-year changes in the trout population? Why would knowledge of the long-term population changes be useful?

Lesson 1 Modeling Sequential Change Using Recursion

MASTER
174   Transparency Master

Think About This Situation

Wildlife management has become an increasingly important issue as modern civilization puts greater demands on wildlife habitat. As an example, consider a fishing pond that is stocked with trout from a Department of National Resources hatchery. Suppose you are in charge of managing the trout population in the pond.

a What are some factors to consider in managing the trout population in the pond? List as many factors as you can.

b How could you estimate the current trout population?

c Why would it be useful to be able to predict the year-to-year changes in the trout population? Why would knowledge of the long-term population changes be useful?

UNIT 7 • DISCRETE MODELS OF CHANGE

LESSON OVERVIEW Throughout the *Contemporary Mathematics in Context* curriculum, students have informally worked with recursion, using *NOW-NEXT* equations. This lesson begins more formal study of recursion. In particular, *NOW-NEXT* equations are represented with subscript notation, and equations of the form $A_n = rA_{n-1} + b$ are introduced.

Lesson Objectives

- ■ To use iteration and recursion to model real-world situations involving sequential change
- ■ To understand the basic concepts of recursive formulas, particularly for equations of the form $A_n = rA_{n-1} + b$
- ■ To understand the effects of changing certain parameters on the long-term behavior of recursive formulas and the situations they model
- ■ To use subscript notation to represent equations that use the words *NOW* and *NEXT* and to take advantage of this notation to analyze recursive formulas more efficiently

LAUNCH full-class discussion

Think About This Situation

See Teaching Master 174.

a Factors include size of the pond, distance from the hatchery, weather, personnel, equipment, money, regulations, food supply, general pond ecology, size of fish population, restocking amount, catch rate, birthrate, death rate, and predators. Students may suggest other factors.

b You might estimate the current population by catch-and-release sampling (for example, catch 100 fish, tag and release them, and then catch another 100 to see what proportion is tagged). You could also use a fishing sonar device.

c It would be useful to predict year-to-year and long-term changes so that short-term and long-term plans could be made for such things as budgets, times and seasons of operation, staffing, and many of the other factors listed in Part a.

INVESTIGATION 1 Modeling Population Change

The main focus of the unit in general and this investigation in particular is to examine the behavior of recursive formulas, starting with the familiar *NOW-NEXT* equations. This investigation is frequently a delight for students and teacher alike, as it is both practical and puzzling. Your students may be surprised to discover that the long-term population of the fish pond is not dependent on the starting population but only on the die-off rate and the restocking amount. The *NOW-NEXT* equation allows for a quick explanation of this result.

When your students are working on Activities 2 through 4, in which these ideas are elicited, encourage them to be as explicit as they can about the relationship between die-off rate or restocking amount and long-term population. Ask them to explain why the initial amount does not influence the long-term population but the other two factors do. Students may have trouble seeing why this should be so, even after they have become convinced from their experiments that it is indeed so. Remind them that a proof should not rely only on examples, and refer them back to the equation *NEXT* = *NOW* − 0.2(*NOW*) + 1,000. Ask what would happen in this equation if the population reached a long-term limit. (The *NEXT* is the same as the *NOW*, so −0.2(*NOW*) + 1,000 = 0. This happens when *NOW* = 5,000.) Give students time to respond to the challenge of figuring out why the initial population is not significant over the long term in this changing situation and why the final population is created by the balancing of the restocking amount and the die-off rate.

Although *NOW-NEXT* equations are the main focus here, you may want to ask your students to write an equation that relates long-term population *L*, restocking amount *A*, and die-off rate *D*. (*A* = *D* · *L*) Those students who discover this relationship will be able to predict the long-term population without any iterations. This equation is also reminiscent of the literal equations that students solved in the "Multiple-Variable Models" unit.

1. **a.** 3,400 fish after 1 year; 3,720 fish after 2 years
   b. *NEXT* = 0.8*NOW* + 1,000 or *NEXT* = *NOW* − 0.2*NOW* + 1,000
   c. There will be 4,580.57 or approximately 4,580 fish after 7 years. There should be some discussion of rounding here since the population must be a whole number of fish. Some students may think that rounding up does not make sense since 0.57 fish does not give another whole fish. However, you may want to discuss that these numbers are estimates and that it really may not matter if students round up or down.

   Students should explain the keystrokes or software features they used so that they know how the calculator or computer procedure relates to the *NOW-NEXT* representation and the situation. *NOW* corresponds to the number (of fish) currently displayed on the calculator screen. *NOW* also corresponds to the "last-answer" feature; it is the answer you have now. *NEXT* corresponds to the number displayed after a calculation.

See additional Teaching Notes on page T549C.

INVESTIGATION 1 ▸ Modeling Population Change

In this lesson, you will build and use a mathematical model to help you predict the changing trout population. As you have seen before, a typical first step in mathematical modeling is simplifying the problem and deciding on some reasonable assumptions. Three factors that you may have listed in the "Think About This Situation" discussion are initial trout population in the pond, annual growth rate of the population, and annual restocking amount, that is, the number of trout added to the pond each year. For the rest of this investigation, use just the following assumptions:

- There are about 3,000 trout currently in the pond.
- Regardless of restocking, the population decreases by about 20% each year due to the combined effect of all causes, including natural deaths and trout being caught.
- 1,000 trout are added at the end of each year.

1. Using these assumptions, build a mathematical model to analyze the population growth in the pond as follows.

   a. Find the population after each of the first two years.

   b. Write an equation using the words *NOW* and *NEXT* to model this situation.

   c. Use the equation from Part b and the last-answer feature of your calculator or computer software to find the population after seven years. Explain how the keystrokes or software features you used correspond to the words *NOW* and *NEXT* in the equation.

2. Now think about the patterns of change in the long-term population of trout in the pond.

   a. Do you think the population will grow without bound? Level off? Die out? Make a conjecture about the long-term population. Compare your conjecture to those made by other students.

   b. Determine the long-term population. Was your conjecture correct? Explain, in terms of the fishing pond ecology, why the long-term population you have determined is reasonable.

   c. Does the trout population change faster around year 5 or around year 25? How can you tell?

3. What do you think will happen to the long-term population of trout if the initial population is different but all other conditions remain the same? Make an educated guess. Then check your guess by finding the long-term population for a variety of initial populations. Describe the pattern of change in long-term population as the initial population varies.

4. Investigate what happens to the long-term population if the annual restocking amount changes but all other conditions are the same as in the original assumptions. Describe your findings about the relationship between long-term population and restocking amount.

5. Describe what happens to the long-term population if the annual decrease rate changes but all other conditions are the same as in the original assumptions.

6. Now consider a situation in which the trout population shows an annual rate of *increase*.

   a. What do you think will happen to the long-term population if the population *increases* at an annual rate? Make a conjecture and then test it by trying at least two different annual increase rates.

   b. Write equations using *NOW* and *NEXT* that represent your two test cases.

   c. Do you think it is reasonable to model the population of trout in a pond with an annual rate of increase? Why or why not?

Checkpoint

Consider this population modeling equation: $NEXT = 0.6NOW + 1,500$.

a Describe a situation involving a population of fish that could be modeled by this equation.

b What additional information is needed to be able to use this equation to predict the population in 3 years?

c What additional information is needed to be able to use this equation to predict the long-term population?

d Consider the following variations in a fish-population situation modeled by an equation like the one above.

   ▪ If the initial population doubles, what will happen to the long-term population?

   ▪ If the annual restocking amount doubles, what will happen to the long-term population?

   ▪ If the annual population decrease rate doubles, what will happen to the long-term population?

e How would you modify the equation above so that it represents a situation in which the fish population increases annually at a rate of 15%? What effect does such an increase rate have on the long-term population?

Be prepared to share your group's thinking with the entire class.

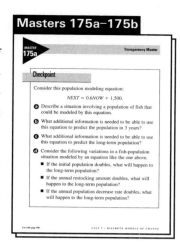

4. Long-term population and restocking amount are directly proportional; for example, if the restocking amount quadruples, so does the long-term population. Encourage students to look closely at this relationship so that they see more than the fact that the factors both increase or decrease. Students may notice that the long-term population is always 5 times the restocking amount. (See the introductory notes for this investigation.)

5. There is an inverse proportional relationship here; for example, if the decrease rate triples, then the long-term population goes down by a factor of $\frac{1}{3}$. Again, encourage students to be as specific as possible when describing this relationship. Some students may determine that the restocking amount divided by the annual decrease rate will give the long-term population. That is, an annual decrease rate of D yields a long-term population of $\frac{1,000}{D}$.

6. **a.** An annual rate of increase, combined with the growth from restocking, will result in the population increasing without bound.

   b. Responses will vary. The *NOW-NEXT* equations should be of the form $NEXT = rNOW + 1,000$, where r is any number larger than 1.

   c. It does not seem reasonable to model the population of trout in a pond with an annual rate of increase and all other assumptions intact, because no fishing pond can have a fish population that grows without bound, as in Part a. The pond ecology (and the finite size of the pond) puts limits on the number of fish possible.

SHARE AND SUMMARIZE   full-class discussion

Checkpoint

See Teaching Masters 175a and 175b.

ⓐ The population has an annual decrease rate of 40% and an annual restocking amount of 1,500 fish. No information is given about initial population.

ⓑ In order to use this equation to predict the population in 3 years, we have to know the initial population.

ⓒ No additional information is needed to be able to use this equation to predict long-term population. Since initial population does not affect long-term population, any initial population can be assumed.

ⓓ Some students may need to create specific examples to help them answer these questions. After they do so, help them generalize their findings.
  ■ Doubling the initial population will not change the long-term population.
  ■ Since this is a direct proportion relationship, doubling the restocking amount will double the long-term population.
  ■ Since this is an inverse proportion relationship, doubling the decrease rate will cut the long-term population in half.

ⓔ The coefficient for *NOW* would become 1.15. This would have the effect of predicting a long-term population that grows without bound.

CONSTRUCTING A MATH TOOLKIT: Following the Checkpoint discussion, students should summarize the analysis of the types of recursive relationships discussed in terms of initial amounts, restocking amounts, and decrease rates as they affect long-term populations.

JOURNAL ENTRY: Describe a situation in which the population will eventually level off, one in which the population will increase without bound, and one in which the population will decrease to zero.

Unit 7

On Your Own

This problem is virtually identical to the trout-population problem, except the parameters are 30 and 10 instead of 3,000 and 1,000.

a. There will be 34 mg after the first six hours and 37.2 mg after the second six hours. (Encourage students to consider why the decimal answers make sense here but did not make sense in the trout problem.)

b. $NEXT = 0.8NOW + 10$ or $NEXT = NOW - 0.2NOW + 10$

c. Two weeks is 56 six-hour periods, and the amount of antibiotic in the patient's system after this number of periods is approximately 50 mg.

d. The goal is to change the long-term amount by a factor of $\frac{1}{2}$. This could be done by changing the regular dosage amount by a factor of $\frac{1}{2}$ or changing the decrease rate by a factor of 2. Since the decrease rate is a function of body metabolism and not under direct control, it makes sense for the doctor to change the prescription by decreasing the regular dosage to 5 mg.

MORE

ASSIGNMENT   *pp. 494 – 504*

Students can now begin Modeling Task 3 from the MORE assignment following Investigation 2.

EXPLORE small-group investigation

INVESTIGATION 2 The Power of Notation

The main point of this investigation is to introduce the standard notation for recursive formulas and to continue to investigate equations of the form $U_n = rU_{n-1} + b$. Since your students are familiar with the meaning of *NOW-NEXT* equations, this notation is only a small change and presents no conceptual difficulties. A greater challenge is to understand and connect the tables, graphs, and equations.

The general recursive formula gives U_n in terms of U_{n-1}. Tables and graphs are easily generated from this equation by a calculator or computer software. Students have used and understand tables and graphs that are the result of some function formula showing, for example, how *y* depends on *x*. However, the entries in the table and the points on the graph in this investigation are generated recursively, one after another, not as a result of some function formula relating U_n to *n*. You can alleviate some possible confusion if you take the time to help students examine these graphical and tabular outputs.

Students may have difficulty choosing window settings for a calculator or computer software. The maximum and minimum values of *n* indicate the number of iterations that is desired, which will create a fixed number of points on the graph. Some calculators continue to use *x* and *y* settings for the graph, which are somewhat clumsy since the variables *x* and *y* do not mean anything in this context. Pairs (n, U_n) are graphed just like (x, y); however, if you set x_{max} to be less than n_{max}, you will not see all the computed pairs.

As students work on these activities, continue to ask them about the meaning of the equation as it relates to the context. When they are creating calculator tables in Activity 3, ask them why it is necessary to enter the starting value. Have them try different values for P_0. Each starting value produces a different table and graph, though not a different long-term value for U_n.

Situations involving sequential change, as in the case of the trout population, are sometimes called **discrete dynamical systems**. A discrete dynamical system is a situation (system) involving change (dynamical) in which the nature of the change is step-by-step (discrete). The method of describing the next step in terms of previous steps is called **recursion**. An important part of analyzing discrete dynamical systems is determining long-term behavior, as you did when you found the long-term population of trout.

▶ On Your Own

A hospital patient is given an antibiotic to treat an infection. He is initially given a 30-mg dose and then receives another 10 mg at the end of every six-hour period thereafter. Through natural body metabolism, about 20% of the antibiotic is eliminated from his system every six hours.

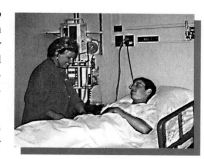

a. Estimate the amount of antibiotic in his system after the first six hours and after the second six hours.

b. Write an equation using the words *NOW* and *NEXT* that models this situation.

c. Find the amount of antibiotic in the patient's system after two weeks.

d. Suppose his doctor decides to modify the prescription so that the long-term amount of antibiotic in his system will be about 25 mg. How should the prescription be modified?

INVESTIGATION ▶ 2 The Power of Notation

A compact notation can be used for equations involving *NOW* and *NEXT* that allows for a detailed analysis of the equations and the situations they model. Using the context of a changing trout population from the last investigation, the **subscript notation** P_n can be used to represent the population after n years. (The notation P_n is read "P sub n.") Thus, P_0 (P sub 0) is the population after 0 years, that is, the initial population. P_1 is the population after 1 year, P_2 is the population after 2 years, and so on.

Recall that the trout-population problem from Investigation 1 was based on these three assumptions:

■ There are about 3,000 trout currently in the pond.

■ Regardless of restocking, the population decreases by 20% each year due to natural causes and trout being caught.

■ 1,000 trout are added at the end of each year.

1. Calculate P_0, P_1, P_2, and P_3 and then sketch a graph of n versus P_n. Describe the pattern of change.

2. The subscript notation relates closely to the way you have used the words *NOW* and *NEXT* to describe sequential change in many contexts.

   a. In the context of a changing fish population, if P_1 is the population *NOW*, what subscript notation represents the population *NEXT* year?

   b. If P_{24} is the population *NEXT* year, what subscript notation represents the population *NOW*?

   c. If P_n is the population *NEXT* year, what subscript notation represents the population *NOW*?

   d. An equation that models the annual change in trout population as described in Investigation 1 is

   $$NEXT = 0.8NOW + 1,000.$$

   Rewrite this equation using P_n and P_{n-1} notation.

3. The equations in Part d of Activity 2 don't tell you what the population is for any given year; they show only how the population changes from year to year. You can analyze situations that involve sequential change, like this one, by using the "recursion mode" on a calculator or computer software. (This activity assumes a calculator is being used.)

   a. Set the mode on your calculator so that you get equations that look like "$P_n = \ldots$" or "$U_n = \ldots$" or "$u(n) = \ldots$." Different calculators may have different names for this mode, and the letters and notation may differ slightly.

Plot1	Plot2	Plot3
nMin	=1	
∴u(n)	=	
u(nMin)	=	
∴v(n)	=	
v(nMin)	=	
∴w(n)	=	
w(nMin)	=	

   b. Rewrite the population equation $NEXT = 0.8NOW + 1,000$ using the notation system of your calculator. (For example, if your calculator uses U_n, then write the equation in the form "$U_n = \ldots$.") Then enter the rule into your calculator. You will also need to enter the initial value.

   c. Use your calculator to produce a table and graph of the rule, with n as the input variable.

   d. Describe any patterns of change you see in the table and graph. Compare the information you get from the table and graph to your analysis of the trout-population situation in Investigation 1. Be sure to describe how the long-term population trend shows up in the table and graph.

4. Reasoning with recursion, as you have been doing with the trout-population problem, is useful in many other contexts. For example, it is often necessary to borrow money for major purchases. Suppose you borrow $5,000 to buy a pre-owned sports utility vehicle, at 9% annual interest, with repayment due in 48 monthly payments. You are told that your monthly payment will be $135. As a wise consumer, you should check to see if this payment amount is correct.

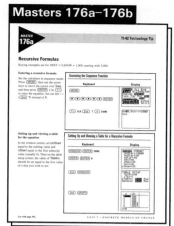

1. $P_0 = 3,000$; $P_1 = 3,400$; $P_2 = 3,720$; and $P_3 = 3,976$. These are the same figures computed in the previous investigation, but now subscript notation is used.

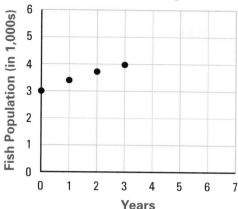

The fish population is increasing, but the amount by which it increases is decreasing.

2. a. If P_1 is the population *NOW*, then P_2 represents the population *NEXT* year.

b. If P_{24} is the population *NEXT* year, then P_{23} represents the population *NOW*.

c. If P_n is the population *NEXT* year, then P_{n-1} represents the population *NOW*.

d. $P_n = 0.8P_{n-1} + 1,000$

3. See Teaching Masters 176a–177b.

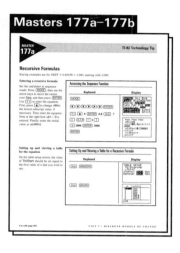

a. Most modern calculators will have a recursion mode. On the TI-82, it is called Seq mode and uses the notation U*n* and V*n*. On the TI-83, it is called Seq mode and uses the notation u(*n*) and v(*n*). On the TI-92, it is called SEQUENCE mode and uses the notation u1(*n*). The text and teacher's notes will use U_n.

b. $U_n = 0.8U_{n-1} + 1,000$

c. Students will use the same keys and menus that have been used to produce graphs and tables for equations in the form "$y = \ldots$", except now there are different choices for the settings. An example is given below.

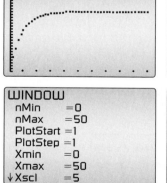

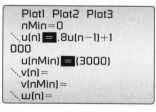

```
Plot1  Plot2  Plot3
nMin=0
\u(n) ■.8u(n-1)+1
000
 u(nMin)■{3000}
\v(n)=
 v(nMin)=
\w(n)=
```

n	u(n)
0	3000
1	3400
2	3720
3	3976
4	4180.8
5	4344.6
6	4475.7

n=6

```
WINDOW
nMin     =0
nMax     =50
PlotStart =1
PlotStep =1
Xmin     =0
Xmax     =50
↓Xscl    =5
```

```
WINDOW
↑PlotStep =1
 Xmin     =0
 XMax     =50
 Xscl     =5
 Ymin     =2900
 Ymax     =6000
 Yscl     =100
```

d. The graph clearly shows a rapid increase in the population during the early years and then a leveling off. This can also be seen in the table. This pattern matches the pattern seen in the last investigation.

See additional Teaching Notes on page T549C.

Unit 7

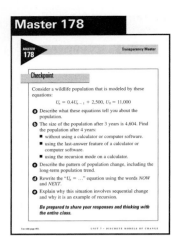

4. **a.** The balance after a given month's payment is computed by first adding the interest for a month to the previous month's balance and then subtracting the payment. Be sure that students realize that the monthly interest rate is 0.75%. The balance after the first payment is \$4,902.50; after the second payment, the balance is \$4,804.27; and after the third payment, the balance is \$4,705.30.

   b. $NEXT = 1.0075NOW - 135$
   $U_n = 1.0075U_{n-1} - 135; U_0 = 5,000$

   c. The balance should be \$0 after the 48th month, but it is $-\$608.27$. The payment is a little high since there is a negative balance. The correct payment is \$124.43.

5. **a.** Forty-eight payments of \$124.43 will pay off the loan. $(48)(124.43) = 5,972.64$. The amount borrowed was \$5,000, so the interest paid is about \$972.64.

   b. The balance is reduced faster at the end of the repayment period. 0.75 percent of \$5,000 is more than 0.75% of \$2,000, for example. So at the beginning, more of the payment must go to pay the interest for that month, and less of the principal gets paid off. Near the end of the four years, most of the payment goes to pay off the principal.

   c. Each month, the balance owed will increase, and the loan will never be paid off! This is not such a good deal, except maybe to the lender. Any payment less than \$37.50 will have this property because 0.75% of 5,000 is 37.5.

SHARE AND SUMMARIZE   full-class discussion

Checkpoint

See Teaching Master 178.

ⓐ The decrease rate is 60%, the restocking amount is 2,500, and the initial population is 11,000.

ⓑ $U_4 = 4,341.6$ (4,341 or 4,342 could be used to represent population.)
   ■ Without a calculator, find 40% of 4,604 and add 2,500.
   ■ Using **ANS** for the last answer, enter **4604** and then calculate **0.4ANS ⊕ 2500**.
   ■ Using the recursion mode, make a table or graph of n versus U_n and find U_4 in the table or on the graph.

ⓒ The population will decrease, quickly at first, and then level off. The long-term population will be approximately 4,166.

ⓓ $NEXT = 0.4NOW + 2,500$

ⓔ This is sequential change since it is step by step, that is, from U_{n-1} to U_n. This is an example of recursion because we are describing the next step (U_n) in terms of the previous step (U_{n-1}).

NOTE: *Difference equation, recurrence relation,* and *recursive formula* are all names for the same thing. In this unit, only the term recursive formula will be used, since it is most descriptive.

CONSTRUCTING A MATH TOOLKIT: Students should write a few examples of recursive formulas (using the vocabulary "recursive formulas"), showing the behavior of the relation for different values of r and b. Suggest using at least two different values for A_0 for each example. Each example should show an equation, a table, and a graph. Students should note how the window settings in the sequence mode relate to the equation being graphed and to the situation being modeled.

---

a. Working as a group, decide how you can determine the amount you still owe, called the *balance*, after a given month's payment. Then find the balance of the auto loan after each of the first three payments. Compare your balances to those of other groups.

b. Write an equation using the words *NOW* and *NEXT* that models the month-by-month change in the balance of the loan. Write an equivalent equation using subscript notation. Be sure to specify the initial balance.

c. Now think about whether the payment amount is correct. If the monthly payment of $135 is correct, what should the balance be after the 48th payment? Use the equations from Part b and your calculator to see if $135 is the correct payment for this loan. If the payment is incorrect, is it too high or too low? How can you tell? Experiment to find the correct monthly payment.

5. Investigate further the loan situation from Activity 4.

a. How much total interest was paid on the $5,000 loan, using the correct monthly payment?

b. Is the balance of the loan reduced faster at the beginning of the repayment period or at the end? Explain and give evidence to support your answer.

c. Suppose someone offers you a "great deal" whereby you have to pay only $35 per month until the loan is paid off. Describe what happens to the repayment process in this situation. Is this such a great deal after all?

Checkpoint

Consider a wildlife population that is modeled by these equations:

$$U_n = 0.4U_{n-1} + 2,500, \quad U_0 = 11,000$$

ⓐ Describe what these equations tell you about the population.

ⓑ The size of the population after 3 years is 4,604. Find the population after 4 years:

- without using a calculator or computer software.
- using the last-answer feature of a calculator or computer software.
- using the recursion mode on a calculator.

ⓒ Describe the pattern of population change, including the long-term population trend.

ⓓ Rewrite the "$U_n = \ldots$" equation using the words *NOW* and *NEXT*.

ⓔ Explain why this situation involves sequential change and why it is an example of recursion.

Be prepared to share your responses and thinking with the entire class.

Unit 7

Equations involving recursion, like those you have been using in this investigation, are called **recursive formulas**. They are also called *recurrence relations* or *difference equations*. The recursive formulas you have studied in this lesson have all been of the general form $A_n = rA_{n-1} + b$, with A_0 as the initial value. Different values for r and b allow you to model many different situations.

On Your Own

Recall the situation (page 491) involving a hospital patient taking an antibiotic to treat an infection. He was initially given a 30-mg dose, and then he took another 10 mg at the end of every six hours. Through natural body metabolism, about 20% of the antibiotic was eliminated from his system every six hours.

a. Write a recursive formula in the form "$U_n = \ldots$" that models this situation.

b. Using your calculator, produce a table and graph of n versus U_n, with n as the input variable.

c. Describe how the amount of antibiotic in the patient's system changes over time, including the long-term change.

MORE
Modeling • Organizing • Reflecting • Extending

Modeling

1. Every ten years, the United States Census Bureau conducts a complete census of the nation's population. In 2000, the census report said that there were about 281 million residents in the United States and its territories. The population changes quite a lot between census reports, but it is too expensive to conduct the census more often. Annual changes can be estimated using estimates like the following:

   ■ Births will equal about 1.5% of the total population each year.

   ■ Deaths will equal about 0.9% of the total population each year.

   ■ Immigrants from other countries will add about 0.8 million people each year.

   (Source: 2001 World Population Data Sheet, Population Reference Bureau, http://www.prb.org.)

On Your Own

a. $U_n = 0.8U_{n-1} + 10$

b.

```
Plot1  Plot2  Plot3
 nMin=0
\u(n) ■.8u(n−1)+1
0
  u(nMin)■{30}
\v(n)=
 v(nMin)=
\w(n)=
```

```
 n    | u(n) |
[0]     30
 1      34
 2      37.2
 3      39.76
 4      41.808
 5      43.446
 6      44.757
n=0
```

```
WINDOW
 nMin    =0
 nMax    =30
 PlotStart =1
 PlotStep =1
 Xmin    =0
 Xmax    =30
↓Xsci    =5
```

```
WINDOW
↑PlotStep =1
 Xmin    =0
 Xmax    =30
 Xscl    =5
 Ymin    =20
 Ymax    =60
 Yscl    =10
```

c. The amount of antibiotic in the patient's body increases over time, rapidly in the beginning, and then eventually levels off at about 50 mg.

MORE

ASSIGNMENT *pp. 494–504*

Modeling: 3 or 5, and choice of one*

Organizing: 1 and choice of one*

Reflecting: Choose one*

Extending: Choose one*

*When choice is indicated, it is important to leave the choice to the student.

NOTE: It is best if Organizing tasks are discussed as a whole class after they have been assigned as homework.

Modeling

1. **a.** The estimated population for 2001 is about 283 million. $281(1.006) + 0.8 = 283.486$. For the year 2010, the estimated population is approximately 307 million people.

    b. $NEXT = 1.006NOW + 0.8$

    c. $U_n = U_{n-1}(1.006) + 0.8$ or $P_{n+1} = P_n(1.006) + 0.8$. The initial value is 281.

    d. In the table and graphs that follow, year 0 represents 2000.

Year	Population	Year	Population	Year	Population
0	281	7	298.72	14	317.19
1	283.49	8	301.31	15	319.90
2	285.99	9	303.92	16	322.62
3	288.50	10	306.54	17	325.35
4	291.03	11	309.18	18	328.10
5	293.58	12	311.84	19	330.87
6	296.14	13	314.51	20	333.66

Beware! Plotting the points in the above table yields the first graph below, which looks linear. Plotting 250 points yields an exponential curve, as shown in the second graph. In the long term, the population grows without bound, according to this model.

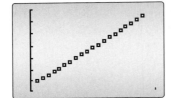 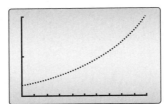

```
WINDOW
 nMin      =0
 nMax      =250
 PlotStart =1
 PlotStep  =1
 Xmin      =0
 Xmax      =250
↓Xscl      =25
```

```
WINDOW
↑PlotStep =1
 Xmin      =0
 Xmax      =250
 Xscl      =25
 Ymin      =0
 Ymax      =2000
 Yscl      =1000
```

e. Any birthrate and death rate such that the death rate is greater than the birthrate will result in a population that levels off over time. For example, the birthrate could be 2.5% of the population, while the death rate could be 3.5% of the population. If immigrants still add 0.9 million people per year, then the population will level off at 90 million people. This relation is modeled by $U_n = 0.99U_{n-1} + 0.9$. Tables and graphs will depend on the specific values chosen but should reflect a leveling off of the population.

2. **a.** $\frac{6,900 + 9,200}{2} = 8,050$

    b. $NEXT = 1.031NOW - 50$

    c. $U_n = 1.031U_{n-1} - 50$ or $P_{n+1} = 1.031P_n - 50$. The initial value is 8,050.

See additional Teaching Notes on page T549D.

a. Using the statistics on the previous page, what population is estimated for the United States in 2001? In the year 2010?

b. Write an equation using the words *NOW* and *NEXT* that represents this situation.

c. Write a recursive formula that represents this situation, and specify the initial value.

d. Produce a table and a graph that show the population estimates through the year 2020. Describe the expected long-term trend in population change over time.

e. Describe some hypothetical birth and death rates that would result in a population that levels off over time. Represent this situation with a recursive formula, a table, and a graph.

2. Commercial hunting of whales is controlled to prevent the extinction of some species. Because of the danger of extinction, scientists conduct counts of whales to monitor their population changes. A status report on the bowhead whales of Alaska estimated that the 1993 population of these whales was between 6,900 and 9,200 and that

the difference between births and deaths yielded an annual growth rate of about 3.1%. No hunting of bowhead whales is allowed, except that Alaskan Inuit are allowed to take, or harvest, about 50 bowhead whales each year for their livelihood. (Source: nmml.afsc.noaa.gov/CetaceanAssessment/bowhead/bmsos.htm)

a. Compute the mean of the high and low population estimates from the report. Use that figure as your estimate of the 1993 population for the rest of this task.

b. Write an equation using the words *NOW* and *NEXT* to model this situation.

c. Write a recursive formula that models this situation; include the initial value.

d. Produce a table and graph showing the change in the bowhead whale population over time. Describe any trends in that change.

e. Suppose that, because of some natural disaster, the current bowhead whale population is reduced to 1,500, but growth rate and number harvested by the Inuit stay the same. Under these conditions, what happens to the long-term population?

3. Retirement is probably not something you are currently concerned about! However, working adults, even very young working adults, should have a financial plan for retirement. If you start saving early and take advantage of compound interest, then you should be in great financial shape by the time you retire. Consider twin sisters with two different retirement savings plans.

Plan I: Cora begins a retirement account at age 20. She starts with $2,000 and then saves $2,000 per year at 7% interest, compounded annually, for 10 years. (*Compounded annually* means that her money will grow at a rate of 7% each year.) Then she stops contributing to the account but keeps her savings invested at the same rate.

Plan II: Mawiyah doesn't save any money in her twenties, but when she turns 30, she starts with $2,000 and then saves $2,000 per year at 7% interest, compounded annually, for 35 years.

Both sisters retire at age 65. Who do you think will have more retirement savings at age 65? Test your conjecture.

4. Chlorine is used to keep swimming pools safe by controlling certain harmful microorganisms. However, chlorine is a powerful chemical, so just the right amount must be used. Too much chlorine irritates swimmers' eyes and can be hazardous to their health; too

little chlorine allows the growth of microorganisms to be uncontrolled, which can be harmful. A pool manager must measure and add chlorine regularly to keep the level just right. The chlorine is measured in parts per million (ppm) by weight. That is, one ppm of chlorine means that there is one ounce of chlorine for every million ounces of water.

Chlorine dissipates in reaction to bacteria and to the sun at a rate of about 15% of the amount present per day. The optimal concentration of chlorine in a pool is from 1 to 2 ppm, although it is safe to swim when the concentration is as high as 3 ppm.

a. Suppose you have a summer job working at a swimming pool, and one of your responsibilities is to maintain a safe concentration of chlorine in the pool. You are required to add the same amount of chlorine to the pool every day. When you take the job, you find that the concentration is 3 ppm. How much chlorine (in parts per million) do you need to add each day in order to maintain a long-term optimal concentration? Write a recursive formula that models your optimal chlorine maintenance plan.

3. **Plan I:** At the end of 10 years of adding to her savings, Cora has approximately $31,567. Then she lets this money sit for 35 years at 7% interest, resulting in a total amount at age 65 of approximately $337,027.

   Plan II: Mawiyah saves $2,000 per year at 7% interest for 35 years, resulting in a total amount at age 65 of approximately $297,827.

   The net result is that Cora, who saved $2,000 per year for only 10 years ($20,000), has about $40,000 more money saved than Mawiyah, who saved $2,000 per year for 35 years ($70,000)!

4. **a.** A recursive formula model looks like $C_n = 0.85C_{n-1} + (daily\ dosage)$, $C_0 = 3$. Students should experiment with different daily dosages to find one that yields a long-term level between 1 and 2 ppm. If the daily dosage is between 0.15 and 0.30 ppm, the long-term chlorine concentration will be between 1 and 2 ppm. For example, a daily dosage of 0.2 ppm will yield a long-term concentration of $\frac{0.20}{0.15}$ or approximately 1.33 ppm.

Unit 7

4. **b.** The pattern is the same as the one for the analysis of the trout-population problem. That is, changing the initial concentration has no effect on the long-term concentration (except that it will change the time it takes to achieve the long-term concentration); changing the daily dosage by a factor of k will result in changing the long-term concentration by the same factor k; and changing the dissipation rate by a factor of k will result in the long-term concentration changing by a factor of $\frac{1}{k}$. These patterns result when you change one factor at a time and leave the others as they were originally.

   c. Students need to convert their ppm dosage from Part a to pounds. In the previous example given, a daily dosage of 0.2 is used. The number of pounds of water in the pool is $50{,}000 \times 8.337$, or 416,850. Thus, the number of pounds of chlorine needed per day is $\frac{0.2}{1{,}000{,}000} \times 416{,}850$, or about 0.083. However, the pellets are only 65% active chlorine, so the amount of pellets needed is $0.083 \div 0.65$, or about 0.128 pounds.

5. **a.** $NEXT = 1.04NOW$

   $U_n = 1.04U_{n-1}$ or $P_{n+1} = 1.04P_n$, $U_0 = P_0 = 100$

   After 10 years there will be $148.02 in the account.

   b. ■ If the interest is compounded monthly and the annual interest rate is 4%, each month you get $\frac{1}{12}$ of the 4%. Therefore, $\frac{4}{12}$% interest is paid each month. $\frac{4}{12}$% = 0.0033, so $U_n = 1.0033U_{n-1}$ or $P_{n+1} = 1.0033P_n$, $U_0 = P_0 = 100$.

   ■ After 1 month, there is $100.33. After 2 months, there is $100.66. After 2 years, there is $108.23. (If students do not round the $\frac{4}{12}$%, they will get $100.67 after 2 months and $108.31 after 2 years.)

   ■ After 10 years, the amount is $148.49 (or $149.08 if $\frac{4}{12}$% is not rounded). The interest that is compounded monthly is a better deal. In this situation, you have $0.47 (or $1.06 if $\frac{4}{12}$% is not rounded) more after 10 years.

   c. ■ $U_n = 1.04U_{n-1} + 50$ or $P_{n+1} = 1.04P_n + 50$, $U_0 = P_0 = 100$

   ■ After 10 years, there is $748.33 in the account.

   ■ The money grows without bound. Once again, the pattern may look linear in the short term, but it is nonlinear. The amount of money is growing at an increasing rate.

b. There are three key factors in this problem: the initial concentration, the daily increase in concentration due to the amount you add, and the dissipation rate. Systematically explore changes in each of these three factors and record the corresponding effects on the long-term chlorine concentration in the swimming pool.

c. Suppose the chlorinating pellets you use are 65% active chlorine, by weight. If the pool contains 50,000 gallons of water, and water weighs 8.337 pounds per gallon, how many pounds of chlorine pellets must you add to the pool each day?

5. If you have money in an interest-bearing savings account, the interest is probably compounded at a rate between 3% and 4.5%. Recursive formulas can be used to analyze how money grows due to compounding of interest. For this task, assume you make no withdrawals from the savings account.

a. Suppose you deposit $100 in a savings account that pays 4% interest, compounded annually. (*Compounded annually* means that your money will grow at a rate of 4% per year.) Write a *NOW-NEXT* equation and a recursive formula that show how the amount of money in your account changes from year to year. Find the amount of money in the account after 10 years.

b. Most savings accounts pay interest that compounds more often than annually. Suppose that you make an initial deposit of $100 into an account that pays 4% annual interest, compounded monthly.

  ■ Write a recursive formula that models the month-by-month change in the amount of money in your account.

  ■ How much money is in the account after 1 month? After 2 months? After 2 years?

  ■ How much money is in the account after 10 years? Compare your answer to the answer you got in Part a. Which kind of interest is a better deal, compounding annually or compounding monthly? How much better?

c. Suppose that, in addition to the initial $100, you deposit another $50 at the end of every year, and the interest rate is 4% compounded annually.

  ■ Write a recursive formula that models this situation.

  ■ How much money is in the account after 10 years?

  ■ Describe the pattern of growth of the money in the savings account.

Organizing

1. In this lesson, you have investigated recursion equations of the form $A_n = rA_{n-1} + b$. Different values for r and b yield models for different situations. Consider some of the possibilities by completing a table like the one below. For each entry in the table, do the following.

   ■ Describe a situation that could be modeled by a recursion equation. (You may use examples from the lesson if you wish.)

   ■ Write the recursive formula.

   ■ Describe the long-term trend.

	$0 < r < 1$	$r > 1$
$b < 0$	A whale population is decreasing by 5% per year due to a death rate higher than the birthrate, and 50 whales are harvested each year. $A_n = 0.95A_{n-1} - 50$ Long-term trend: Extinction	
$b > 0$		

2. In this lesson, you used a specific and very common subscript notation to represent sequential change. However, there are other ways to represent sequential change with subscript and related notation. You may see some of these other ways when using different textbooks and calculators. Consider again the trout population modeling equation $NEXT = 0.8NOW + 1{,}000$, which you represented as $P_n = 0.8P_{n-1} + 1{,}000$.

   a. If U_n is the population NOW, what subscript notation represents the population $NEXT$ year? Rewrite the NOW-$NEXT$ equation above using U_n and U_{n+1}.

   b. If $A(n)$ is the population NOW, what notation represents the population $NEXT$ year? Rewrite the NOW-$NEXT$ equation above using $A(n)$ and $A(n+1)$.

   c. You now have four different equations representing the same trout population: an equation using the words NOW and $NEXT$, an equation using P_n and P_{n-1}, an equation using U_n and U_{n+1}, and an equation using $A(n)$ and $A(n+1)$. Suppose that one of your classmates has not completed this task. Write a paragraph or two to the classmate explaining how all four equations accurately represent the changing trout population.

Organizing

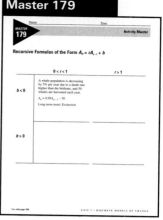

Master 179

1. **See Teaching Master 179.**

    ### Recursive Formulas of the Form $A_n = rA_{n-1} + b$

	$0 < r < 1$	$r > 1$
	A whale population is decreasing by 5% per year due to a death rate higher than the birthrate, and 50 whales are harvested each year.	A whale population is increasing by 20% per year due to a birthrate higher than the death rate, and 50 whales are harvested each year.
	$A_n = 0.95A_{n-1} - 50$	$A_n = 1.2A_{n-1} - 50$
$b < 0$	Long-term trend: Extinction	Long-term trend: Unbounded population growth (if initial population is over 250)
	Note: This combination of parameters will always lead to extinction.	**Note:** In this situation, if $A_0 > \frac{b}{1-r}$, then the long-term trend will be unbounded growth. If $A_0 < \frac{b}{1-r}$, then the long-term trend will be extinction. If $A_0 = \frac{b}{1-r}$, then the population will remain constant at A_0.
	A whale population is decreasing by 5% per year due to a death rate higher than the birthrate, and 50 whales are added to the stock each year.	A whale population is increasing by 20% per year due to a birthrate higher than the death rate, and 50 whales are added to the stock each year.
$b > 0$	$A_n = 0.95A_{n-1} + 50$	$A_n = 1.2A_{n-1} + 50$
	Long-term trend: A fixed population of $\frac{50}{0.05}$ or 1,000	Long-term trend: Unbounded growth
	Note: This combination will always lead to a long-term population equal to $\frac{b}{1-r}$.	**Note:** This combination will always produce unbounded growth.

2. **a.** U_{n+1} represents the population next year. $U_{n+1} = 0.8U_n + 1,000$
    b. $A(n+1)$ represents the population next year. $A(n+1) = 0.8A(n) + 1,000$
    c. The fish population changes from one year to the next by a factor of 0.8, plus an added 1,000. This pattern of change is accurately described by all four equations. One way to see that they are all accurate representations is to use each one to compute the changing fish population and see that you get the same values. The symbolic notation is different in the different forms; however, the equations using *NOW* and *NEXT*, P_n and P_{n-1}, U_n and U_{n+1}, and $A(n)$ and $A(n+1)$ all compute the population of the following year given the current population.

3. **a.** From Activity 2 of Investigation 1, we know that the trout population levels off at 5,000. This means that the graph has a horizontal asymptote at 5,000. The graph of the equation given here is a reflection across the x-axis and then a translation, up 5,000 units, of the exponential function $f(x) = 2,000(0.8)^x$. Since the graph of $f(x)$ has the x-axis as an asymptote, P_n will have an asymptote of $P_n = 5,000$. In addition, this graph will increase quickly at first and then level off, just as the underlying function does.

    b. $P_1 = -2,000(0.8) + 5,000 = 3,400$
    $P_5 = -2,000(0.8)^5 + 5,000 = 4,344.64$
    These values match P_1 and P_5 found earlier.

    c. To get the initial population from the new equation, substitute $n = 0$. This gives $-2,000 + 5,000$, or 3,000.

    d. To find the long-term population, substitute a very large number for n. This makes $(0.8)^n$ very small. Thus, $-2,000(0.8)^n$ is very small, and you can see that $-2,000(0.8)^n + 5,000$ is very close to 5,000. So the long-term population is easily seen to be 5,000.

4. The practical domain is all nonnegative integers, and the practical range is integers between 3,000 and 5,000.

5. **a.** $AB = [0.8(3,000) + 1,000] = [3,400]$. This is the value of P_1.

    b. $AC = [3,400 \ 1]$. Multiply this answer matrix by C to find P_2. This would be the same as AC^2. Similarly, AC^3 will produce P_3.

3. In Activity 2 of Investigation 2 (page 492), you found the following recursive formula to model a trout population:

$$P_n = 0.8P_{n-1} + 1,000, \text{ with } P_0 = 3,000$$

Another equation that represents this situation is the following:

$$P_n = -2,000(0.8)^n + 5,000$$

a. Using ideas from the "Families of Functions" unit, explain why this new equation is reasonable.

b. Verify that the new equation gives the same values for P_1 and P_5 as those found using the recursive formula.

c. Verify that the new equation yields an initial population of 3,000.

d. Use the new equation to verify the long-term population you found in Activity 3 of Investigation 1 (page 489). Explain your thinking. How is the long-term population revealed in the symbolic form of the new equation?

4. You can represent recursive formulas with subscript notation or function notation. For example, in the trout-population problem, you can represent the population P as a function of the number of years n and write P_n or $P(n)$. In the case of the trout-population problem, what are the practical domain and practical range of the function P?

5. Think about how matrix multiplication can be used to calculate successive values generated by recursive formulas of the form $A_n = rA_{n-1} + b$. For example, consider the recursive formula for the original trout-population situation at the beginning of this lesson: $P_n = 0.8P_{n-1} + 1,000$, with $P_0 = 3,000$.

a. A first attempt at a matrix multiplication that would be equivalent to evaluating the recursive formula might use the following matrices.

$$A = [3,000 \ \ 1] \quad \text{and} \quad B = \begin{bmatrix} 0.8 \\ 1,000 \end{bmatrix}$$

Compute AB and compare it to P_1.

b. AB is just a 1×1 matrix and so is not much good for repeated multiplication. Thus, you can't use repeated multiplication of these matrices to successively evaluate the recursive formula. A better try might be to use the following matrices.

$$A = [3,000 \ \ 1] \quad \text{and} \quad C = \begin{bmatrix} 0.8 & 0 \\ 1,000 & 1 \end{bmatrix}$$

Compute AC and compare it to P_1. What matrix multiplication would you use next to find P_2? To find P_3?

LESSON 1 • MODELING SEQUENTIAL CHANGE USING RECURSION   **499**

c. There is just one finishing touch needed: Modify the matrices so that the multiplication computes not only the successive values but also the number of the year. Consider the following matrices.

$$A = [0 \quad 3{,}000 \quad 1] \quad \text{and} \quad D = \begin{bmatrix} 1 & 0 & 0 \\ 0 & 0.8 & 0 \\ 1 & 1{,}000 & 1 \end{bmatrix}$$

Compute AD, AD^2, AD^3, AD^4, and AD^5, and compare the results to P_1 through P_5.

d. Use matrix multiplication to generate three successive values of the recursive formula $P_n = 1.04P_{n-1} - 350$, with $P_0 = 6{,}700$.

e. Explain why this matrix multiplication method works to find successive values of a recursive formula.

Reflecting

1. When using some graphing calculators, you have the option of graphing in "connected" mode or "dot" mode. Find out what the difference is between these two modes of graphing. Which do you think is more appropriate for the graphing you have been doing in this lesson? Why?

2. You can use a calculator to produce the successive values of a recursive formula in several different ways. For example, you can use the last-answer key, you can use recursion mode to generate a table, or you can use recursion mode to generate a graph and then trace the graph.

   a. Use each of the above methods to find the successive values of the recursive formula $A_n = 0.65A_{n-1} + 90$, with $A_0 = 200$.

   b. Use any other method you can think of to find some successive values.

   c. Do you prefer one method over the others? If you have your choice of methods, how will you decide which one to use?

3. In this lesson, you used recursive formulas to model sequential change in several situations, such as population growth, drug concentration, chlorine concentration, and money saved or owed. Describe one result of your investigations that was particularly interesting or surprising.

4. Recursive formulas are also sometimes called *difference equations*. What difference would be of interest in studying a recursive formula?

5. c. $P_1 = 3,400$; $P_2 = 3,720$; $P_3 = 3,976$; $P_4 = 4,180.8$; $P_5 = 4,344.64$
$AD = [1\ \ 3,400\ \ 1]$; $AD^2 = [2\ \ 3,720\ \ 1]$; $AD^3 = [3\ \ 3,976\ \ 1]$;
$AD^4 = [4\ \ 4,180.8\ \ 1]$; $AD^5 = [5\ \ 4,344.64\ \ 1]$
Note that the first entry in the matrix is the year and the second entry is the population for that year.

d. $A = [0\ \ 6,700\ \ 1]$ and $B = \begin{bmatrix} 1 & 0 & 0 \\ 0 & 1.04 & 0 \\ 1 & -350 & 1 \end{bmatrix}$

$AB = [1\ \ 6,618\ \ 1]$; $AB^2 = [2\ \ 6,532.72\ \ 1]$; $AB^3 = [3\ \ 6,444.03\ \ 1]$
The second entries of these matrices are the first three successive values of the recursive formula.

e. To explain why this matrix multiplication works and how someone might have thought of it in the first place, students might reason as follows. First of all, it seems reasonable to try to use repeated matrix multiplication, and particularly matrix powers, to mimic the iteration of a recursive formula, since computing a matrix power is an iterative process. A first attempt at matrix multiplication using $A = [3,000\ \ 1]$
and $B = \begin{bmatrix} 0.8 \\ 1,000 \end{bmatrix}$ is reasonable because you set up the simplest matrices which,
when multiplied, will yield P_1. However, this result is just a 1×1 matrix and is, therefore, not much good for repeated multiplication. Add an extra column to B so that the multiplication will yield a 1×2 matrix, which can then be used for further multiplications. Then the last step is to modify the matrices so that the multiplication computes not only the successive values but also the number of the iteration. This is done by using the matrices as given in Part c.

Reflecting

1. Connected mode will draw a continuous graph by connecting the computed values with line segments. Dot mode is discontinuous or discrete; it will show the graph as a series of dots. The dot mode is most appropriate in this lesson since the change is sequential (for example, from year to year) and there are no computed values between steps.

2. a. Students should use all three methods. The sequence of values will be as follows:

n	0	1	2	3	4	5	6	...
A_n	200	220	233	241.45	246.94	250.51	252.83	...

b. Students might calculate by hand or use a spreadsheet.

c. Responses may vary. For example, some students may choose to use the last-answer key because they like to see the values unfold one by one; others might like the graph because it is more visual; and others may like the table because it shows all the values listed out at once, along with the values of n.

3. Student responses may vary. For example, it is interesting that when $|r| < 1$ in $A_n = rA_{n-1} + b_n$, no matter what you pick for an initial value, the sequence will reach the same long-term value $\frac{b}{1-r}$ (as in the trout-population problem or the antibiotic problem).

4. The differences between any two successive values are of interest in studying a recursive formula. The speed at which these differences change gives important information about the sequence of numbers. (Students will see in the next lesson, it is the pattern in these differences that helps them determine if the associated sequence is arithmetic, geometric, or neither.)

Extending

NOTE: In this context of population, it is reasonable to truncate all decimal numbers.

1. Students might use ClarisWorks®, Lotus®, Excel® or other spreadsheet programs to complete Modeling Task 4 on chlorine concentration.

2. **a.**

L_1	L_2	L_1	L_2	L_1	L_2
0	3,000	7	4,580	14	4,912
1	3,400	8	4,664	15	4,929
2	3,720	9	4,731	16	4,943
3	3,976	10	4,785	17	4,954
4	4,180	11	4,828	18	4,963
5	4,344	12	4,862	19	4,971
6	4,475	13	4,890	20	4,976

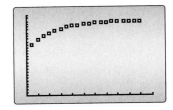

```
WINDOW
Xmin =0
Xmax =22
Xscl =2
Ymin =0
Ymax =5400
Yscl =200
Xres =1
```

b. Students first need to realize that this graph has the general shape of a transformed exponential model. If the plot is transformed by first reflecting it across the *x*-axis and then translating it up 5,000 units, the graph looks like a standard exponential model of the form $y = ab^x, 0 < b < 1$. The original scatterplot and the transformed data are shown below.

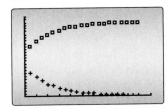

```
WINDOW
Xmin =0
Xmax =22
Xscl =2
Ymin =0
Ymax =5400
Yscl =200
Xres =1
```

This modification to the lists can be completed by letting $L_3 = -L_2 + 5,000$. Using a calculator to find the exponential regression equation for the data in L_1 and L_3 produces $y = 2,000(0.8)^x$.

c. You can transform the modified data back into the original data by reflecting them across the *x*-axis and then shifting up 5,000. This is accomplished by the equation $y = -2,000(0.8)^x + 5,000$.

d. The graph and scatterplot are shown below. The graph matches the scatterplot perfectly. $-2,000(0.8)^{20} + 5,000 = 4,976.94$, which is the same as P_{20}.

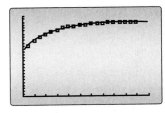

```
WINDOW
Xmin =0
Xmax =22
Xscl =2
Ymin =0
Ymax =5400
Yscl =200
Xres =1
```

Extending

1. Spreadsheets are designed to take advantage of the power of recursion. In particular, recursive formulas can be evaluated and analyzed using spreadsheets. Use some spreadsheet software to complete one of the Modeling tasks from this lesson.

	A	B	C
1	2		
2	14		
3	50		
4			
5			
6			
7			
8			
9			
10			

2. In this lesson, you modeled a trout population with the recursive formula $P_n = 0.8P_{n-1} + 1{,}000$, with $P_0 = 3{,}000$. You can get another modeling formula for this situation by fitting a curve to the population data and finding the equation for that curve. Use the following steps to carry out this plan.

   a. Use the formula $P_n = 0.8P_{n-1} + 1{,}000$, with $P_0 = 3{,}000$, to generate the sequence of population figures for 20 years and put these figures into a data list, say L_2, on your calculator or computer. Generate another list, say L_1, that contains the sequence of years 0 through 20. Produce a scatterplot of L_1 versus L_2.

   b. Modify your scatterplot by transforming the data in the lists so that the plot matches one of the standard regression models of your calculator or computer software. Use the regression model feature to find an equation that fits the transformed data.

   c. Now, transform your regression equation so that it fits the original data.

   d. Test your equation. Does the graph fit the original scatterplot? Compare the function value for $n = 20$ to what you get when you find P_{20} using the recursive formula $P_n = 0.8P_{n-1} + 1{,}000$, with $P_0 = 3{,}000$.

3. These days, almost every state has a lottery, and the jackpots are often quite large. But are they really as large as they seem? Suppose you win $500,000 in a lottery (which you will, of course, donate to the mathematics department at your school). Typically, these large jackpots are paid over time. For example, suppose you receive your $500,000 over 20 years at $25,000 per year. To accurately analyze how much you have *really* won in this situation, you need to include the effect of compound interest.

Unit 7

a. Suppose you deposit $500,000 in a bank account paying 3.5% annual interest, and you withdraw $25,000 at the end of every year. Write a recursive formula that models this situation, and calculate how much money will be in the account after 20 years.

b. Experiment to find an initial deposit that will yield a balance of $0 after 20 years.

c. The result from Part b is called the **present value** of your lottery winning. The present value is the lump sum amount that, if deposited now at 3.5% annual interest, would generate payments of $25,000 per year for 20 years. The present value is what your lottery winning is really worth, taking into account the reality of compound interest. So in this situation, how much is a $500,000 jackpot paid over 20 years really worth?

d. Find the actual value, that is, the present value, of a lottery winning of $1,000,000 that is paid at $50,000 per year for 20 years, if you can invest money at 5% annual interest.

e. Actual present values are even lower than what you have calculated here. What do you think causes even lower present values?

4. The Towers of Hanoi is a mathematical game featured in an old story about the end of the world. As the story goes, monks in a secluded temple are working on this game, and when they are finished the world will end! The people of the world would like to know how long it will take the monks to finish the game.

The game is played with 3 pegs mounted on a board and 64 golden disks of successively larger sizes with holes in the center. (Commercial games such as the example above have many fewer disks.) The game begins with all 64 disks stacked on one peg, from largest to smallest. The goal of the game is to move all 64 disks onto another peg, subject to these rules: (1) Only one disk may be moved at a time. (2) You are not allowed to put a larger disk on top of a smaller disk. (3) Disks may be placed temporarily on any peg, including the one on which the disks were originally stacked. (4) Eventually, the disks must be stacked from largest to smallest on a new peg.

3. **a.** $U_n = 1.035U_{n-1} - 25,000$. After 20 years, there will be $287,902 in the account.
    b. If you start with $355,310, you get -0.16 after 20 years.
    c. A $500,000 jackpot is really worth about $355,310.
    d. The actual cash value of a $1,000,000 jackpot, if there is 5% annual interest for 20 years, is $623,110.50. This can be found using the recursive formula $U_n = 1.05U_{n-1} - 50,000$.
    e. Inflation can diminish the actual present value even more.

Unit 7

4. a.

Number of Disks	Fewest Number of Moves
1	1
2	3
3	7
4	15
5	31
6	63

b. $U_n = 2U_{n-1} + 1$ or $U_n = 2^n - 1$

c. It would take 18,446,744,073,709,551,615 moves. There are $365 \cdot 24 \cdot 60 \cdot 60$ or 31,536,000 seconds in a year. Therefore, it would take 584,942,417,355 years to complete the game, over 40 times the estimated age of the *universe*. Clearly, we don't need to worry about the end of the world because of monks finishing a game!

5. a. $t_n - t_{n-1} = k(t_{n-1} - s)$

b. t_0: initial temperature $= 180°F$

t_1: temperature after one minute $= 171°F$

s: temperature of the surrounding environment $= 72°F$

$171 - 180 = k(180 - 72)$

$$-9 = 108k$$

$$k = -\frac{9}{108}$$

$$k = -\frac{1}{12}$$

Thus, $t_n - t_{n-1} = k(t_{n-1} - s)$ becomes $t_n - t_{n-1} = -\frac{1}{12}(t_{n-1} - 72)$.

c. $t_n = \frac{11}{12}t_{n-1} + 6$

d. After 5 minutes, the temperature will be 141.9°F. You will have to wait 12 minutes for the coffee to cool to 110°F.

Unit 7

a. You may not have 64 golden disks to play this game, but to get an idea of how it works, you can play with some homemade disks and pegs. Cut out 4 successively larger squares of paper to use as disks (or use different size coins for the disks). Put 3 large dots on a piece of paper to use as pegs mounted on a board. Play the game several times, first with just one disk stacked on the starting peg, then with two disks, then three, and so on. As you play each game, keep track of the *fewest* number of moves it takes to finish the game. Make a table listing the number of disks in the game and the fewest number of moves it takes to finish the game.

b. By thinking about strategies for how to play the game with more and more disks and by looking for patterns in the table from Part a, find a recursive formula and any other formula you can for the fewest number of moves needed to finish the game with n disks.

c. What is the fewest number of moves needed to finish a game with 64 disks? If the monks in the story move one disk every second and work nonstop, should we worry about the world ending soon? Explain.

5. You undoubtedly have noticed how a hot drink will cool down as it sits in a room. In the 1700s, Sir Isaac Newton discovered a mathematical model for this situation, called **Newton's Law of Cooling**: The change in an object's temperature from one time period to the next is proportional to the difference between the temperature of the object at the earlier time period and the temperature of the surrounding environment.

a. To say that one thing, X, is proportional to another, Y, means that there is some constant, k, such that $X = kY$. If t_n is the temperature of a cup of hot coffee after n minutes, s is the temperature of the surrounding environment, and k is the constant of proportionality, find a formula for Newton's Law of Cooling.

b. Suppose that the temperature of a cup of hot coffee is initially 180°F and that, after sitting in a room at temperature 72°F for one minute, the coffee cools down to 171°F. Use this information to find t_0, s, and k. Rewrite the formula from Part a so that it models this particular situation.

c. Rewrite the formula from Part b in the "standard" form $A_n = rA_{n-1} + b$.

d. Find the temperature of the cup of hot coffee if it remains sitting in the room for 5 minutes. How long will you have to wait before it cools down to 110°F?

Unit 7

e. Use the formula to compute the long-term behavior of the temperature of the cup of coffee. Did you expect this behavior? Explain why this behavior makes sense in terms of the cooling coffee.

f. *Optional:* Compare your analysis of the cooling coffee to actual data. Obtain a temperature probe that will connect to your calculator or to an available computer.

Use the probe to gather data on the minute-by-minute temperature of a cooling cup of hot coffee. Use Newton's Law of Cooling to predict the cooling behavior. Compare the observed temperature changes to the predicted changes. Discuss any discrepancies. Use the statistical regression capability of your calculator or computer to fit a curve to the observed data and get another formula describing the cooling. Check that your new formula produces results reasonably close to the results using your original formula. Which of these formulas is recursive?

5. **e.** The long-term temperature of the coffee is $\frac{6}{\frac{1}{12}}$ or 72°F. The coffee will cool until it hits room temperature. Then it will remain constant.

f. Responses will vary. There will be some discrepancies between the theoretical values generated by Newton's Law and the actual measured values, but they should be close. Using statistical regression will give the functional formula (approximately) for Newton's recursive formula. The functional formula will be an exponential equation. If students use exponential regression on a calculator, they will have to shift the data down first so that the *x*-axis is the asymptote of the data. Then they will have to let the calculator fit a curve and finally shift it up the same amount to fit the original data.

See Assessment Resources pages 264–269.

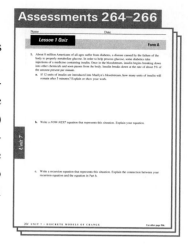

Assessments 264–266

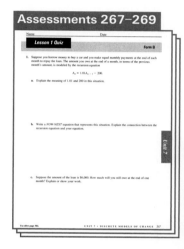

Assessments 267–269

Lesson **2** *A Discrete View of Function Models*

LESSON OVERVIEW The main topics of study in this lesson are arithmetic and geometric sequences and series. In addition, sequences generated by polynomial functions are investigated using finite differences tables.

Lesson Objectives

■ To understand arithmetic sequences and their connections to linear functions, using recursive formulas, function formulas, and applications

■ To understand geometric sequences and their connections to exponential functions, using recursive formulas, function formulas, and applications

■ To understand and apply arithmetic and geometric series (sums of sequences)

■ To use finite differences tables to find function formulas for certain recursive formulas and to describe the connection between such tables and polynomial functions

■ To use linear, exponential, and polynomial functions to model discrete situations

LAUNCH   full-class discussion

Think About This Situation

See Teaching Master 180.

a Students should be able to find recursive and function formulas for the distance D fallen each second using their past knowledge of recursion and linear functions.

■ $D_n = D_{n-1} + 32$, starting at 16.

■ $D(n) = 32n - 16$

Students may find this equation using algebraic methods such as those learned in Course 1, "Linear Models" or by linear regression. In this lesson, students will learn how to find this equation by finding the function formula for an arithmetic sequence.

b

Seconds n	1	2	3	4	5
Total Distance Fallen T_n	16	64	144	256	400

The total distance fallen is increasing very rapidly. The pattern is not linear as in Part a.

c Although some students may be able to find an equation as a result of the work they previously did with falling objects, it is okay if students do not come up with equations at this time. This situation will be revisited using finite differences in Organizing Task 2, page 522. A function rule for the total distance fallen after n seconds is $T(n) = 16n^2$. A recursive formula is $T_n = T_{n-1} + 32(n-1) + 16$ or $T_n = T_{n-1} + 32n - 16$.

Lesson 2

A Discrete View of Function Models

In the previous lesson, you investigated a variety of situations that were modeled by recursive formulas, including population growth, consumer loans, and medicine dosage. In each of these situations, you examined a sequence of numbers and looked for patterns. In this lesson, you will take a closer look at sequences of numbers. As you do so, you will extend your understanding of recursion, and you will revisit three important function families: linear, exponential, and polynomial. To begin, consider the exciting but dangerous sport of skydiving.

Think About This Situation

Imagine a sky diver jumping from a plane at a height of about 5,000 feet. Because of Earth's gravity and ignoring wind resistance, the sky diver will fall 16 feet in the first second. Thereafter, until the parachute opens, the distance fallen during each second will be 32 feet more than the distance fallen during the previous second.

a Think about the pattern of change in the distance the sky diver falls each second. How would you describe the number of feet fallen during each second:

- using a recursive formula?
- as a function of the number of seconds n?

b Now consider the pattern of change in the *total* distance fallen. How far has the sky diver fallen after each of the first five seconds? Describe any patterns you see in this sequence of numbers. Compare this sequence to the sequence of distances fallen during each second.

c How would you describe the total distance fallen after each second using an algebraic equation? How might the sky diver use this equation in planning the jump?

INVESTIGATION 1 ▶ Arithmetic and Geometric Sequences

As you can imagine, skydiving requires considerable training and careful advance preparation. Although the sport of bungee jumping may require little or no training, it too requires careful preparation to ensure the safety of the jumper. In Course 1, you may have explored the relationship between jumper weight and bungee cord length by conducting an experiment with rubber bands and weights.

1. In one such experiment, for each ounce of weight added to a 3-inch rubber band, the rubber band stretched about $\frac{1}{2}$ inch.

a. Describe the relationship between weight added and rubber band length, using words, graphs, tables, and equations. What type of function models this relationship?

b. Complete a data table like the one below.

Bungee Experiment													
Weight (in ounces)	0	1	2	3	4	5	...	50	...	99	...	n
Length (in inches)							...		...		...	

c. The sequence of numbers that you get for the lengths is called an *arithmetic sequence*. An **arithmetic sequence** of numbers is one in which you add the same constant to each number in the sequence to get the next number. An arithmetic sequence models **arithmetic growth**. Explain why the sequence of rubber band lengths is an arithmetic sequence.

d. Which, if any, of the sequences in the "Think About This Situation" is an arithmetic sequence? Why?

2. There are several different equations that can be used to represent the weight-length relationship.

a. Write an equation using the words *NOW* and *NEXT* that shows how the length changes as weight is added.

b. Write a recursive formula that models this situation; that is, write an equation for this situation that looks like

$$L_n = (\text{expression involving } L_{n-1}).$$

This is called a *recursive formula for the sequence*.

INVESTIGATION 1 ▸ Arithmetic and Geometric Sequences

Although many of the ideas in this investigation are so familiar to your students that much of this may seem like a review, you may want to ask them probing questions as they work on the following activities, to keep them from overgeneralizing these ideas to sequences for which the ideas do not apply. For example, you might ask if the entries in the table produced in the fish-population problem of Lesson 1 are also an arithmetic or geometric sequence and if these entries can be obtained using a function formula. (They are neither arithmetic nor geometric, and, while they can be obtained through a function formula, it is not at all obvious what that formula should be.) The goal is for your students to realize that arithmetic sequences are connected to linear functions and that, in those cases, U_n can be expressed using both function and recursive formulas. Also, geometric sequences are related to exponential functions. In Investigation 2, the sums of arithmetic and geometric series are developed, and in Investigation 3, more complicated recursive formulas are related to polynomial functions.

NOTE: All sequences in this investigation will begin with U_0. Starting sequences with subscript 0 is common and is often the most natural choice when using sequences to model situations in the real world. For example, the first term is often the initial value at time 0; thus, it is represented with subscript 0. Using other starting subscripts will be explored in Investigation 2 and some of the MORE tasks.

Unit 7

1. Note that this bungee jumping activity was done in the "Linear Models" unit of Course 1. It is not necessary that students remember the activity to proceed here, but it is expected that they retain some familiarity with the analysis of such a situation using a function in the form "$y = \ldots$".

   a. The rubber band length will increase by 0.5 inch for each ounce of weight added. Thus, this is a situation of a constant rate of change of length with respect to weight. A graph for this situation is shown at the right. Equations that students might use to model the situation include $NEXT = NOW + 0.5$ (starting with 3) and $y = 0.5x + 3$. The table will show constant rate of change and will be similar to the table in Part b. This relationship is modeled by a linear function. (Note, of course, that the rubber band will eventually break, ending the sequence.)

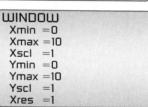

   b. **Bungee Experiment**

Weight (in ounces)	0	1	2	3	4	5	...	50	...	99	...	n
Length (in inches)	3	3.5	4	4.5	5	5.5	...	28	...	52.5	...	$3 + 0.5n$

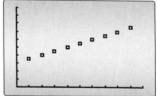

```
WINDOW
 Xmin =0
 Xmax =10
 Xscl =1
 Ymin =0
 Ymax =10
 Yscl =1
 Xres =1
```

   c. 0.5 is added to each term of the sequence to produce the next term of the sequence.

   d. The sequence of distances fallen each second is an arithmetic sequence. Each second the distance fallen during that second increases by 32.

2. a. $NEXT = NOW + 0.5$

   b. $L_n = L_{n-1} + 0.5, L_0 = 3$

2. **c.** Using the recursion mode on a calculator (or calculating by hand), students should determine that the length of the rubber band, with 15 ounces of weight, is 10.5 inches.

 d. $L_n = 3 + 0.5n$

 It makes sense to call this a function formula because it is a formula that gives one length for each value of n. The function formula is also written in the form of a function; n is the input (independent variable), and L is the output (dependent variable). That is, L (length) is a function of n (weight). In fact, for this situation, function notation can be used instead of subscript notation: $L(n) = 3 + 0.5n$.

 NOTE: Students are very familiar with this type of function. Although the recursive formula in Part b can also be considered in terms of functions, where L_n is a function of L_{n-1}, this is a more complicated function and to keep the recursive aspect of the formula clear, *recursive formula* is a more apt description.

---

 e. $L_{15} = 3 + 0.5(15) = 3 + 7.5 = 10.5$ inches

 f. When using the recursive formula, you must use the formula fifteen times, adding 0.5 to the previous result each time. When using the function formula, only one evaluation of the formula, by substituting 15 for n, is needed.

3. **a.** The recursive formula is $P_n = P_{n-1} + 0.40$, $P_0 = 1.25$. The function formula is $P(n) = 1.25 + 0.40n$.

 b. The recursive formulas both have a coefficient of 1 on the P_{n-1} or L_{n-1} term. The constant added in each case is the difference between consecutive terms. Both function formulas are linear equations. In both function formulas, the constant from the recursive formula is the coefficient of n, and the initial value of the recursive formula is the constant in the function formula.

4. **a.** Each of the function formulas in Activities 2 and 3 is a linear function.

 b. The graph of each function formula is a line with y-intercept equal to the initial value and slope equal to the difference between consecutive terms.

 c. The slope of the graph in Activity 2 is 0.5. The slope of the graph in Activity 3 is 0.40. The slope is what you add to *NOW* or U_{n-1} in the recursive formulas, and it is the coefficient of n in the function formula.

5. **a.** $t_0, t_0 + d, t_0 + 2d, t_0 + 3d, t_0 + 4d$

 Recursive formula: $t_n = t_{n-1} + d$, starting with t_0

 Function formula: $t_n = t_0 + nd$

c. Use the recursive formula to predict the rubber band length when 15 ounces of weight are attached.

d. Write an equation for this situation that looks like

$$L_n = \text{(expression involving } n \text{ with no subscripts)}.$$

An equation in this form can be called a **function formula** for the sequence of lengths. Explain why it makes sense to call such a formula a function formula.

e. Use the function formula to predict the rubber band length when 15 ounces of weight are attached.

f. Describe the difference between the processes of using the recursive formula and using the function formula to compute the rubber band length when 15 ounces of weight are attached.

3. Cellular phones, pagers, and telephone calling cards afford convenient ways to stay in contact with friends and family. A calling card at a convenience store may cost $1.25 plus 40 cents per minute.

a. Determine recursive and function formulas for the sequence of calling card prices.

b. Compare these formulas to those you found for the rubber band experiment in Activity 2. How are they similar? How are they different?

4. Now think about possible connections between arithmetic sequences and other mathematical models you have studied.

a. What type of function is represented by each of the function formulas in Activities 2 and 3?

b. In each case, describe the shape of the graph of the function formula.

c. What is the slope of each graph? How does the slope appear in each of the recursive and function formulas you have been examining?

5. Suppose t_0 is the initial term of a *general* arithmetic sequence for which you add d to each term of the sequence to get the next term of the sequence.

a. Write the first five terms of this sequence and then find recursive and function formulas for the sequence. Compare your formulas to those of other groups. Resolve any differences.

b. How would you interpret t_0, d, and n in the context of the rubber band experiment?

c. The constant d is sometimes called the **common difference** between terms. Explain why it makes sense to call d the common difference.

d. Suppose an arithmetic sequence t_0, t_1, t_2, ... begins with $t_0 = 84$ and has a common difference of -6. Find function and recursive formulas for this sequence and then find the term t_{87}.

6. Now consider the growth sequence of bacteria cells if a cut by a rusty nail puts 25 bacteria cells into a wound and then the number of bacteria doubles every quarter-hour.

a. Use words, graphs, tables, and equations to describe the relationship between the number of quarter-hours and the number of bacteria. What type of function models this relationship?

b. Complete a data table like the one below for this situation.

Bacterial Growth

Number of Quarter-Hours	0	1	2	3	4	5	...	50	...	99	...	n
Bacteria Count							...		...		...	

c. The sequence of numbers that you get for the bacteria count is called a *geometric sequence*. A **geometric sequence** of numbers is one in which each number in the sequence is multiplied by a constant to get the next number. A geometric sequence models **geometric growth**. Explain why the sequence of bacteria counts is a geometric sequence.

d. Which, if any, of the sequences in the "Think About This Situation" (page 505) is a geometric sequence? Why?

7. If B_n represents the bacteria count after n quarter-hours, then there are several different equations that can be used to model this situation.

a. Write an equation using the words *NOW* and *NEXT* that shows how the bacteria count increases as time passes.

b. Write a recursive formula beginning "$B_n = ...$" for the sequence of bacteria counts. Use the recursive formula to predict the bacteria count after 18 quarter-hours.

5. b. In the context of the rubber band experiment, t_0 is the initial length of the rubber band (3 inches), d is the constant amount of stretch (0.5 inch) for each ounce of weight added, and n is the number of ounces of weight added.

c. It makes sense to call d the common difference because the difference (subtraction) of *any* two successive terms is d.

d. Recursive formula: $t_n = t_{n-1} - 6$, $t_0 = 84$
Function formula: $t_n = 84 - 6n$
$t_{87} = -438$

6. **Note that this bacterial growth activity was done in the "Exponential Models" unit of Course 1. It is not necessary that students remember the activity to proceed here, but it is expected that they retain some familiarity with the analysis of such a situation using a function in the form "$y = ...$".**

a. The number of bacteria doubles each quarter-hour. Thus, this is not a constant rate of change. The pattern of change is exponential since 2 is a common multiplier between all successive time periods. A graph of this relationship is shown below. Equations that students might use to describe this relationship include $NEXT = 2NOW$ (starting with 25); $B_n = 2B_{n-1}$, where $B_0 = 25$; and $y = (25)2^x$. A table for this situation will show nonconstant rate of change and will be similar to the table in Part b. This relationship can be modeled by an exponential function.

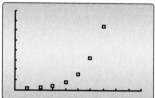

```
WINDOW
Xmin =0
Xmax =10
Xscl =1
Ymin =0
Ymax =4000
Yscl =500
Xres =1
```

b. Bacterial Growth

Number of Quarter-Hours	0	1	2	3	4	5	...	50	...	99	...	n
Bacteria Count	25	50	100	200	400	800	...	25×2^{50}	...	25×2^{99}	...	25×2^n

c. Two is the constant multiplier. That is, you multiply each term by 2 to get the next term.

d. None of the sequences in the "Think About This Situation" section is a geometric sequence since none of them has a constant multiplier.

7. a. $NEXT = 2NOW$

b. $B_n = 2B_{n-1}$, $B_0 = 25$
$B_{18} = 6{,}553{,}600$ bacteria

7. c. $B_n = (25)2^n$

$B_{18} = (25)2^{18} = 6{,}553{,}600$ bacteria

d. Using the recursive formula requires multiplying the previous result by 2 eighteen times, while using the function formula requires only one step, substituting 18 for n and computing the result.

8. a. The area of the carpet at each stage is $\frac{8}{9}$ of the area of the carpet at the preceding stage.

Recursive formula: $A_n = \frac{8}{9} A_{n-1}, A_0 = 1$

Function formula: $A_n = \left(\frac{8}{9}\right)^n$

b. In each of the recursive formulas, there is no constant term. The coefficient of the U_{n-1} term is the constant multiplier that takes you from one term to the next.

Each of the function formulas is an exponential equation of the form $y = a(b^x)$. The value of a is the initial value of the function, and b is the common multiplier.

9. a. $t_0, rt_0, r^2t_0, r^3t_0, r^4t_0$

Recursive formula: $t_n = rt_{n-1}$, starting with t_0

Function formula: $t_n = t_0 r^n$

b. In the context of bacterial growth, t_0 is the initial size of the bacteria population (25), r is the constant multiplier (2), and n is the number of quarter-hours.

c. The term *common ratio* is a sensible term to use because r is the ratio of *any* two successive terms in the sequence (common to all successive pairs).

d. Recursive formula: $t_n = 3t_{n-1}, t_0 = -4$

Function formula: $t_n = -4(3)^n$

$t_{17} = -516{,}560{,}652$

10. In this activity, students should generate a variety of sequences and then describe and identify them. They should note that an arithmetic sequence is characterized by adding a constant to get from term to term and that a geometric sequence is characterized by multiplying by a constant to get from term to term. There are many examples of sequences that exhibit neither pattern, such as 2, 3, 5, 8, 12, 17, 23, … (add 1, then add 2, then add 3, then add 4, and so on).

Unit 7

c. Write a function formula beginning "$B_n = \ldots$" for the sequence of bacteria counts. Use the function formula to predict the bacteria count after 18 quarter-hours.

d. Describe the difference between the processes of using the recursive formula and using the function formula to compute the bacteria count after 18 quarter-hours.

8. One of the simplest fractal patterns is the *Sierpinski carpet*. Starting with a solid square "carpet" one meter on a side, smaller and smaller squares are cut out of the carpet. The first two stages in forming the carpet are shown below.

Stage 0

Stage 1

Stage 2

a. Find recursive and function formulas for the sequence of carpet area that remains at each stage.

b. Compare your formulas to those you found for the bacteria present after a cut by a rusty nail, in Activity 7. How are they similar? How are they different?

9. Now, suppose t_0 is the initial term of a *general* geometric sequence for which each term of the sequence is multiplied by r ($r \neq 1$) to get the next term of the sequence.

a. Write the first five terms of this sequence and then find recursive and function formulas for the sequence. Compare your formulas to those of other groups. Resolve any differences.

b. What are t_0, r, and n in the situation involving bacterial growth?

c. The constant r is sometimes called the **common ratio** of terms. Explain why it makes sense to call r the common ratio.

d. Suppose a geometric sequence t_0, t_1, t_2, $\ldots$ begins with $t_0 = -4$ and has a common ratio of 3. Find function and recursive formulas for this sequence and then find the term t_{17}.

10. Working individually, write the first five terms for three different sequences. One sequence should be arithmetic, one should be geometric, and the third should be neither. Challenge your groupmates to correctly identify your sequences. Similarly, identify the sequences prepared by the other members of your group. Write a summary of how you can tell by inspection whether a given sequence is arithmetic, geometric, or neither.

Unit 7

Checkpoint

In this investigation, you studied two important patterns of growth: arithmetic growth, modeled by arithmetic sequences, and geometric growth, modeled by geometric sequences.

ⓐ How are arithmetic and geometric sequences different? How are they similar? Describe one real-world situation different from those you studied in this investigation that could be modeled by an arithmetic sequence. Do the same for a geometric sequence.

ⓑ What is the connection between arithmetic and geometric sequences and linear and exponential functions?

ⓒ Describe the difference between a recursive formula and a function formula for a sequence. What information do you need to know to find each type of formula?

ⓓ What is one advantage of a recursive formula for a sequence? What is one disadvantage? What is one advantage of a function formula? What is one disadvantage?

ⓔ In the first lesson of this unit, you investigated situations that could be modeled by recursive formulas of the form $A_n = rA_{n-1} + b$. You can think of these formulas as *combined recursive formulas*. What is the connection between such combined recursive formulas and recursive formulas for arithmetic and geometric sequences? Why does it make sense to call these formulas "combined recursive formulas"?

Be prepared to share your group's thinking with the entire class.

▶On Your Own

For each of the sequences below and on the next page, do the following.

- Complete a copy of the table.
- State whether the sequence is arithmetic, geometric, or neither.
- For those sequences that are arithmetic or geometric, find a recursive formula and a function formula.
- If a sequence is neither arithmetic nor geometric, find whatever formula you can that describes the sequence.

a.

n	0	1	2	3	4	5	6	...	10	...	100	...
A_n	2	6	18	54	162			...		...		...

Checkpoint

See Teaching Masters 181a and 181b.

ⓐ They are different in that arithmetic sequences are generated by adding a constant to each term to get the next term and geometric sequences are generated by multiplying each term by a constant to get the next term. They are similar in that in each case you use a constant to generate the terms.

Students' situations may vary. For example, a taxi fare that begins with a flat rate and then increases by a fixed amount each tenth of a mile can be modeled by an arithmetic sequence. The growth of an initial deposit of money in an interest-bearing savings account can be modeled by a geometric sequence.

ⓑ The function formula for an arithmetic sequence is a linear function. The function formula for a geometric sequence is an exponential function.

ⓒ The recursive formula tells you how to get from one term to the next, but it does not directly tell you what the nth term is. The function formula gives you a formula for directly computing the nth term.

Students may say that the same information is needed to find the two types of formulas, namely, the initial term and the constant that is added or multiplied. However, strictly speaking, for the recursive formula you need to know just the constant that is multiplied or added to get from one term to the next. The initial value does not show up in the recursive formula directly, although it is an additional piece of important information.

ⓓ One advantage of a recursive formula is that you can easily see the patterns of change. One disadvantage is that it may be time-consuming to find a term far into the sequence. One advantage of a function formula is that finding any desired term is straightforward. One disadvantage is that the relationship between successive terms is not as clear.

ⓔ Recursive formulas for geometric and arithmetic sequences are special cases of combined recursive formulas of the form $A_n = rA_{n-1} + b$. If $b = 0$, you get the recursive formula for geometric sequences, and if $r = 1$ you get the recursive formula for arithmetic sequences.

APPLY individual task

On Your Own

a. ■

n	0	1	2	3	4	5	6	...	10	...	100	...
A_n	2	6	18	54	162	486	1,458	...	118,098	...	$(2)3^{100}$	...

■ The sequence is geometric since you multiply each term by 3 to get the next term.

■ $A_n = 3A_{n-1}, A_0 = 2$

$A_n = (2)3^n$

Unit 7

MORE

ASSIGNMENT *pp. 519–529*

Students can now begin Modeling Task 1 or 2; Organizing Task 1 or 7; Reflecting Task 1, 2, 4, or 5; or Extending Task 3 from the MORE assignment following Investigation 3.

b. ■

n	0	1	2	3	4	5	6	...	10	...	100	...
B_n	1	2	5	10	17	26	37	...	101	...	10,001	...

■ The sequence is neither arithmetic nor geometric since getting from one term to the next does not involve adding a constant or multiplying by a constant.

■ $B_n = n^2 + 1$
$B_n = B_{n-1} + (2n - 1)$
(Students may not be able to identify this equation until they study Investigation 2.)

c. ■

n	0	1	2	3	4	5	6	...	10	...	100	...
C_n	3	7	11	15	19	23	27	...	43	...	403	...

■ The sequence is arithmetic since you add 4 to each term to get the next term.

■ $C_n = C_{n-1} + 4, C_0 = 3$
$C_n = 3 + 4n$

EXPLORE small-group investigation

INVESTIGATION 2 Some Sums

In this investigation, students study finite sums of arithmetic and geometric sequences, also known as *series*. The term *series* is not given until page 515, after the Checkpoint.

1. a. After three seconds, the sky diver has fallen 144 feet.
After five seconds, the sky diver has fallen 400 feet.
After ten seconds, the sky diver has fallen 1,600 feet.

b. D_n is an arithmetic sequence; the common difference is 32.

c. ■ $D_1 = 16 + (0)32 = 16$
$D_5 = 16 + (4)32 = 144$
■ $D_{18} = 16 + (17)32 = 560$
$D_{19} = 16 + (18)32 = 592$
$D_{20} = 16 + (19)32 = 624$

d. The most obvious response here is to calculate all 20 distances and then add them together. Some students might use what they know about gravity and falling objects and write the formula $S(n) = 16n^2$. Accept any responses here that will answer the question. Students will further explore finding a sum of an arithmetic sequence in the next several activities.

b.

n	0	1	2	3	4	5	6	...	10	...	100	...
B_n	1	2	5	10	17				...		...	...

c.

n	0	1	2	3	4	5	6	...	10	...	100	...
C_n	3	7	11	15	19				...		...	...

INVESTIGATION 2 Some Sums

In the "Think About This Situation" at the beginning of this lesson, you considered the distance fallen by a sky diver during each second of a free fall and the total or *accumulated* distance fallen. Predicting the accumulated distance for various times in the jump is critical to determining when to open the parachute.

1. The table below shows the distance in feet fallen by a sky diver, assuming no wind resistance, during *each* of the first 10 seconds of a jump.

Skydiving										
Time n (in seconds)	1	2	3	4	5	6	7	8	9	10
Distance Fallen D_n (in feet)	16	48	80	112	144	176	208	240	272	304

   a. What is the total distance fallen after three seconds? After five seconds? After 10 seconds?

   b. What kind of sequence is D_n?

   c. Notice that the sequence of distances fallen, D_1, D_2, D_3, ..., begins with subscript 1 rather than subscript 0 like the other sequences you have studied in this lesson. From Investigation 1, you know that the function formula for an arithmetic sequence beginning with subscript 0 and having common difference d is $t_n = t_0 + nd$. As you know from the "Families of Functions" unit, a horizontal shift will affect the function formula in a predictable way. Since the D_n sequence has subscripts shifted by 1, the corresponding function formula is $D_n = 16 + (n - 1)(32)$. (To explore the situation of shifted subscripts more fully, see Extending Task 2 on page 526.)

   ■ Use the function formula to verify the entries for D_1 and D_5.

   ■ Use the function formula to find D_{18}, D_{19}, and D_{20}.

   d. How would you determine the total distance fallen by the sky diver after 20 seconds?

e. One approach to finding the sum of the first 20 terms of the sequence D_n is based on a method reportedly discovered by Carl Friedrich Gauss (1777–1855) when he was only 10 years old. Gauss, considered to be one of the greatest mathematicians of all time, noticed that the sum of the terms of an arithmetic sequence, such as $16 + 48 + 80 + \ldots + 560 + 592 + 624$, could be quickly calculated by first writing the sum in reverse order and then adding pairs of corresponding terms.

$$\begin{array}{c} 16 + 48 + 80 + \ldots + 560 + 592 + 624 \\ \underline{624 + 592 + 560 + \ldots + 80 + 48 + 16} \\ 640 \end{array}$$

- What is the sum of each pair of terms? How many pairs are there?
- What is the total distance fallen after 20 seconds?

f. Use your function formula from Part c and Gauss's method to determine the total distance the sky diver would fall in 30 seconds and in 35 seconds.

g. An expert sky diver typically free-falls to about 2,000 feet above Earth's surface before pulling the rip cord on the parachute. If the altitude of the airplane was about 5,000 feet when the sky diver began the jump, how much time can the sky diver safely allow for the free-fall portion of the flight?

2. You can use Gauss's idea in Activity 1 and algebraic reasoning to derive a general formula for the *sum of the terms of an arithmetic sequence* with common difference d.

a. If $a_0, a_1, a_2, \ldots, a_n$ is an arithmetic sequence with common difference d, explain why the sum S_n of the terms a_0 through a_n can be expressed by the equation

$$S_n = a_0 + (a_0 + d) + (a_0 + 2d) + \ldots + (a_n - 2d) + (a_n - d) + a_n.$$

b. If you rewrite S_n in reverse order and then add pairs of corresponding terms as in Activity 1, what is the sum of each pair of terms? How many pairs are there?

c. Write a formula for S_n in terms of a_0, a_n, and n. Compare your formula to those of others and resolve any differences.

d. Toni developed the following formula for the sum of the terms of an arithmetic sequence:

$$S = \frac{(\textit{initial term} + \textit{final term})(\textit{number of terms})}{2}$$

Explain why this formula makes sense.

e. Find the sum of the terms of the sequence

$$7, 12, 17, 22, \ldots, 52.$$

1. **e.** ■ The sum of each pair is 640. There are 20 pairs. (Note that students computed $D_{20} = 624$ so they know that 624 is the twentieth term.)

   ■ Since each distance has been used twice, the total distance fallen after 20 seconds is $\frac{1}{2}(20)(640)$ or 6,400 feet.

   f. Using the function formula from Part c, we get $D_{30} = 16 + 32(29) = 944$. Now using Gauss's method, each pair sums to $D_1 + D_{30}$, which is $16 + 944$ or 960. There will be 30 pairs, so the total distance fallen will be $\frac{30}{2}(960)$ or 14,400 feet.

   $D_{35} = 16 + 32(34) = 1,104$. Using Gauss's method, there will be 35 pairs, each with a sum of $16 + 1,104$ or 1,120. Thus, the total distance fallen in 35 seconds is $\frac{35}{2}(1,120)$ or 19,600 feet.

   g. At this point, students may have to guess and check to find the correct time. They will develop a formula for S_n in the next activity. The sky diver can free-fall about 3,000 feet. From Part e, students know that the time available for free fall is less than 20 seconds. Since $D_{13} = 16 + 12(32) = 400$, the total distance fallen in the first thirteen seconds is $\frac{13}{2}(16 + 400)$ or 2,704 feet. After fourteen seconds, the sky diver will have fallen a total of 3,136 feet. Thus, the sky diver can fall for approximately thirteen seconds.

2. **Now students will derive a formula for the sum of an arithmetic sequence. For consistency with the notation used in Investigation 1, the initial subscript of the sequence will be 0.**

   a. Since the sequence is arithmetic, the terms of the sequence can be expressed as the first term a_0 plus multiples of the common difference (or the last term a_n minus multiples of the common difference). So the right-hand side of the given equation is the sum of the terms a_0 through a_n, which is also S_n.

   b. The sum of each pair is $a_0 + a_n$. There are $n + 1$ such pairs.

   c. $S_n = \frac{(n + 1)(a_0 + a_n)}{2}$

   d. This formula makes sense because, using Gauss's idea, the terms of the sequence are paired up in such a way that (*sum of each pair*) = (*initial term*) + (*final term*), and the number of pairs is the number of terms. Since each term is added twice in this method, you must divide by 2.

   e. The sum is 295. In order to use the formula developed in Parts c and d, students will need to figure out what value of n corresponds to 52. Try to encourage them to find a method other than writing out all the terms between 22 and 52. By looking at the general pattern or by using the function formula for the terms of the sequence, they should be able to determine that 52 is the tenth term. Thus, $n = 9$ in the formula. (The function formula for the terms of this sequence is $t_n = 7 + 5n$, or specifically for this case, $52 = 7 + 5n$. Solving gives $n = 9$.) Once they know $n = 9$, students can apply the formula from Part c and obtain $S_9 = \frac{10(7 + 52)}{2} = 5(59) = 295$. Alternatively, once students figure out that there are 10 terms, they can compute $\frac{(\text{initial term} + \text{final term})(\text{\# of terms})}{2} = \frac{(7 + 52)(10)}{2} = \frac{590}{2} = 295$.

Unit 7

3. **a.** The first six terms are 1, 3, 9, 27, 81, and 243. The total number of sick people at the end of day 5 is 243, which is the last of the six terms.

   b. The first six terms are 1, 3, 9, 27, 81, and 243. The total number of sick people at the end of day 5 is $1 + 3 + 9 + 27 + 81 + 243$ or 364, which is the sum of the six terms.

   c. You sum the terms in the second situation (Part b) because each term is the *additional* number of sick people each day. In the first situation (Part a), each term already represents the total number of sick people through that day; thus, a given term gives the total directly, and there is no need to sum the terms.

4. **Note that it is important to clarify the starting point of the sequence and the appropriate subscript notation. In this case, $S_0 = 1$, $S_1 = 3$, $S_2 = 3^2$, and so on.**

   a.

$S_n = 1 + 3 + 3^2 + 3^3 + 3^4 + \ldots + 3^n$	Given
$3(S_n) = 3(1 + 3 + 3^2 + 3^3 + 3^4 + \ldots + 3^n)$	Multiply both sides by 3
$= 3 + 3^2 + 3^3 + 3^4 + \ldots + 3^n + 3^{n+1}$	Distribute the 3
$3(S_n) - S_n = 3^{n+1} - 1$	Subtract the first equation from the third equation
$(3 - 1)S_n = 3^{n+1} - 1$	Factor out S_n
$S_n = \dfrac{3^{n+1} - 1}{3 - 1}$	Divide by $(3 - 1)$

   b. At the end of day 5, the number of sick people is S_5, which is $\frac{3^6 - 1}{3 - 1}$ or 364. This is the same value as the one in Part b of Activity 3.

   c.
   $$S_n = 1 + r + r^2 + r^3 + \ldots + r^n$$
   $$rS_n = r + r^2 + r^3 + r^4 + \ldots + r^n + r^{n+1}$$
   $$rS_n - S_n = r^{n+1} - 1$$
   $$(r - 1)S_n = r^{n+1} - 1$$
   $$S_n = \frac{r^{n+1} - 1}{r - 1}$$

5. **a.** If the epidemic begins with two people, the original sequence is $2, 2 \cdot 3$, $2 \cdot 3^2, \ldots, 2 \cdot 3^n$. Thus, the total number of sick people will be $S_n = 2 + 2 \cdot 3 + 2 \cdot 3^2 + \ldots + 2 \cdot 3^n = 2(1 + 3 + 3^2 + \ldots + 3^n)$. The total number of sick people will be twice the total number when the epidemic begins with only one person. So there will be 2(121) or 242 sick people after day 4. Students may provide reasoning other than the formula to support this doubling relationship. One possibility is that each of the initial two people will infect 121 people, so there will be a total of 242 people infected.

If you have never had **Chicken Pox**, <u>**DO NOT ENTER**</u> this room.

In modeling a situation involving sequential change, it is important to decide whether the situation involves a pattern of change in *additional* amount or a pattern of change in *accumulated* amount.

3. It may happen that in two different situations, you get the same sequence of numbers, but it makes sense to add the terms of the sequence in only one of the situations. Consider an epidemic that begins at day 0 with one infected person and spreads rapidly through a population. A health official states, "The number of sick people triples every day."

   a. Suppose the statement is interpreted to mean, "The *accumulated* number of sick people triples every day." Write the first six terms of the sequence of accumulated numbers of sick people. What is the total number of sick people at the end of day 5 (assuming no sick person gets well in that time)?

   b. Suppose the statement is interpreted to mean, "The *additional* number of sick people triples every day." Write the first six terms of the sequence of additional numbers of sick people. Under this interpretation, what is the total number of sick people at the end of day 5 (assuming no sick person gets well in that time)?

   c. Look back at Parts a and b. Explain why it makes sense to sum the terms of the sequence in one situation but not in the other.

4. In the epidemic example from Activity 3, assume that the epidemic begins at day 0 with one sick person and the *additional* number of sick people triples every day. Then the total number of sick people at the end of day n is given by

   $$S_n = 1 + 3 + 3^2 + 3^3 + 3^4 + \ldots + 3^n.$$

   a. Using algebraic reasoning, you can derive a formula for quickly calculating this sum, as shown below. Provide reasons for each step in the following derivation.

   $$S_n = 1 + 3 + 3^2 + 3^3 + 3^4 + \ldots + 3^n$$
   $$3(S_n) = 3(1 + 3 + 3^2 + 3^3 + 3^4 + \ldots + 3^n)$$
   $$= 3 + 3^2 + 3^3 + 3^4 + \ldots + 3^n + 3^{n+1}$$
   $$3(S_n) - S_n = 3^{n+1} - 1$$
   $$(3 - 1)S_n = 3^{n+1} - 1$$
   $$S_n = \frac{3^{n+1} - 1}{3 - 1}$$

   b. Use this formula to calculate the total number of sick people at the end of day 5. Compare your answer to your response to Part b of Activity 3.

   c. Using similar reasoning, prove that the *sum of the terms of the geometric sequence* $1, r, r^2, r^3, r^4, \ldots, r^n$, where $r \neq 1$, is

   $$1 + r + r^2 + r^3 + r^4 + \ldots + r^n = \frac{r^{n+1} - 1}{r - 1}.$$

5. Consider sums of geometric sequences when the initial term is not 1.

   a. Suppose an epidemic begins with two infected people and the additional number of infected people triples every day. What is the total number of sick people at the end of day 4?

Unit 7

b. Suppose an ice cream store sold 22,000 ice cream cones in 2002. Based on sales data from other stores in similar locations, the manager predicts that the number of ice cream cones sold will increase by 5% each year. Find the total predicted number of ice cream cones sold during the period from 2002 to 2008. Show how this problem can be solved using the formula for the sum of a geometric sequence, which you developed in Part c of Activity 4. (You may find it helpful to write the sum term-by-term and then factor out 22,000.)

6. Now suppose $a_0, a_1, a_2, \ldots, a_n$ is a geometric sequence with common ratio r, where $r \neq 1$. Write a formula for calculating the sum S_n in terms of a_0, r, and n. Provide an argument for why your formula is correct.

7. It is also possible to use the geometric sum formula when the common ratio is less than 1. Consider a geometric sequence with initial term $t_0 = 48$ and common ratio of $\frac{1}{4}$.

a. Find a recursive formula and a function formula for this sequence.

b. Find the sum of the terms of this sequence through t_8.

Checkpoint

In this investigation, you examined total change in situations involving arithmetic growth and geometric growth or decay.

a In such situations, it may be that the *accumulated* amount increases by a constant d or a factor r every time period, or it may be that the *additional* amount increases by a constant d or a factor r every time period. Give an example of each case for each growth model. In which case would you sum an arithmetic sequence to find the total amount after 12 time periods? In which case would you sum a geometric sequence to find the total amount?

b Suppose an arithmetic sequence has initial term a_0 and common difference d.

- Write recursive and function formulas for the sequence.
- Write a formula for the sum of the terms up through a_n.

c Suppose a geometric sequence has initial term a_0 and common ratio r.

- Write recursive and function formulas for the sequence.
- Write a formula for the sum of the terms up through a_n.

Be prepared to explain your thinking and formulas to the entire class.

5. b. $22{,}000 + 1.05(22{,}000) + 1.05^2(22{,}000) + \ldots + 1.05^6(22{,}000) =$
$22{,}000(1 + 1.05 + 1.05^2 + 1.05^3 + 1.05^4 + 1.05^5 + 1.05^6) =$
$22{,}000\left(\frac{1.05^{6+1} - 1}{1.05 - 1}\right) \approx 179{,}124$
For the period from 2002 to 2008, the predicted sales are approximately 179,124 ice cream cones.

6. $S_n = \frac{a_0(r^{n+1} - 1)}{r - 1}$. Students might provide an algebraic argument similar to the proofs in Parts a and c of Activity 4, or they may factor a_0 out of the sequence and use the formula from Activity 4 Part c.

7. a. Recursive formula: $t_n = 0.25t_{n-1}$, $t_0 = 48$
Function formula: $t_n = 48(0.25)^n$

   b. The sum of the terms of the sequence up through term t_8 is $48\left(\frac{0.25^{8+1} - 1}{0.25 - 1}\right)$ or approximately 64.

SHARE AND SUMMARIZE   full-class discussion

Checkpoint

See Teaching Masters 182a and 182b.

a An example of an arithmetic sequence in which the *accumulated* amount increases by a constant d is the amount of money in a young child's piggy bank if a dollar is placed into the piggy bank each week. An example of an arithmetic sequence in which the *additional* amount increases by a constant d is the number of times a grandfather clock chimes each hour (beginning at 1:00). You would sum an arithmetic sequence to find the total number of times the clock chimes in 12 hours.

An example of a geometic sequence in which the *accumulated* amount increases by a factor of r every time period is population growth. An example of a geometic sequence in which the *additional* amount increases by a factor of r every time period is a situation in which the number of hamburgers served increases by a constant factor each year. You would sum the geometric sequence to find the total number of hamburgers served in 10 years.

b ■ Recursive formula: $a_n = a_{n-1} + d$, starting with a_0
Function formula: $a_n = a_0 + nd$
■ Sum of the terms: $S_n = \frac{(n+1)(a_0 + a_n)}{2}$

c ■ Recursive formula: $a_n = ra_{n-1}$, starting with a_0
Function formula: $a_n = a_0 r^n$
■ Sum of the terms: $S_n = a_0\left(\frac{r^{n+1} - 1}{r - 1}\right)$

CONSTRUCTING A MATH TOOLKIT: Students should summarize the concepts involving arithmetic and geometric growth, including accumulated increases by a constant or a factor, additional increases by a constant or a factor, recursive and function formulas, and sums of sequences.

NOTE: When thinking about S_n, for either arithmetic or geometric series, it may be helpful to emphasize that S_n has $n + 1$ terms when summing from a_0 to a_n.

Unit 7

ASSIGNMENT pp. 519–529

Students can now begin
Modeling Task 3, Organizing
Task 5 or 6, Reflecting Task 3,
or Extending Task 2 from the
MORE assignment following
Investigation 3.

APPLY individual task

On Your Own

You may wish to discuss the connection between the term number and subscript notation before students begin these tasks.

a. $t_{10} = 8 + 3(10) = 38$; $S_{10} = \frac{11(8 + 38)}{2} = 253$

b. The sum is $\frac{1(2.5^{13} - 1)}{2.5 - 1}$ or approximately 99,340.41.

c. The sum of A_0 through A_{14} is $\frac{2(3^{15} - 1)}{3 - 1}$ or 14,348,906.
    The term B_{14} is $95 + (14)(-5)$ or 25 so, the sum of B_0 through B_{14} is $\frac{15(95 + 25)}{2}$ or 900.

d. The predicted total number of shoes sold was $\frac{5,700(1.03^7 - 1)}{1.03 - 1}$ or approximately 43,676.

EXPLORE small-group investigation

INVESTIGATION 3 Finite Differences

In this investigation, students use finite differences tables to help them determine the polynomial function that generates a sequence. This method works only for polynomial functions. As a result of the three investigations in this lesson, students will be able to identify a sequence as having been generated by a linear, exponential, or polynomial relation and to write a function formula for the nth term in such sequences.

As a launch for this investigation, you might consider writing several tables on the board and asking your students to describe the entries in the tables using a recursive formula or a function formula. Your tables should include an arithmetic sequence, a geometric sequence, and some others. Some patterns are easier to see from the recursive formula and some from the function formula. It is not important that your students find both formulas for each, but they should realize that there are patterns other than arithmetic and geometric and that sometimes the same pattern can be generated in two ways. You may want to return to these tables later. Tables could include the following:

n	U_n		n	U_n		n	U_n		n	U_n		n	U_n
0	?		0	?		0	?		0	?		0	?
1	4		1	3		1	6		1	11		1	2
2	7		2	6		2	8		2	15		2	5
3	10		3	12		3	11		3	24		3	10
4	13		4	24		4	15		4	40		4	17
5	16		5	48		5	20		5	65		5	26

(The first table shows an arithmetic sequence, $U_n = U_{n-1} + 3$, $U_0 = 1$, or $U_n = 1 + 3n$; the second table shows a geometric sequence, $U_n = 2U_{n-1}$, $U_0 = 1.5$, or $U_n = 1.5(2)^n$; the third is generated by $U_n = U_{n-1} + n$, $U_0 = 5$, or $U_n = 0.5n^2 + 0.5n + 5$; the fourth is $U_n = U_{n-1} + n^2$, $U_0 = 10$, or $U_n = \left(\frac{1}{3}\right)n^3 + \left(\frac{1}{2}\right)n^2 + \left(\frac{1}{6}\right)n + 10$; and the last is $U_n = U_{n-1} + 2n - 1$, $U_0 = 1$, or $U_n = n^2 + 1$.)

Tell your students that they are going to investigate another class of sequences that can be described using recursive and function formulas and that they will develop a way to discover what the function formula is from the clues in a table.

An expression denoting the sum of the terms of a sequence is called a **series**. The series $a_0 + a_1 + a_2 + \ldots + a_n$ is called an **arithmetic series** or a **geometric series**, depending on the sequence that generates the terms.

▶ **On Your Own**

Find the indicated sum for each of the sequences below.

a. If $t_0 = 8$ and $d = 3$ in an arithmetic sequence, find S_{10}.

b. If $t_0 = 1$ and $r = 2.5$ in a geometric sequence, find the sum of the terms up through t_{12}.

c. Find the sum of the first 15 terms of each sequence below.

n	0	1	2	3	4	5	6	...	14	...
A_n	2	6	18	54	162			...		...

n	0	1	2	3	4	5	6	...	14	...
B_n	95	90	85	80	75			...		...

d. A popular shoe store sold 5,700 pairs of athletic shoes in 1998. Projections were for a 3% increase in sales each year for several years after 1998. What was the projected total number of athletic shoes sold during the period from 1998 to 2004?

INVESTIGATION 3 ▶ **Finite Differences**

So far, you have been able to find a function formula for a sequence by detecting and generalizing a pattern. Sometimes that is not so easily done. In this investigation, you will explore a method called *finite differences* to find the function formula for certain sequences.

1. To see how the method works, it's best to start with a sample function formula. Suppose you *toss* a rock straight down from a high bridge. If the rock is thrown from a bridge 300 feet above the river with an initial velocity of 10 feet per second, then the distance D_n of the rock from the river after n seconds is given by the function formula

$$D_n = -16n^2 - 10n + 300.$$

An analysis of the pattern of change in the distance between the rock and the river is shown in the following table.

Number of Seconds n	D_n	1st Difference	2nd Difference
0	300		
		−26	
1	274		−32
		−58	
2	216		—
		—	
3	—		—
		—	
4	—		

a. Make a copy of the table and complete the D_n column.

b. The third column contains differences between consecutive terms of the sequence D_n. How was the "−58" calculated? Find the remaining entries in the "1st Difference" column.

c. The fourth column contains differences between consecutive terms of the "1st Difference" column. Verify the entry "−32" and find the remaining entries in the "2nd Difference" column.

d. A table like this is called a **finite differences table**. Describe any patterns you see in the completed table.

It is a fact that for any function formula that is a quadratic equation, such as the equation in Activity 1, the 2nd differences in a finite differences table will be a constant. (See Extending Task 4 on page 528.) Conversely, if the 2nd differences are a constant, then the function formula is a quadratic. For example, consider the following counting problem involving vertex-edge graphs.

2. A **complete graph** is a graph in which there is exactly one edge between every pair of vertices. The diagram below shows a complete graph with 4 vertices. In this activity, you will investigate the number of edges E_n in a complete graph with n vertices.

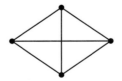

At the end of this lesson, you may want to assign some practice with the ideas and skills developed in this investigation. You could use the examples in the launch for practice or have students generate their own tables with "mystery" polynomial functions and challenge other students to find the function formula.

1. Note that in these finite differences tables, you should subtract the upper number from the lower number, rather than subtracting in the other order. In general, either order of subtraction is acceptable, as long as it is done consistently, but it is more common to subtract D_{n-1} from D_n. Subtracting in this manner models the real-world situation better. Think about time passing and computing the average velocity for each one-second interval. Such a computation requires that you subtract D_{n-1} from D_n. Velocity should be negative because the distance is decreasing over time.

   a.

Number of Seconds n	D_n	1st Difference	2nd Difference
0	300		
		−26	
1	274		−32
		−58	
2	216		−32
		−90	
3	126		−32
		−122	
4	4		

   b. The "−58" was calculated $216 - 274$. In general, the entries in the "1st Difference" column are found by evaluating $D_n - D_{n-1}$. See the table in Part a for the remaining entries in the "1st Difference" column.

   c. $-58 - (-26) = -32$. See Part a for the completed table.

   d. The most obvious pattern is that the 2nd differences are all –32. Students might also notice that the distances are decreasing in the D_n column, which makes the 1st differences negative; likewise, the 1st differences are decreasing (becoming more negative), which makes the 2nd differences negative. Some students may notice that -32 is the acceleration due to the force of gravity.

Unit 7

Complete
Graph with
2 Vertices

Complete
Graph with
3 Vertices

Complete
Graph with
5 Vertices

2. a. Complete Graphs

Number of Vertices n	0	1	2	3	4	5
Edge Count E_n	0	0	1	3	6	10

b.

Number of Vertices n	E_n	1st Difference	2nd Difference
0	0		
		0	
1	0		1
		1	
2	1		1
		2	
3	3		1
		3	
4	6		1
		4	
5	10		

Patterns in the table include all 1s in the "2nd Difference" column and the sequence of counting numbers in the "1st Difference" column.

c. Given the fact stated in the paragraph before Activity 2, the constant entries in the "2nd Difference" column indicate that the formula for edge counts must be a quadratic equation. That is, $E_n = an^2 + bn + c$.

d. Students should be encouraged to develop and try methods for finding the coefficients a, b, and c. For example, they may use some values for n and E_n from the table and solve some equations, or they may use statistical regression. Don't let them spend too much time here, however. In Part e, they will use a matrix method. The matrix method is powerful, and it is a good review of matrices and systems of equations. In the MORE tasks, students will have a chance to use a different matrix method and also use statistical regression.

e. If students already used this method in Part d, then they can skip this activity. If not, they should now use this method.
   i. From the table, $E_1 = 0$. A complete graph with 1 vertex has 0 edges.
   ii. From the table, $E_2 = 1$. So $1 = a(2)^2 + b(2) + c = 4a + 2b + c$.
   iii. $9a + 3b + c = 3$

f. Students should make sure that their equations are the same as those given in Part e. Having students talk to each other about the equations will help them really understand where the equations come from.

g.

$$\begin{bmatrix} 1 & 1 & 1 \\ 4 & 2 & 1 \\ 9 & 3 & 1 \end{bmatrix} \begin{bmatrix} a \\ b \\ c \end{bmatrix} = \begin{bmatrix} 0 \\ 1 \\ 3 \end{bmatrix}$$

This matrix equation looks like $AX = C$. The solution is $X = (A^{-1})(C) = \begin{bmatrix} 0.5 \\ -0.5 \\ 0 \end{bmatrix}$.

Thus, $a = 0.5$, $b = -0.5$, and $c = 0$. Note that the calculator may give c as a very small number. Students must interpret this number in terms of round-off error and conclude that $c = 0$.

a. Complete a table like the one below. Draw complete graphs to help you, as needed.

Complete Graphs						
Number of Vertices n	0	1	2	3	4	5
Edge Count E_n						

b. Make a finite differences table for the sequence of edge counts E_n. Describe any patterns you see in the table.

c. What pattern in the finite differences table tells you that the function formula for the sequence of edge counts must look like $E_n = an^2 + bn + c$?

d. How could you find the coefficients a, b, and c? With some classmates, brainstorm some ideas and try them out.

e. One way to find a, b, and c is to set up and solve a system of three linear equations. You can get this system of equations by letting n equal any three values, for example, 1, 2, and 3.

  i. To get the first equation, suppose $n = 1$.

  ■ Explain what the value of E_1 in your table means in terms of complete graphs and numbers of edges.

  ■ If you substitute $n = 1$ in the equation $E_n = an^2 + bn + c$, you get
  $$E_1 = a(1)^2 + b(1) + c = a + b + c.$$
  So you know that $E_1 = a + b + c$ and, from your table, that $E_1 = 0$. Thus, one equation is $a + b + c = 0$.

  ii. Use similar reasoning with $n = 2$ to get the second equation.

  iii. To get the third equation, let $n = 3$. What is the equation that results from this choice of n?

f. Compare the system of three linear equations you found in Part e to the systems found by others. Resolve any differences.

g. You can solve systems of three equations like these using matrices, as you did for the case of systems of two linear equations in "Matrix Models," Unit 1 of Course 2. Written in matrix form, the system looks like this (fill in the missing entries):

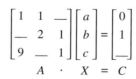 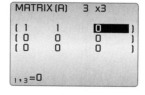

Solve this matrix equation.

h. Use the results of Part g to write the function formula for the number of edges in a complete graph with n vertices. Use this formula to check the entries in the table from Part a.

i. Now find a recursive formula for the sequence of edge counts by examining the table in Part a.

3. So far in this investigation, you have examined situations in which the function formula is a quadratic equation. Now consider the case of a higher-degree function formula. Suppose $A_n = 4n^3 + 2n^2 - 5n - 8$. Make a prediction about which column in the finite differences table for this sequence will be constant. Construct the finite differences table to check your conjecture.

In general, it is possible to compute more than just 2nd or 3rd differences. If the function formula is an rth degree polynomial, then the rth differences will be constant. The converse is also true. These facts can be used to find function formulas for certain sequences.

Checkpoint

Think about the method of finite differences and how it can be used.

ⓐ Describe how to construct the finite differences table for a sequence of numbers.

ⓑ If the 4th differences in the finite differences table for a sequence are constant, what do you think the function formula for the sequence will look like? How would you go about finding the specific formula?

ⓒ In general, what kind of function formulas can be found using finite differences tables?

Be prepared to share your descriptions and thinking with the entire class.

▶ **On Your Own**

Use a finite differences table and matrices to find a function formula for the sequence below.

n	0	1	2	3	4	5	6	7	8	9	10	11
A_n	3	12	25	42	63	88	117	150	187	228	273	322

2. **h.** Substituting these values into $E_n = an^2 + bn + c$ gives $E_n = 0.5n^2 - 0.5n$. Using this formula to check the entries in the table from Part a gives the following:

$E_0 = (0.5)0^2 - (0.5)0 = 0$　　　$E_1 = (0.5)1^2 - (0.5)1 = 0$

$E_2 = (0.5)2^2 - (0.5)2 = 1$　　　$E_3 = (0.5)3^2 - (0.5)3 = 3$

$E_4 = (0.5)4^2 - (0.5)4 = 6$　　　$E_5 = (0.5)5^2 - (0.5)5 = 10$

i. A recursive formula is $E_n = E_{n-1} + (n - 1)$. Note that you cannot use a *NOW-NEXT* equation in this situation because of the $(n - 1)$ term.

3. Since this equation is a polynomial of degree 3, the 3rd differences should be constant. The finite differences table is shown below, and the 3rd differences are indeed constant.

n	A_n	1st Difference	2nd Difference	3rd Difference
0	−8			
		1		
1	−7		28	
		29		24
2	22		52	
		81		24
3	103		76	
		157		24
4	260		100	
		257		24
5	517		124	
		381		
6	898			

SHARE AND SUMMARIZE　full-class discussion

Checkpoint

See Teaching Master 183.

ⓐ Make a table in which the first column consists of the subscripts, that is, 0, 1, 2, 3, …, which might represent numbers of seconds or numbers of vertices or just subscripts for the terms of the sequence. In the second column, list the actual terms of the sequence. The third column is the 1st differences, that is, the differences between successive terms in the sequence; the fourth column is the 2nd differences, that is, the differences between successive terms in the previous column; and so on.

ⓑ If the 4th differences in the finite differences table for a sequence are constant, then the function formula for the sequence must be a quartic equation (degree 4). The function formula will be of the form $A_n = an^4 + bn^3 + cn^2 + dn + e$. (To find the specific formula, students can use a calculator or computer software to solve the matrix equation

$$\begin{bmatrix} 1 & 1 & 1 & 1 & 1 \\ 16 & 8 & 4 & 2 & 1 \\ 81 & 27 & 9 & 3 & 1 \\ 256 & 64 & 16 & 4 & 1 \\ 625 & 125 & 25 & 5 & 1 \end{bmatrix} \begin{bmatrix} a \\ b \\ c \\ d \\ e \end{bmatrix} = \begin{bmatrix} a_1 \\ a_2 \\ a_3 \\ a_4 \\ a_5 \end{bmatrix}$$

where $a_1, a_2, a_3, a_4,$ and a_5 are the output values for terms 2–6 of the sequence.)

See additional Teaching Notes on page T549D.

ASSIGNMENT *pp. 519–529*

Modeling: 1 or 2, and 3*
Organizing: 2, 3, and choice of
          one*
Reflecting: Choose one*
Extending: Choose one*

*When choice is indicated, it is important to
leave the choice to the student.*
NOTE: *It is best if Organizing tasks are discussed as a whole class after they have been
assigned as homework.*

Modeling

1. **a.** College Education, One Year

Year	Cost
0	$9,500
1	$10,260
2	$11,080.80
3	$11,967.26
4	$12,924.65
5	$13,958.62

   b. The sequence is geometric. The constant multiplier is 1.08.

   c. Recursive formula: $C_n = C_{n-1}(1.08)$, $C_0 = 9,500$
       Function formula: $C_n = 9,500(1.08)^n$, where n is the number of years

   d. Responses will vary depending on your students. For students who are juniors, the average cost for the four years will be $\frac{11,080.80 + 11,967.26 + 12,924.65 + 13,958.62}{4}$ or approximately $12,483 per year.

   e. Assuming the child will start college in 18 years and spend four years in college, the cost is represented by $C_{18} + C_{19} + C_{20} + C_{21}$. This is approximately 37,962 + 40,999 + 44,279 + 47,821 or $171,061. (Some students might choose to find this value by evaluating $S_{21} - S_{17}$.)

2. **a.** It appears that the data would be better modeled by an arithmetic sequence. The added constant seems to be approximately 4. (Note that the table is not set up with one degree increments in temperature.) Also, if you plot the data, the graph appears to be linear, which indicates a constant increase or decrease and, thus, an arithmetic sequence.

   b. $U_n = U_{n-1} + 4$. Using $U_{45} = 20$ or $U_{60} = 80$, the recursive formula predicts 140 chirps per minute when the temperature is 75° ($U_{75} = 140$).

   c. The crickets would stop chirping at about 40°F. The recursive formula can be interpreted to mean that for each 1° decrease in temperature, the number of chirps per minute will decrease by 4. From 45° we need a decrease of 5° to get to 0 chirps per minute.

   d. The temperature would be about 65°F, based on an increase of 4 chirps per minute for a 1° increase in temperature and 80 chirps per minute at 60°F.

Modeling • Organizing • Reflecting • Extending

Modeling

1. For many people, a college education is a desirable and worthwhile goal. But the cost of a college education is growing every year. Suppose that the average tuition cost for a year of college education is now $9,500 and that the cost is rising at a rate of 8% per year.

   a. Make a table showing the average cost of a year of college education for the next 5 years.

   b. Is the sequence of increasing costs arithmetic, geometric, or neither?

   c. Determine a recursive and function formula for the sequence of costs.

   d. Use your formulas to predict the average cost of a year of your college education.

   e. Predict the cost of four years of college for a child born this year.

2. Animal behavior often changes as the outside temperature changes. One curious example of this is the fact that the frequency of cricket chirps varies with the outside temperature in a very predictable way. Consider the data below for one species of cricket.

   Cricket Chirps

Temperature (in degrees F)	45	47	50	52	54	55	60
Frequency (in chirps/min)	20	28	41	50	57	61	80

   a. If you were to choose an arithmetic sequence or a geometric sequence as a model for the frequency sequence, which type of sequence would you choose? Why?

   b. As is often the case in mathematical modeling, the model you chose in Part a does not fit the data exactly. Nevertheless, it may be quite useful for analysis of the situation. Find a recursive formula for the frequency sequence, based on the sequence you chose in Part a. Use the formula to predict the frequency of cricket chirps for a temperature of 75°F.

   c. At what temperature would you expect crickets to stop chirping?

   d. You can use the relationship between the frequency of cricket chirps and the temperature as a kind of thermometer. What would you estimate the temperature to be if a cricket is chirping at 100 chirps per minute?

Unit 7

3. Sandy has a sales job which pays him a monthly commission. He made $250 in his first month. His supervisor tells him that he should be able to increase his commission income by 10% each month for the next year. For this problem, assume that the supervisor's prediction is correct.

   a. Find recursive and function formulas for the sequence of monthly commission income.

   b. How much total commission income will Sandy earn in his first ten months on the job?

4. In this task, you will use the idea of sequential change to investigate the number of diagonals that can be drawn in a regular n-sided polygon.

   a. Draw the first few regular n-gons and make a table showing the number of diagonals that can be drawn in each of them.

   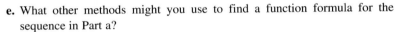

   b. Determine a recursive formula for the number of diagonals that can be drawn in a regular n-gon.

   c. Use the method of finite differences to find a function formula for the number of diagonals that can be drawn in a regular n-gon.

   d. Use your formulas to predict the number of diagonals in a regular 20-gon.

   e. What other methods might you use to find a function formula for the sequence in Part a?

5. The square Sierpinski carpet you constructed in Investigation 1, page 509, is an example of a *fractal* in that small pieces of the design are similar to the design as a whole. Other fractal shapes can also be constructed using recursive procedures.

   a. A *Sierpinski triangle* is constructed through a sequence of steps illustrated by the figures below.

   $n = 0$ $n = 1$ $n = 2$ $n = 3$

   At stage $n = 0$, you construct an equilateral triangle whose sides are all of length 1 unit. In succeeding stages, you remove the "middle triangles," as shown in stages $n = 1, 2$, and 3. This process continues indefinitely. Consider the sequence of areas of the figures at each stage. Find recursive and function formulas for the sequence of areas.

3. **a.** Recursive formula: $I_n = 1.1I_{n-1}$, $I_1 = 250$
   Function formula: $I_n = 250(1.1)^{n-1}$, where n = number of months

   b. *Total income* $= 250 + 250(1.1) + 250(1.1)^2 + \ldots + 250(1.1)^9$
   $$= 250(1 + 1.1 + 1.1^2 + \ldots + 1.1^9)$$
   $$= 250\left(\frac{1.1^{10} - 1}{1.1 - 1}\right)$$
   $$\approx \$3,984.36$$

4. **a.** **Regular *n*-gons**

Number of Sides	Number of Diagonals
3	0
4	2
5	5
6	9
7	14
8	20

   b. $D_n = D_{n-1} + (n-2)$

   c.

Number of Sides	Number of Diagonals	1st Difference	2nd Difference
3	0		
		2	
4	2		1
		3	
5	5		1
		4	
6	9		1
		5	
7	14		1
		6	
8	20		

   The 2nd differences are constant, so the function formula is a quadratic function.

   One matrix equation is $\begin{bmatrix} 9 & 3 & 1 \\ 16 & 4 & 1 \\ 25 & 5 & 1 \end{bmatrix} \begin{bmatrix} a \\ b \\ c \end{bmatrix} = \begin{bmatrix} 0 \\ 2 \\ 5 \end{bmatrix}$. Solving gives $D_n = 0.5n^2 - 1.5n$.

   d. The number of diagonals is D_{20}, which is $0.5(20)^2 - 1.5(20)$ or 170.

   e. One could look for a pattern in the table and try to find a formula that describes the pattern. In fact, another (equivalent) closed-form equation is $D_n = \frac{n(n-3)}{2}$. One could also use the regression features of a calculator or computer software.

5. **a.** The area of the initial triangle ($n = 0$) is $\frac{\sqrt{3}}{4}$. Each successive figure has $\frac{3}{4}$ the area of the previous figure. Thus, the formulas for the geometric sequence of areas are as follows.

   Recursive formula: $A_n = \frac{3}{4}A_{n-1}$, $A_0 = \frac{\sqrt{3}}{4}$

   Function formula: $A_n = \frac{\sqrt{3}}{4}\left(\frac{3}{4}\right)^n = \frac{3^n(\sqrt{3})}{4^{n+1}}$

Unit 7

5. b. The perimeter of the initial "snowflake" is 3. The perimeter of each succeeding figure is $\frac{4}{3}$ times the perimeter of the previous figure. Thus, the formulas for the geometric sequence of perimeters are as follows.

Recursive formula: $P_n = \frac{4}{3}P_{n-1}$, $P_0 = 3$

Function formula: $P_n = 3\left(\frac{4}{3}\right)^n$

6. This is a geometric sequence. The percentage of words in the list that are still in use n years later, expressed as a decimal, is given by the formulas below.

Recursive formula: $W(n) = (0.99978)W(n-1)$, $W(0) = 1$

Function formula: $W(n) = 1(0.99978)^n$

The number of words still in use is about $(0.99978)^{1,000}(500) = 401$.

Organizing

1. a.

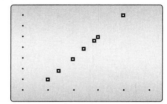

```
WINDOW
  Xmin =40
  Xmax =65
  Xscl =5
  Ymin =10
  Ymax =85
  Yscl =10
  Xres =1
```

Linear regression gives $y = -160.53 + 4.024x$. Given this problem situation, it seems reasonable to round the coefficients to whole numbers. Thus, a function formula would be $C_n = -160 + 4n$. Students may also reason that they need to multiply the change in temperature by 4 and add 20, so $C_n = 4(n - 45) + 20$, which is equivalent to the rounded linear regression model.

b. Evaluating the function in Part a for 47° and 60° gives $C_{47} = -160 + 4(47) = 28$ and $C_{60} = -160 + 4(60) = 80$. These values match the values in the table.

b. Another interesting fractal is the *Koch snowflake*. The procedure for constructing the Koch snowflake also begins with an equilateral triangle whose sides are of length 1 unit. At each stage you remove the segment that is the middle third of each side and replace it with two outward-extending segments of the same length, creating new equilateral triangles on each side as shown in the diagrams below. The process continues indefinitely.

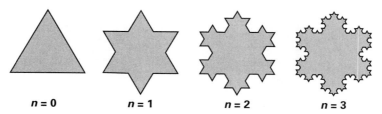

n = 0	*n* = 1	*n* = 2	*n* = 3

Find recursive and function formulas for the sequence of perimeters of the snowflake.

6. *Glottochronology* is the study of changes in languages. Over time, certain words in a language are no longer used. In effect, they disappear from the language. Suppose a linguist examines a list of 500 words used in a language 1,000 years ago. Let $W(n)$ be the percentage of the words in this list that are still in use n years later, given as a decimal. It is commonly assumed that $W(n)$ is proportional to $W(n-1)$. Glottochronologists have determined that the constant of proportionality can be estimated to be about 0.99978. Find recursive and function formulas for this sequence. According to this model, about how many of the 500 words are still in use today?

Organizing

1. In Modeling Task 2, page 519, you may have established that the sequence of chirping frequencies for one species of cricket is approximately an arithmetic sequence with recursive formula

$$C_n = C_{n-1} + 4.$$

a. Plot the (*temperature*, *frequency*) data from the table on page 519 and find an equation that fits the data.

b. Using the equation from Part a, write a function formula for the sequence. Check that your formula does generate the values given in the table for the chirping frequencies at temperatures of 47°F and 60°F.

Unit 7

2. In the "Think About This Situation" for Lesson 2, page 505, you considered two sequences related to the free fall of a sky diver: the sequence D_n of distance fallen each second and the sequence T_n of total distance fallen after each second.

   a. Use the information given in the "Think About this Situation" to verify that the two sequences below, D_n and T_n, are accurate models if you assume Earth's gravity and no air resistance.

Distances Fallen

n	D_n	T_n	n	D_n	T_n
1	16	16	6	176	576
2	48	64	7	208	784
3	80	144	8	240	1,024
4	112	256	9	272	1,296
5	144	400	10	304	1,600

   b. Use the method of finite differences to find function formula that describes the sequence of total distance fallen.

   c. Use calculator- or computer-based regression methods to find function formula relating total distance fallen to the number of seconds in the fall.

   d. For the "Think About This Situation" questions, you wrote recursive and function formulas for the sequence D_n. Note that each term (after the first) of T_n is the result of adding the corresponding term of D_n to the previous term of T_n. Use this fact to help you find a recursive formula for T_n.

3. Below is the sequence from the "On Your Own" task on page 518.

n	0	1	2	3	4	5	6	7	8	9	10	11
A_n	3	12	25	42	63	88	117	150	187	228	273	322

   a. Produce a scatterplot of n versus A_n using a graphing calculator or computer software. Describe the shape of the graph. Which function family would best model this data pattern?

   b. Use calculator- or computer-based regression methods to find the equation of the model that seems to best fit the scatterplot. Compare this equation to the function formula you derived in the "On Your Own" task using the finite differences method. Describe and resolve any differences in the two solutions.

   c. Do you think statistical regression methods will work to find a function formula for any sequence? Explain.

4. Use a finite differences table and matrices to find the function formula for the sequence given by $B_n = B_{n-1} + 3n$, with $B_0 = 2$.

2. a. To verify D_n, students can use the fact given in the "Think About This Situation" on page 505 that the sky diver will fall 32 feet farther each second. To verify T_n, they can find the total distance fallen up to that point by finding the sum $D_1 + D_2 + \ldots + D_n$.

b.

n	T_n	1st Difference	2nd Difference
1	16		
		48	
2	64		32
		80	
3	144		32
		112	
4	256		32
		144	
5	400		

Since the 2nd differences are the same, the function formula is quadratic. The matrix equation is shown in the margin. Solving this equation gives $a = 16$, $b = 0$, and $c = 0$. Thus, the function formula is $T_n = 16n^2$.

$$\begin{bmatrix} 1 & 1 & 1 \\ 4 & 2 & 1 \\ 9 & 3 & 1 \end{bmatrix} \begin{bmatrix} a \\ b \\ c \end{bmatrix} = \begin{bmatrix} 16 \\ 64 \\ 144 \end{bmatrix}$$

c. Using quadratic regression will also give $T_n = 16n^2$.

d. A recursive formula for T_n is $T_n = T_{n-1} + D_n = T_{n-1} + (32n - 16)$. See the notes for the "Think About This Situation" on page T505 for further discussion of this formula.

3. a. The rate of change is not constant, so a linear model is not a good choice. There is not a constant multiplier, so an exponential model is not a good choice. The graph could be a parabola, so a quadratic model would be appropriate to try. A power model will fit well if the A_n data are shifted down by 3 so that the data go through the origin. (However, because many calculators compute a power model by using logarithms, students will get an undefined error unless they remove the (0, 0) point before trying to fit a power model.) Then the 3 must again be added to the equation. Doing this yields a function that is a little too high at first and a little too low for the last few points. So the best family of functions in this situation is the quadratic functions.

b. Using quadratic regression, the equation is $A_n = 2n^2 + 7n + 3$. This is the same formula found using finite differences.

c. Sequences can have many different patterns, but they also may be random. Many sequences do not have a function formula. So statistical regression will clearly not work to find the function formula for any sequence. However, it can be a useful tool in many cases. It is most useful when you already have a good idea about the pattern of the sequence, and that pattern is one that is included in the statistical regression options on calculators or computers. Then regression can be used to find the "best-fitting" model of a certain type (based on the criterion of least squares). For example, in this task, after students suspect that the scatterplot is a parabola, they can use quadratic regression to find the best-fitting quadratic model. Students continuing on to Course 4 will take a more technical look at how to use statistics to fit functions to data.

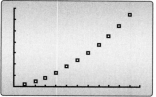

```
WINDOW
Xmin =0
Xmax =12
Xscl =1
Ymin =0
Ymax =350
Yscl =50
Xres =1
```

4. The 2nd differences are constant (3), so the function formula is a quadratic function with the form $B_n = an^2 + bn + c$. Solve the system:

$$\begin{aligned} a + b + c &= 5 \\ 4a + 2b + c &= 11 \\ 9a + 3b + c &= 20 \end{aligned}$$

The function formula is $B_n = an^2 + bn + c = 1.5n^2 + 1.5n + 2$.

5. a. $A_4 = r(r^3A_0 + r^2b + rb + b) + b = r^4A_0 + r^3b + r^2b + rb + b$
    $A_5 = r(r^4A_0 + r^3b + r^2b + rb + b) + b = r^5A_0 + r^4b + r^3b + r^2b + rb + b$
    $A_n = r^nA_0 + r^{n-1}b + r^{n-2}b + \ldots + rb + b$

    b. $r^{n-1}b + r^{n-2}b + \ldots + rb + b$ is the sum of a geometric sequence of n terms with initial term b and constant factor r. So this part of A_n sums to $b\left(\frac{r^n-1}{r-1}\right)$. Thus, $A_n = r^nA_0 + b\left(\frac{r^n-1}{r-1}\right)$.

    c. $A_n = 0.8^n(3,000) + (1,000)\left(\frac{0.8^n-1}{0.8-1}\right)$
    $A_2 = (0.8^2)(3,000) + (1,000)\left(\frac{0.8^2-1}{0.8-1}\right) = 3,720$
    $A_{10} = (0.8^{10})(3,000) + (1,000)\left(\frac{0.8^{10}-1}{0.8-1}\right) = 4,785.25$

    To find the long-term population, let n be a large number, such as 1,000. (When rounding to the hundredths place, n can be as low as 58 to round to the long-term population.)
    $A_{1,000} = (0.8^{1,000})(3,000) + (1,000)\left(\frac{0.8^{1,000}-1}{0.8-1}\right) \approx 5,000$
    These values should match those obtained earlier.

    d. Because $|r| < 1$, if you choose a very large value for n (corresponding to the long-term population), r^n will be very close to zero. Thus, $A_n = r^nA_0 + b\left(\frac{r^n-1}{r-1}\right) \approx 0 + b\left(\frac{0-1}{r-1}\right) = \frac{-b}{r-1} = \frac{b}{1-r}$. If we apply this formula to the trout-population problem, we get $\frac{1,000}{1-0.8}$ or 5,000. This is the same long-term population that we obtained in Part c.

    e. These two formulas look different, but they are equivalent, as shown below.
    $A_n = 0.8^n(3,000) + (1,000)\left(\frac{0.8^n-1}{0.8-1}\right)$
    $\quad = 0.8^n(3,000) + \frac{1,000(0.8^n-1)}{-0.2}$
    $\quad = 0.8^n(3,000) - 5,000(0.8^n-1)$
    $\quad = 0.8^n(3,000) - 5,000(0.8^n) + 5,000$
    $\quad = -2,000(0.8^n) + 5,000$

6. **In order to use the formulas developed in this lesson for the sum of a sequence, students will first have to determine how long each sequence is. They may do this by solving equations, as shown below, or by computing and counting terms.**

    a. This sequence is a geometric sequence with $r = 2$ and initial value 13.
    $6,656 = 13(2^n)$
    $512 = 2^n$
    $9 = n$
    $S_9 = 13\left(\frac{2^{10}-1}{2-1}\right) = 13,299$

    b. This is an arithmetic sequence with $d = -0.75$ and initial value 13. So $1 = 13 - 0.75n$ and $n = 16$. $S_{16} = \frac{17(13+1)}{2} = 119$

    c. The sequence is neither arithmetic nor geometric, but it is described by $a_n = n^2$ if the subscripts start with 1 or $a_n = (n+1)^2$ if the subscripts start with 0. The sum of the indicated terms is 1,240.

    d. The sequence is geometric with $r = 0.8$ and initial value 5.
    $0.8388608 = 5 \cdot (0.8^n)$
    $0.16777216 = 0.8^n$
    $8 = n$
    $S_8 = 5\left(\frac{0.8^9-1}{0.8-1}\right) = 21.6445568$

5. In this lesson, you found function formulas for arithmetic and geometric sequences. In Lesson 1, you studied combined recursive formulas of the form $A_n = rA_{n-1} + b$. You can now use what you know about geometric sequences and their sums to find a function formula for such combined recursive formulas.

a. Complete the following list of terms for the combined recursive formula $A_n = rA_{n-1} + b$. Examine the list for patterns so that you can write a function formula for A_n.

$$A_0 = A_0$$

$$A_1 = rA_0 + b$$

$$A_2 = rA_1 + b = r(rA_0 + b) + b = r^2A_0 + rb + b$$

$$A_3 = r(r^2A_0 + rb + b) + b = r^3A_0 + r^2b + rb + b$$

$$A_4 = ?$$

$$A_5 = ?$$

$$\vdots$$

$$A_n = ?$$

b. The expression you have for A_n at the end of Part a is a function formula, but it can be simplified. To simplify, use what you know about the sum of the terms of a geometric sequence.

c. Now reconsider the combined recursive formula that modeled the trout-population problem in Lesson 1: $A_n = 0.8A_{n-1} + 1{,}000$, with $A_0 = 3{,}000$. Use the general function formula from Part b to write a function formula that models the trout population. Then use that formula to find A_2 and A_{10}. Choose a year far in the future and find the long-term population. Compare your results to those you found in Lesson 1, using other methods.

d. Suppose the combined recursive formula $A_n = rA_{n-1} + b$ represents year-to-year population change. Assume that r is a positive number less than 1. Use the function formula from Part b to explain why the long-term population in this situation is $\frac{b}{1-r}$. Use this fact to find the long-term population in the trout-population problem, and compare it to what you found before.

e. Compare the function formula you obtained in Part c to the one given in Organizing Task 3 of Lesson 1, page 499. Explain and resolve any differences.

6. As you complete this task, think about the defining characteristics of arithmetic and geometric sequences and how those characteristics are related to the sum of their terms. For each sequence below, determine if the sequence is arithmetic, geometric, or neither. Then find the sum of the indicated terms.

a. 13, 26, 52, 104, …, 6,656

b. 13, 12.25, 11.5, 10.75, …, 1

c. 1, 4, 9, 16, …, 225

d. 5, 4, 3.2, 2.56, …, 0.8388608

Unit 7

7. In Course 2 of *Contemporary Mathematics in Context*, you may have investigated the waiting-time distribution in the context of a modified Monopoly® game in which 36 students are in jail and a student must roll doubles to get out of jail.

a. The probability of rolling doubles is $\frac{1}{6}$. Thus, the probability of getting out of jail on any given roll of the dice is similarly $\frac{1}{6}$. What is the probability of remaining in jail on any given roll of the dice?

b. Complete the following table. The waiting-time distribution refers to the first two columns, since you want to know how long a student has to wait to get out of jail. The last column provides important related information.

Rolling Dice to Get Doubles

Number of Rolls to Get Doubles	Expected Number of Students Released on the Given Number of Rolls	Expected Number of Students Still in Jail
1	6	30
2	5	
3		
4		
5		

c. Consider the sequence of numbers in the last column.

■ Is the sequence an arithmetic or geometric sequence? Why?

■ Determine the recursive and function formulas for the sequence. (Use 36 as the initial term of the sequence since that is the initial number of students in jail.)

■ Use the formulas to find the expected number of students left in jail after 20 rolls.

d. Sketch a histogram for the waiting-time distribution shown in the first two columns.

■ Write a recursive formula that shows how the height of any given bar compares to the height of the previous bar.

■ What kind of sequence is the sequence of bar heights?

7. a. $P(\text{left in jail}) = \frac{5}{6}$

b. Rolling Dice to Get Doubles

Number of Rolls to Get Doubles	Expected Number of Students Released on the Given Number of Rolls	Expected Number of Students Still in Jail
1	6	30
2	5	25
3	4.17	20.83
4	3.47	17.36
5	2.89	14.47

c. ■ It is a geometric sequence, since each entry is $\frac{5}{6}$ of the previous entry.
■ Recursive formula: $J_n = \left(\frac{5}{6}\right)J_{n-1}$; $J_0 = 36$
  Function formula: $J_n = 36\left(\frac{5}{6}\right)^n$
■ $J_{20} = 0.94$ students left in jail

d.

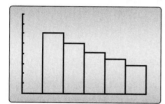

```
WINDOW
Xmin =0
Xmax =6
Xscl =1
Ymin =0
Ymax =8
Yscl =1
Xres =1
```

■ $H_n = \left(\frac{5}{6}\right)H_{n-1}$, $H_1 = 6$
■ It is a geometric sequence with a constant multiplier of $\frac{5}{6}$, starting with 6.

Unit 7

Reflecting

1. The function formula is a much more efficient way to find the 100th term of the sequence. It involves only one application of a formula rather than 100 applications of the recursive formula. However, the recursion capabilities of the calculator allow for rather easy calculations even using the recursive formula, although it would take the calculator some time to compute the 100th term of a sequence.

2. Responses will vary. The height of a bouncing ball dropped from a certain height could be modeled by a geometric sequence. An exercise program for which you add 10 minutes per week to an exercise routine until you reach 6 hours per week would be modeled by an arithmetic sequence.

3. **a.** ■ $\frac{\sum_{i=1}^{n} x_i}{n}$

   ■ $\sqrt{\frac{\sum_{i=1}^{n}(x_i - \bar{x})^2}{n}}$, where $\bar{x}$ is the mean of $x_1, x_2, \ldots, x_n$

   b. $\sum_{k=0}^{12} 3k = 0 + 3 + 6 + 9 + 12 + 15 + 18 + 21 + 24 + 27 + 30 + 33 + 36$
   $= \frac{13(36 + 0)}{2}$
   $= 234$

   c. $\sum_{i=3}^{10} 2^i = 2^3 + 2^4 + 2^5 + 2^6 + 2^7 + 2^8 + 2^9 + 2^{10} = \frac{8(2^8 - 1)}{2 - 1} = 2,040$

   d. $3 + 5 + 7 + 9 + 11 + 13 + 15 = \sum_{n=1}^{7}(2n+1)$

4. Responses will vary. Arithmetic sequences grow slowly and steadily, while geometric sequences grow very quickly once they get started. Thus, if food supply growth is arithmetic and population growth is geometric, there will come a time when population growth far outpaces the food supply available to support the population. This would be an "apocalyptic" situation, with mass starvation due to lack of food. Although there are countries that experience famine and severe starvation, this situation of mass starvation due to global lack of food has not happened. Nevertheless, the comparison of arithmetic growth to geometric growth, particularly where population growth or even compound interest is concerned, is an important perspective that is useful for understanding the changing world in which we live.

5. **a.** Responses will vary. The function formula may be thought of as "explicit" because it explicitly says how to compute a given term of the sequence, as opposed to the recursive form. In some sense, the recursive form is "implicit" in that you can't compute a given term directly but rather must first find the previous terms.

   b. Responses will vary. "Closed form" seems to capture the idea that to find any term in the sequence you just substitute and calculate; it's closed because you don't need any information other than the formula and one input. For example, to find A_{100}, you just substitute 100 for n in the formula for A_n and compute. This is in contrast to the more "open-ended" recursive form, in which to find A_{100} you must know A_{99}, which requires knowing A_{98}, and so on. Therefore, evaluating A_{100} requires computing again and again (iteration).

6. The matrix A will always be the same in quadratic situations when using 1, 2, and 3 as values for n. This observation allows us to solve similar problems by immediately using matrix A, without going through the derivation each time.

Reflecting

1. Suppose you want to find the 100th term of a sequence of numbers. You have both a recursive formula and a function formula. Which formula would you use? Why?

2. Describe one situation in your daily life or in the daily newspaper that could be modeled by a geometric sequence. Describe another situation that could be modeled by an arithmetic sequence.

3. A series $a_0 + a_1 + a_2 + \ldots + a_n$ can be written in a more compact form using sigma notation: $\sum_{i=0}^{n} a_i$. You used sigma notation (without subscripts) when writing a formula for standard deviation in Unit 5.

   a. Suppose $x_1, x_2, x_3, \ldots, x_n$ are sample data values. Use sigma notation with subscripts to write an expression for

   ■ the mean of this distribution.

   ■ the standard deviation of this distribution.

   b. Write $\sum_{k=0}^{12} 3k$ in *expanded form* and then find the sum.

   c. Write $\sum_{i=3}^{10} 2^i$ in expanded form and then find the sum.

   d. Complete this equation: $3 + 5 + 7 + 9 + 11 + 13 + 15 = \sum_{n=?}^{?}(2n + 1)$.

4. The English economist Thomas Malthus (1766–1834) is best remembered for his assertion that *food supply grows arithmetically while population grows geometrically*. Do some research and write a brief essay about this idea. Your essay should address the following questions: What is the meaning of Malthus's statement in terms of sequences you have studied? Do you think it is a reasonable statement? What are its consequences? Why has this statement been called "apocalyptic"? Have the events of the last 200 years borne out the statement? What can we learn from the statement even if it is not completely accurate?

5. You have represented sequences using recursive and function formulas.

   a. A function formula for a sequence is sometimes called an *explicit formula*. Why do you think the term "explicit" is used? What is explicit about a function formula?

   b. A function formula is also sometimes called a *closed-form formula*. Why do you think this term is used?

6. On page 517, you solved the matrix equation $AX = C$ to find the coefficients of a quadratic equation. Examine matrix A on page 517. Do you think this matrix will change if you work a similar problem that involves different data? Explain.

Unit 7

Extending

1. You may have seen a stack of oranges in a grocery store that was in the shape of a pyramid with a square base. The number of oranges in such a stack depends on the number of layers in the stack.

a. Complete a table like the one below.

Pyramid of Oranges

Number of Layers in a Stack	0	1	2	3	4	5	6
Number of Oranges in a Stack	0	1	5				

b. Find a recursive formula for the sequence of number of oranges in a stack.

c. Use the method of finite differences to find a function formula for the sequence of number of oranges in a stack. How many oranges are in a stack with 15 layers?

2. In this lesson, you mainly considered sequences that started with subscript 0; that is, A_0 was the initial term. It is certainly possible to use other notation. For example, you might represent the initial term as A_1. Changing the notation like this does not, of course, change the pattern of the sequence, but it will change the form of the function formula. Consider the arithmetic sequence 4, 7, 10, 13, ...

a. Determine a recursive formula and a function formula for this sequence, using $A_0 = 4$.

b. Now determine the function formula for the sequence labeling the initial term, 4, as A_1 instead of A_0. (That is, $A_1 = 4$.)

c. The recursive formula doesn't change, no matter how you label the initial term, because it just describes how you get from one term to the next. However, the function formula will change if you change the subscript of the initial term, as you saw in Parts a and b. What will be the function formula for this same sequence if you label the initial term A_2?

d. Sometimes a sequence may start with a much higher value of n. Consider the sequence of chirping frequencies for the species of crickets in Modeling Task 2, page 519. That sequence is reproduced below.

Cricket Chirps

Temperature (in degrees F)	45	47	50	52	54	55	60
Frequency (in chirps/min)	20	28	41	50	57	61	80

It is probably easiest to consider the part of the sequence shown in the table as beginning with $n = 45$ (*temperature* = 45°); that is, the initial term is A_{45}. Find a function formula for this sequence.

Extending

1. **a.** Pyramid of Oranges

Number of Layers in a Stack	0	1	2	3	4	5	6
Number of Oranges in a Stack	0	1	5	14	30	55	91

b. $U_n = U_{n-1} + n^2$

c.

Number of Layers	Number of Oranges	1st Difference	2nd Difference	3rd Difference
0	0			
		1		
1	1		3	
		4		2
2	5		5	
		9		2
3	14		7	
		16		2
4	30		9	
		25		2
5	55		11	
		36		
6	91			

Since the 3rd differences are constant, the general form of the function formula for the number t_n of oranges in a stack will be

$t_n = an^3 + bn^2 + cn + d$
$t_0 = 0 = d$
$t_1 = 1 = a + b + c + d = a + b + c$
$t_2 = 5 = 8a + 4b + 2c + d = 8a + 4b + 2c$
$t_3 = 14 = 27a + 9b + 3c + d = 27a + 9b + 3c$

So one matrix equation is $\begin{bmatrix} 1 & 1 & 1 \\ 8 & 4 & 2 \\ 27 & 9 & 3 \end{bmatrix} \begin{bmatrix} a \\ b \\ c \end{bmatrix} = \begin{bmatrix} 1 \\ 5 \\ 14 \end{bmatrix}$. Solving this equation gives

$a = \frac{1}{3}$, $b = \frac{1}{2}$, and $c = \frac{1}{6}$. So the function formula is $t_n = \frac{1}{3}n^3 + \frac{1}{2}n^2 + \frac{1}{6}n$. There are 1,240 oranges in a stack with 15 layers.

2. **a.** Recursive formula: $A_n = A_{n-1} + 3$, $A_0 = 4$
   Function formula: $A_n = 4 + 3n$

   b. The function formula is now $A_n = 4 + 3(n - 1)$.

   c. The function formula will be $A_n = 4 + 3(n - 2)$.

   d. The function formula is $A_n = 20 + 4(n - 45)$.

2. **e.** $t_n = t_1 + d(n - 1)$

f. $t_n = t_1 r^{n-1}$

g. If the initial term is A_1 instead of A_0, then the formulas for S_n, the sum of the terms a_1 through a_n, are as follows.

Arithmetic sequence: $S_n = \dfrac{n(a_1 + a_n)}{2}$

Geometric sequence: $S_n = a_1\left(\dfrac{r^n - 1}{r - 1}\right)$

3. **a.** *NEXT = NOW + PREVIOUS*

b. $F_{n+1} = F_n + F_{n-1}$

c. ■ You cannot list the terms with the information given because you don't have the initial terms.

■ Two initial values are needed. Students' choices of initial values will vary.

For initial values 2 and 4, the sequence is 2, 4, 6, 8, 10, 12, ...

For initial values 1 and 5, the sequence is 1, 5, 9, 13, 17, 21, ...

Both of the sequences are arithmetic, and the common difference is the difference between the two initial values.

■ An equivalent recursive form is $A_n = A_{n-1} + (A_1 - A_0)$.

d. Three initial values are needed. For example, if the first three terms are 1, 3, and 8, then the first six terms are 1, 3, 8, 18, 47, and 121.

e. The following are good resources on the Fibonacci sequence.

Barnard, Jane. Those fascinating fibonaccis! Student Math Notes in the *NCTM News Bulletin*, January 1996.

Garland, Trudi Hammel. *Fascinating Fibonaccis: Mystery and Magic in Numbers*. Palo Alto, CA: Dale Seymour Publications, 1987.

Hoggatt, Verner E., Jr. *Fibonacci and Lucas Numbers*. Boston: Houghton-Mifflin Publishing Co., 1969.

e. What is the function formula for an arithmetic sequence with initial term t_1 and common difference d?

f. What is the function formula for a geometric sequence with initial term t_1 and common ratio r?

g. Investigate and prepare a brief report on how the formulas for the sum of the terms of arithmetic and geometric sequences change if the initial term is a_1 instead of a_0.

3. In this unit, you have investigated recursive formulas and sequences that can be modeled by equations using the words *NOW* and *NEXT*. This means that to find *NEXT*, you need to use only *NOW*, one step before *NEXT*. However, there are sequences for which finding *NEXT* requires using more than one step before *NEXT*. One of the most famous sequences of this type is called the *Fibonacci sequence*, named after the mathematician Leonardo Fibonacci (c.1175–c.1250), who first studied the sequence.

a. Here is the Fibonacci sequence: 1, 1, 2, 3, 5, 8, 13, 21, 34, 55, 89, 144, ... Using the words *NEXT*, *NOW*, and *PREVIOUS*, describe the pattern of the sequence.

b. Let F_{n+1} represent *NEXT*, and use F_{n+1}, F_n, and F_{n-1} to write a recursive formula for the Fibonacci sequence.

c. Here is a recursive formula for a sequence similar to the Fibonacci sequence: $A_n = 2A_{n-1} - A_{n-2}$.

- Why can't you list the terms of this sequence?

- Choose some initial values and list the first six terms of the sequence. Then choose different initial values and list the first six terms of the sequence. Compare the two sequences. Describe any patterns you see.

- Write a recursive formula for this sequence that uses only A_n, A_{n-1}, A_1, and A_0.

d. Consider the sequence given by $A_n = A_{n-1} + A_{n-2} + 7A_{n-3}$. Choose some initial values and list the first six terms of this sequence.

e. *Optional:* The Fibonacci sequence has many interesting patterns and shows up in the most amazing places. In the photo at the left, the flower has 34 spirals in the counterclockwise direction and 21 in the clockwise direction; these two numbers are successive terms in the Fibonacci sequence. Sunflowers and pine cones also have spirals with numbers from the Fibonacci sequence, as do many other things in nature.

In fact, entire books and journals have been written about this sequence. Find an article or book about the Fibonacci sequence and write a brief report on one of its patterns or applications.

Unit 7

4. In Investigation 3, pages 515–518, you used the method of finite differences to find a function formula for certain sequences. You used the fact that the function formula for a sequence is a quadratic equation if and only if the 2nd differences in a finite differences table are constant. In this task, you will prove that fact.

   a. Suppose a sequence has a quadratic function formula ($A_n = an^2 + bn + c$). Construct a finite differences table and verify that the 2nd differences are constant. Describe any relationship you see between the constant 2nd differences and the function formula.

   b. Now, conversely, suppose the 2nd differences are constant. Show that the function formula is a quadratic equation.

5. In Activity 6 of Investigation 2, page 514, you found a formula for the sum of a *finite* number of terms of a geometric sequence. A sequence can also have an *infinite* number of terms. It is possible to analyze mathematically the sum of an infinite number of terms. Consider the sequence $\frac{1}{2}, \frac{1}{4}, \frac{1}{8}, \frac{1}{16}, \ldots, \frac{1}{2^n}, \ldots$.

   a. Explain why this is a geometric sequence. Find recursive and function formulas for this sequence.

   b. Find the sum of the terms up through $\frac{1}{2^n}$.

   c. This sequence has infinitely many terms. Does the geometric model of this sequence shown below suggest what the infinite sum of all the terms of the sequence might be?

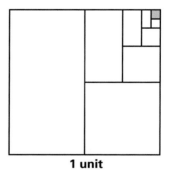

1 unit

   d. A mathematical analysis of infinite sums involves thinking about what happens to the sum of *n* terms as *n* gets very large. Examine the formula for the sum of terms up through $\frac{1}{2^n}$ from Part b. What happens to this formula as *n* gets very large? Your answer should give you the infinite sum.

4. a.

n	A_n	1st Difference	2nd Difference
0	c		
		$a + b$	
1	$a + b + c$		$2a$
		$3a + b$	
2	$4a + 2b + c$		$2a$
		$5a + b$	
3	$9a + 3b + c$		$2a$
		$7a + b$	
4	$16a + 4b + c$		

Note that the 2nd differences are constant. Also note that the 2nd difference is twice the leading coefficient of the polynomial.

b. Suppose the 2nd differences are a constant k. $(A_{n+2} - A_{n+1}) - (A_{n+1} - A_n) = k$. So $A_{n+2} = 2A_{n+1} - A_n + k$.

Now, we will use this fact to find a function formula for A_n and see if it is quadratic. To do this, we will list the terms of the sequence and look for a pattern.

A_0

A_1

$A_2 = 2A_1 - A_0 + k$ (using the equation above)

$A_3 = 2(2A_1 - A_0 + k) - A_1 + k = 3A_1 - 2A_0 + 3k$

$A_4 = \ldots = 4A_1 - 3A_0 + 6k$

$$\vdots$$

$$A_n = nA_1 - (n-1)A_0 + \frac{n(n-1)}{2}k$$
$$= \frac{k}{2}n^2 + \left(A_1 - A_0 - \frac{k}{2}\right)n + A_0$$

This last equation is a function formula for A_n, and it is a quadratic equation. Thus, we have shown that if the 2nd differences are constant, then the function formula is a quadratic equation.

5. a. This is a geometric sequence because there is a common ratio of $\frac{1}{2}$.

Recursive formula: $a_n = \frac{1}{2}a_{n-1}, a_0 = \frac{1}{2}$

Function formula: $a_n = \frac{1}{2}\left(\frac{1}{2}\right)^n$

b. The formula for the sum of the terms of the finite geometric sequence $a_n = \frac{1}{2}a_{n-1}$, $a_o = \frac{1}{2}$ is $S_n = a_0\left(\frac{r^{n+1}-1}{r-1}\right)$. Thus, the sum of the terms of this sequence up through $\frac{1}{2^n}$ is given by the following.

$$S_n = \frac{1}{2}\left(\frac{\left(\frac{1}{2}\right)^{n+1} - 1}{\frac{1}{2} - 1}\right) = -\left[\left(\frac{1}{2}\right)^{n+1} - 1\right] = 1 - \left(\frac{1}{2}\right)^{n+1}$$

c. It requires some delicate mathematics to make sense of adding infinitely many terms. The theory of infinite limits provides the necessary mathematical machinery. In this task, students will get just a taste of that theory. Intuition can be misleading when it comes to thinking about infinity, so the conjectures that students make may vary considerably. Some may think that the sum must be infinite since infinitely many terms are added. Others may think that there is some finite sum. However, by looking at the square, they should be able to reason that the sum will be 1.

d. If n is very large in the formula from Part b, then S_n becomes very close to 1. Thus, we take 1 to be the sum of all the (infinitely many) terms of the sequence.

Unit 7

Assessments 270–272

Assessments 273–275

5. **e.** The finite sum formula is $S_n = a_0\left(\frac{r^{n+1}-1}{r-1}\right)$. If n is very large, then S_n becomes very close to $\frac{a_0}{1-r}$, since r^n gets very close to 0 as n gets very large. Thus, $S = \frac{a_0}{1-r}$ is a formula for the sum of the terms in an infinite geometric sequence when $0 < r < 1$.

   f. Using the formula in Part e, the sum of the terms in the infinite geometric sequence given at the beginning of this task is $\frac{\frac{1}{2}}{1-\frac{1}{2}}$ or 1. This is the same answer as the one found in Part d.

   g. Responses will vary, depending on sequences. Consider the sequence $4, \frac{8}{3}, \frac{16}{9}, \frac{32}{27}, \ldots$, where the common ratio is $\frac{2}{3}$. The sum of the infinitely many terms is $\frac{4}{1-\frac{2}{3}}$ or 12.

6. The area of the figure can be found by finding the infinite sum $1 + \frac{1}{2} + \ldots + \frac{1}{2^n} + \ldots$. From Activity 5 we know that this sum is 2.

   The perimeter can be represented by the sum $1 + 2\frac{1}{2} + 2\frac{1}{4} + 2\frac{1}{8} + 2\frac{1}{16} + \ldots$. Clearly, this sum will grow without bound since each new rectangle will add a little more than 2 to the perimeter of the figure. The area is finite partly because the area of each new rectangle is getting closer and closer to zero. But the amount each new rectangle adds to the perimeter is always at least 2. Thus, the area is finite, but the perimeter is infinite! Students may have a very hard time believing that this can be the case.

See Assessment Resources pages 270–275.

e. Consider a general geometric sequence with terms t_n and common multiplier r. Suppose that $0 < r < 1$. Determine a general formula for the infinite sum by considering what happens to the finite sum formula if n is very large.

f. Use the general infinite sum formula for $0 < r < 1$ to find the infinite sum of the sequence $\frac{1}{2}, \frac{1}{4}, \frac{1}{8}, \frac{1}{16}, \ldots, \frac{1}{2^n}, \ldots$. Compare the sum to your answer for Part d.

g. Construct a geometric sequence of your choice with $0 < r < 1$. Use the general infinite sum formula from Part e to find the infinite sum.

6. Extending Task 5 involved infinite geometric sums. Infinite sums lead to some surprising results. Consider a figure that consists of the rectangles of width 1 and height $\frac{1}{2^n}$ arranged as shown below.

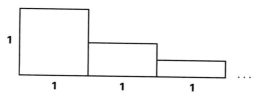

There are infinitely many rectangles that comprise this figure. Find the area of this figure. Find the perimeter. Do you think it is possible for a figure to have finite area but infinite perimeter? Explain.

Lesson **3** — *Iterating Functions*

Functions and recursive (*NOW-NEXT*) thinking are both important and unifying ideas in the *Contemporary Mathematics in Context* curriculum. In this lesson, you will explore a connection between recursive formulas and functions, and you will use this connection to further analyze processes of sequential change.

A function can be considered a process that accepts inputs and produces outputs. For example, for the function $f(x) = x^2$, an input of 2 produces an output of 4. Imagine starting with a specific input, such as 2, and then sequentially feeding the outputs back into the function as new inputs.

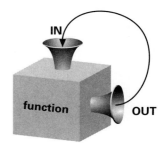

Think About This Situation

Think about the function $f(x) = x^2$ as an input-output process.

a Start with an input of 2. The resulting output is 4.

- Put 4 in as a new input. What is the new output?
- Put the new output in as the next input. What is the next output?
- Continue this process of feeding outputs back in as new inputs for several more steps.
- What do you think will be the long-term behavior of the sequence of numbers generated by this process?

b Suppose you carry out the same process for the same function, except this time start with an input of $\frac{1}{2}$. What do you think will be the long-term behavior of the resulting sequence of numbers in this case?

c What happens when you carry out the same process with a starting input of $x = 1$?

d In what way is this process of feeding outputs back in as inputs a recursive process?

Lesson 3 *Iterating Functions*

Master 184

MASTER 184   Transparency Master

Think About This Situation

Think about the function $f(x) = x^2$ as an input-output process.

ⓐ Start with an input of 2. The resulting output is 4.
- Put 4 in as a new input. What is the new output?
- Put the new output in as the next input. What is the next output?
- Continue this process of feeding outputs back in as new inputs for several more steps.
- What do you think will be the long-term behavior of the sequence of numbers generated by this process?

ⓑ Suppose you carry out the same process for the same function, except this time start with an input of $\frac{1}{2}$. What do you think will be the long-term behavior of the resulting sequence of numbers in this case?

ⓒ What happens when you carry out the same process with a starting input of $x = 1$?

ⓓ In what way is this process of feeding outputs back in as inputs a recursive process?

Use with page 530.   UNIT 7 • DISCRETE MODELS OF CHANGE

LESSON OVERVIEW Although some real-world contexts are investigated, this lesson deals primarily with "pure" mathematics, albeit in an exploratory, hands-on manner. The mathematical topic explored, function iteration, is a fascinating and growing area of current mathematical development, with many applications. It leads to such contemporary topics as fractals and chaos. Although the term *function composition* is never used or explicitly discussed, function iteration consists of composing a function with itself. Thus, this lesson gives some introduction to function composition, which will be formalized in Course 4, Unit 3, "Logarithmic Functions and Data Models."

Lesson Objectives

- **To iterate functions and describe the resulting patterns, the long-term behavior in particular**
- **To describe the connection between function iteration and recursive formulas**
- **To analyze long-term behavior when iterating linear functions, using graphical iteration, numerical iteration, and algebraic methods, including fixed point analysis and connections to slope**
- **To provide an implicit introduction to the composition of functions**

LAUNCH   **full-class discussion**

Think About This Situation

See Teaching Master 184.

Doing the experiments here will set the stage for a closer investigation of function iteration, which is an example of sequential change and discrete dynamical systems. As usual, with discrete dynamical systems, it is important and interesting to analyze long-term behavior.

ⓐ ■ 16
  ■ 256
  ■ The following terms in the sequence will be 65,536 and 4,294,967,296.
  ■ The long-term behavior is that the sequence grows without bound.

ⓑ Starting with $\frac{1}{2}$, the sequence of numbers is $\frac{1}{2}, \frac{1}{4}, \frac{1}{16}, \frac{1}{256}, \frac{1}{65,536}, \ldots$. The long-term behavior of this sequence is that the numbers get smaller and smaller, tending toward 0.

ⓒ Starting with 1, the sequence is 1, 1, 1, 1, … . The long-term behavior is that the terms of the sequence will be 1.

ⓓ This is a recursive process because to get the next output, you need the previous output; thus, it is a *NOW-NEXT* (recursive) process.

INVESTIGATION 1 Play It Again ... and Again

This investigation is designed to establish the connection between evaluating recursive formulas and iterating functions and to give students an experience of the richness of long-term behavior that is possible when you iterate even simple functions.

In Lesson 1, students investigated the recursive formula $U_n = rU_{n-1} + b$ and found that the long-term behavior could be influenced by the parameters r and b and also by the initial value. In this investigation, they find that iterating different functions can create an amazing diversity of outcomes, including oscillations that eventually converge to a single value, oscillations that do not converge, and chaotic behavior. Small changes in parameters can cause surprising results. In this investigation, many questions are raised without attempting to reach closure on them, since the mathematics required for such closure is beyond the scope of high school mathematics. However, the details of iterating *linear* functions are investigated more closely in Investigation 2 of this lesson.

Iterating a function is fundamentally the same idea as sequentially evaluating a recursive formula. Students need time to think about how these processes relate both to each other and to evaluating a function.

x	$f(x) = 2x + 1$		n	$U_n = 2U_{n-1} + 1,$ $U_0 = 1$		x	iterating $f(x) = 2x + 1$
0	1		0	1		0	1
1	3		1	3		1	3
2	5		2	7		3	7
3	7		3	15		7	15
⋮	⋮		⋮	⋮		⋮	⋮

Your students may say that the third table above, iterating a function, is like a selection of the inputs and outputs from the first table, function evaluation. The second and third tables have the same outputs but for different input values. You may wish to lead a full-class discussion clarifying these processes following Activity 2 or with the Checkpoint discussion on page 533.

1. **a.** Using the *NOW-NEXT* equation with an initial value of 1 yields the sequence 1, −3, 13, 333.

    b. $U_n = 2(U_{n-1})^2 - 5$;. $U_0 = 1$. $U_1 = -3$; $U_2 = 13$; $U_3 = 333$.

    c. Iterating $f(x)$ three times starting with $x = 1$ yields the sequence 1, −3, 13, 333.

    d. The sequences in Parts a, b, and c are the same. Iterating the function $f(x) = 2x^2 - 5$ is the same as evaluating the recursive formula $U_n = 2(U_{n-1})^2 - 5$, which is the same as finding successive values of the *NOW-NEXT* equation. All three processes produce identical sequences. It is just the notation that is different.

See additional Teaching Notes on page T549E.

Unit 7

INVESTIGATION 1 ▶ Play It Again … and Again

The process of feeding the outputs of a function back into itself as inputs is called **iterating a function**. Imagine making a reduced copy on a copying machine, then making a reduced copy of your copy, then making a reduced copy of that copy, and so on.

As you might expect, there is a close connection between iterating a function and evaluating a recursive formula.

1. Consider the equation $NEXT = 2(NOW)^2 - 5$.

a. Use an initial value of 1 and find the next three values.

b. Rewrite the equation as a recursive formula using U_n and U_{n-1}. Let $U_0 = 1$ and then find U_1, U_2, and U_3.

c. Now think about iterating a function, as illustrated in the diagram before the "Think About This Situation" on page 530. Iterate $f(x) = 2x^2 - 5$ three times, starting with $x = 1$.

d. Compare the sequences of numbers you got in Parts a, b, and c.

2. Think about iterating the function $f(x) = 3x + 1$, starting with $x = 2$. A table that shows the iteration process is similar to function tables you have used before, but with a new twist.

a. Complete a table like the one below.

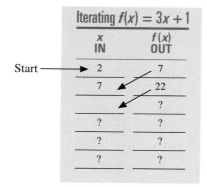

b. How would the table be different if you started with $x = 0$?

3. Consider the recursive formula $U_n = (U_{n-1})^2 + 3U_{n-1} + 4$, with $U_0 = 1$.

   a. Rewrite the recursive formula as an equation using the words *NOW* and *NEXT*.

   b. What function can be iterated to yield the same sequence of numbers generated by the recursive formula? Check your answer by iterating your function, starting with an input of 1, and comparing the result to the corresponding sequence generated by the recursive formula.

4. Now consider the function $g(x) = -0.7x + 6$.

   a. What recursive formula yields the same sequence of numbers generated by iterating $g(x)$?

   b. Use the last-answer feature of your calculator or computer software to iterate $g(x)$ at least 30 times, starting with 14. Describe any patterns that you see in the iteration sequence.

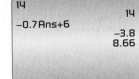

   c. Use the recursion mode on your calculator or computer software to produce a graph illustrating the iteration of $g(x)$, starting with $x = 14$.

As with any process of sequential change, it is important to study the long-term behavior of function iteration.

5. Suppose $f(x) = \sqrt{x}$. Iterate this function, starting with $x = 256$. Describe the long-term behavior of the resulting sequence of numbers.

6. Now suppose $h(x) = 1 - x$. Iterate this function and describe the long-term behavior of the iteration sequence for each of the following starting values.

   a. $x = 5$

   b. $x = -28$

   c. $x = \frac{1}{2}$

In the next activity, you will iterate functions of the form $f(x) = rx(1 - x)$. This is a broadly useful equation in mathematics, called the **logistic equation**. For different values of r, you get different functions, each of which may have a different behavior when iterated. Iterating these functions has proven to be a very useful method of modeling certain population growth situations. Also, the study of the behavior of these functions has contributed to many important developments in modern mathematics over the last several decades.

7. For each of the function iterations below, use $x = 0.02$ as the starting value and describe any patterns you see, including the long-term behavior.

   a. Iterate $f(x) = 2.7x(1 - x)$.

   b. Iterate $g(x) = 3.2x(1 - x)$.

   c. Iterate $h(x) = 3.5x(1 - x)$.

   d. Iterate $j(x) = 3.83x(1 - x)$.

   e. Iterate $k(x) = 4x(1 - x)$.

3. **a.** $NEXT = NOW^2 + 3NOW + 4$

   b. $f(x) = x^2 + 3x + 4$. The sequence generated starting at 1 is 1, 8, 92, 8,744, 76,483,772. Be sure students can iterate the function, as well as use the recursive formula.

4. **a.** Iterating the recursive formula $U_n = -0.7U_{n-1} + 6$ will yield the same sequence of numbers as iterating the function $g(x) = -0.7x + 6$, as long as you start with the same initial value.

   b. Patterns that students may notice include an oscillation between positive and negative numbers at the beginning, but then they are all positive and eventually seem to approach a number near 3.529. If you iterate even further, you get convergence, to 9 decimal places, to 3.529411765. Students may also notice that as the numbers approach 3.529411765, they are alternately above and below that limit. The convergence point will be carefully explored in the next investigation, so you should not expect students to explain it now. (The exact number to which the sequence tends in the long term is $\frac{6}{1.7}$, which is the solution to the equation $x = -0.7x + 6$. This value is sometimes called a "fixed point" since, if you ever get to it, you never move from it. See Activity 3 of Investigation 2, on page 535.)

   c.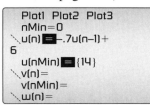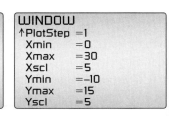

5. The iteration sequence is 256, 16, 4, 2, 1.414, 1.189, 1.091, … . The long-term behavior tends to 1. Students could enter 256, type in $\sqrt{ANS}$, and press ENTER repeatedly. Or they might put their calculator in "recursion mode," enter $U_n = \sqrt{U_{n-1}}$, and then look at a table of values.

6. **a.** 5, −4, 5, −4, 5, …
      The long-term behavior is that the sequence oscillates between 5 and −4.

   b. −28, 29, −28, 29, …
      The long-term behavior is that the sequence oscillates between −28 and 29.

   c. 0.5, 0.5, 0.5, 0.5, …
      This sequence is fixed at 0.5.

7. **In this activity, students investigate the logistic equation. Much has been studied and written about this equation. For example, see *Chaos* by James Gleick (Viking, 1987) or *Chaos, Fractals, and Dynamics* by Robert Devaney (Addison-Wesley, 1990). Here, students try a few experiments to see the richness of iterative behavior. Note that the experiments show "convergence" to one number, a two-cycle, a four-cycle, a three-cycle, and "chaos." By varying the parameter *r*, it is possible to get cycles of all possible lengths, although they become difficult to find by computer experimentation. One of the fundamental results in this field of mathematics is that if there is a three-cycle, as in Part d, then there will be a cycle of every other length, as well as completely chaotic cycles, as in Part e.**

   a. Converges to a single value $\frac{1.7}{2.7}$ or approximately 0.6296296.

See additional Teaching Notes on page T549E.

Unit 7

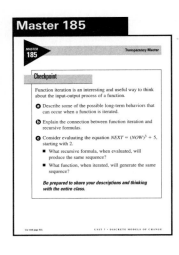

Checkpoint

See Teaching Master 185.

ⓐ Possible long-term behaviors seen in this investigation are no change at all, eventual convergence to a single value, oscillation among several values, and "chaos."

ⓑ If the function and the recursive formula express the same pattern of change, then function iteration and sequential evaluation of recursive formulas produce the same output values for the same starting value.

ⓒ ▪ $U_n = (U_{n-1})^3 + 5$, $U_n = 2$
    ▪ $f(x) = x^3 + 5$, starting with 2

CONSTRUCTING A MATH TOOLKIT: Students should summarize in their Math Toolkits what it means to iterate a function and include examples of function iteration and its connection to recursive formulas.

MORE

ASSIGNMENT pp. 537–545

Students can now begin Organizing Task 4 or 5 or Reflecting Task 1, 4, or 5 from the MORE assignment following Investigation 2.

APPLY individual task

▶On Your Own

a. The iteration sequence converges to approximately 0.739085. (This is the x value of the intersection point of the graphs of $y = x$ and $y = \cos x$.)
   ▪ $A_n = \cos(A_{n-1})$, $A_0 = 10$
   ▪ $NEXT = \cos(NOW)$, starting with 10

b. Responses will vary. You may wish to have students share their results with others in their group.

Checkpoint

Function iteration is an interesting and useful way to think about the input-output process of a function.

ⓐ Describe some of the possible long-term behaviors that can occur when a function is iterated.

ⓑ Explain the connection between function iteration and recursive formulas.

ⓒ Consider evaluating the equation $NEXT = (NOW)^3 + 5$, starting with 2.
- What recursive formula, when evaluated, will produce the same sequence?
- What function, when iterated, will generate the same sequence?

Be prepared to share your descriptions and thinking with the entire class.

Function iteration is a relatively new field of mathematical study. There are many unanswered questions in this area, including questions about the behavior of logistic equations like the ones you investigated in Activity 7. Function iteration is related to such contemporary mathematical topics as *fractals* and *chaos*. Applications of function iteration are being discovered every day, in areas like electronic transmission of large

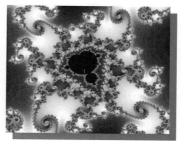

The Mandelbrot Set (fractal)

blocks of data, computer graphics, and modeling population growth. You will explore some of these ideas and applications in the MORE set at the end of this lesson.

▶On Your Own

Function iteration can be applied to any function.

a. Iterate $g(x) = \cos x$, starting with $x = 10$. (Be sure you are using radian mode, not degrees.) Describe the long-term behavior of the iteration sequence.
- What recursive formula yields the same sequence as iterating $g(x)$?
- Rewrite your recursive formula using the words *NOW* and *NEXT*.

b. Choose any function not used in this investigation and several different starting points. Iterate your function, starting with each of your starting points, and describe the long-term behavior of the iteration sequences.

INVESTIGATION 2 ▶ Iterating Linear Functions

In Investigation 1, you iterated a variety of functions, both linear and nonlinear. The iterative behavior of nonlinear functions is not yet completely understood and is currently a lively area of mathematical research. On the other hand, iteration of linear functions is understood well.

1. Just as with many other ideas in mathematics, the process of function iteration can be represented visually. To see how *graphical iteration* works, consider the function $f(x) = 0.5x + 2$. The graphs of $y = x$ and $y = 0.5x + 2$ are shown below on the same set of axes. Think graphically about how an input becomes an output, which then becomes the next input, which produces the next output, and so on.

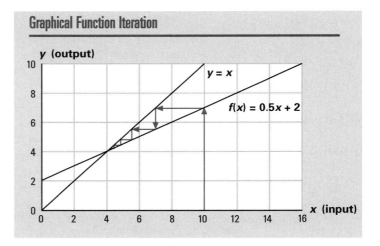

Graphical Function Iteration

In the diagram above, 10 has been chosen as the original input. To find an input's (x value's) resulting output (y value), you go up to the graph of the function you are iterating. Next, according to the process of function iteration, the output gets put back into the function as an input. This is accomplished graphically by moving horizontally to the $y = x$ graph, since on this line the y value (the current output) is identical to the x value (the new input). Now go vertically again to find the output associated with the new input. The process continues in this way until, in this example, you are drawn into the inter-section point of the two graphs. This is the process of **graphical iteration**.

   a. From this graphical perspective, what is the long-term behavior of the function $f(x) = 0.5x + 2$ when iterated? Use your calculator to iterate $f(x)$, starting with $x = 10$, and see if the numerical result matches the graphical result.

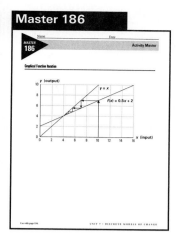

INVESTIGATION 2 Iterating Linear Functions

In this investigation, students are challenged to determine the influence of *a* and *b* when the linear function $f(x) = ax + b$ is iterated. A new technique is introduced: creating a web graph. This technique is difficult for some students, since they are already working with functions in two ways: evaluating $y = f(x)$ to get outputs for *any x* in the domain and iterating $f(x)$ to generate a sequence of outputs, each of which is the next input. Now a web graph is superimposed on the graph of the function, and, in a sense, the web graph selects points on the complete graph of a function to mirror the way that iterating a function selects input/output pairs from the "complete" table of a function. As it does this, the long-term behavior of the iterated function becomes apparent.

Activities 1–3 flow together, and it may be helpful to pause after these activities and have a full-class discussion to be sure that students understand what the web graph does and how it relates to a recursive formula and to iterating a function. After Activities 1–3, you may want to have students examine $U_n = 0.5U_{n-1} + 2$ using a "last-answer" feature or key, by making a graph of U_n, by examining a calculator- or computer-produced table of U_n, and by iterating $y = 0.5x + 2$ in a handmade table, in addition to using the web graph. Ask what the relation $y = 0.5x + 2$ would mean in the trout-population context from Lesson 1, and ask what the fixed point means in that context. Taking time here to try all these techniques on a few different linear functions and making connections among all the representations is time well spent. You will want to use small integer values for the parameters at this point to facilitate graphing, but in each case you can ask what the relation would mean in the trout-population context. Students will then be more confident about adding yet another technique in Activity 4 and continuing on with their investigation of fixed points.

Some students persist in thinking that fixed points exist only when the iterated function sequence is convergent. That is, they seem to equate "attracting" and "fixed." This confusion is understandable, and you will want to take time to discuss it.

Iteration of nonlinear functions is not investigated here, but students have an opportunity to experiment with these in Modeling Tasks 2 and 3.

1. **See Teaching Master 186.**

   a. The graph seems to indicate that the long-term iterative behavior of $f(x)$ is that it will converge at 4. Iterating the function shows that the long-term behavior is steady at 4, just as in the graphical iteration.

Unit 7

1. **b.** Student responses may vary. Examples follow.

   ■ For a function $y = f(x)$, x is the input and y is the output. You get y (the output) by substituting for x (the input). This substitution gives an ordered pair (x, y) on the graph of $f(x)$. But the conventional rule for graphing is that (x, y) means to go horizontally to x and then vertically to y. Thus, to find the output using the graph, you first find x on the horizontal (input) axis, and then you go vertically to the graph to find the y (output) that goes with it.

   ■ Roughly, to turn an output into an input means to turn y into x, and that's what the $y = x$ line does. Graphically, you want to reflect the y (output) value onto the x (input) axis.

      A more detailed explanation might be the following: An output is on the vertical axis; if you want to use it as the next input, then you need to get it onto the horizontal (input) axis. However, you want to keep the same distance from the origin along the axis, because you want the same numerical value. Moving over to the line $y = x$ and looking down to the x-axis will accomplish this.

   c. The graphical iteration starting with $x = 1$ also converges to 4.

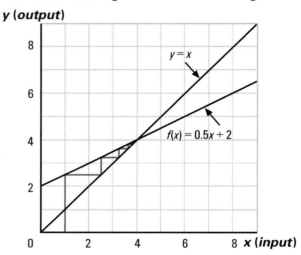

2. The iteration shown here begins with $x = 1$. The iteration is converging to $\frac{8}{1.5}$ or approximately 5.33. In Activity 1, the pattern was a "stair step," while here the pattern is more of a spiral or a "cobweb." Similar patterns occur whenever the slope of the iterated function is negative. Accept any reasonable conjecture. Students will study iteration patterns more as the lesson progresses.

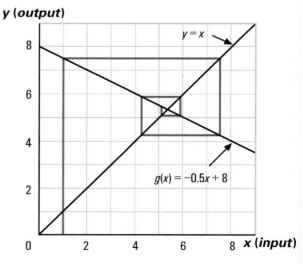

See additional Teaching Notes on page T549F.

b. Now, think about the process of graphical iteration as illustrated in the diagram on the previous page.

- Explain, in your own words, why you can graphically find the output of a function for a given input by moving vertically to the graph of the function.

- Explain, in your own words, why you can graphically turn an output into the next input by moving horizontally from the graph of the function to the graph of $y = x$.

c. Carefully draw the graphs of $y = 0.5x + 2$ and $y = x$ on graph paper and illustrate the process of graphical iteration using $x = 1$ as the original input. What do you notice?

2. Sketch graphs and illustrate the process of graphical function iteration for the function $g(x) = -0.5x + 8$. Choose your own starting value. Compare the overall pattern of the graphical iteration to the patterns you saw in Activity 1. Make a conjecture about what kinds of linear function rules yield graphical iteration patterns like the one you found in this activity. You will test your conjecture later in this lesson.

3. As you have seen, sometimes when you iterate a function, you are drawn to a particular value, and if you reach that value, you never leave it. Such a value is called a *fixed point*.

a. Look back at Activity 1. What is the fixed point when iterating the function $f(x) = 0.5x + 2$?

b. What is the fixed point when iterating the function $f(x) = -0.7x + 6$?

c. The precise definition of a **fixed point** is a value x such that $f(x) = x$. Explain why this definition fits the above description of a fixed point: "If you reach that value, you never leave it."

4. One method that sometimes works to find a fixed point is iterating the function, either numerically or graphically, and seeing what happens. Another method for finding a fixed point is to use the definition of a fixed point. That is, set the rule for the function equal to x and solve. Use this symbolic method to find the fixed point when iterating the function $f(x) = 0.5x + 2$, and compare your answer to your response in Part a of Activity 3.

5. For each of the functions on the following page, try to find a fixed point using each of these three methods.

- Iterate by using the last-answer feature of your calculator or computer software or by producing a table (numeric method).

- Iterate graphically (graphic method).

- Solve the equation $f(x) = x$ (symbolic method).

Organize your work as follows.

- Try a variety of starting values for each function.

- Keep a record of what you try, the results, and any patterns that you notice.

Each student should use all three of the methods on the previous page for Parts a and b.

a. $s(x) = 0.6x + 3$

b. $u(x) = 4.3x + 1$

For Parts c through h, share the workload among members of your group.

c. $t(x) = 0.2x - 5$ **d.** $v(x) = 3x - 4$

e. $w(x) = x + 2$ **f.** $f(x) = -0.8x + 4$

g. $h(x) = -x + 2$ **h.** $k(x) = -2x + 5$

6. Three important characteristics to look for when iterating functions are *attracting fixed points*, *repelling fixed points*, and *cycles*. An **attracting fixed point** is a fixed point such that iteration sequences that start close to it get pulled into it. In contrast, iteration sequences move away from a **repelling fixed point**, except of course for the sequence that begins at the fixed point. A **cycle** is a set of numbers that an iteration sequence repeats over and over.

   a. For each of the linear functions you iterated in Activity 5, decide as a group whether it has an attracting fixed point, a repelling fixed point, a cycle, or none of these.

   b. Is there a connection between the slope of the graph of a linear function and the function's behavior when iterated? If so, explain how you could complete Part a of this activity simply by knowing the slope of each linear function's graph.

Checkpoint

In this investigation, you have seen that linear functions have rich and varied behavior when iterated.

ⓐ Describe what a fixed point is and how to find one. Give as many different descriptions of how to find a fixed point as you can.

ⓑ Attracting fixed points seem to pull you into them. But do you ever actually get to a fixed point? Explain.

ⓒ Describe the different long-term behaviors that can occur when a linear function is iterated. For each of the behaviors described, explain how that behavior is completely characterized by the slope of the graph of the iterated function.

ⓓ In the first lesson of this unit, you investigated situations that could be modeled by combined recursive formulas of the form $A_n = rA_{n-1} + b$. What is the connection between these combined recursive formulas and iterating linear functions?

Be prepared to share your descriptions and thinking with the entire class.

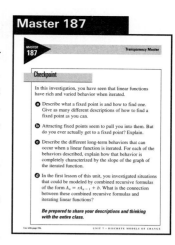

5. **a.** $s(x) = 0.6x + 3$: The fixed point is 7.5. You are pulled into the fixed point no matter where you start; the graphical pattern as you approach the fixed point is a stair step.

    b. $u(x) = 4.3x + 1$: The fixed point is $-\frac{10}{33}$. With numerical and graphical iteration, you will never find this fixed point unless you start right at it; all numerical and graphical iterations from starting values that are not the fixed point itself are pushed away from the fixed point; the graphical iteration pattern is a stair step.

    c. $t(x) = 0.2x - 5$: The fixed point is -6.25. Same general pattern and analysis as in Part a.

    d. $v(x) = 3x - 4$: The fixed point is 2. Same general pattern and analysis as in Part b.

    e. $w(x) = x + 2$: There is no fixed point. Graphical iteration will produce a stair step pattern; all numerical and graphical iteration sequences tend to positive infinity.

    f. $f(x) = -0.8x + 4$: The fixed point is $\frac{20}{9}$. Graphical iteration produces a spiral pattern; all numerical and graphical iteration sequences are pulled into the fixed point.

    g. $h(x) = -x + 2$: The fixed point is 1. The graphical iteration pattern is a "cycle"; each starting value (except the fixed point) is part of its own two-cycle, and the other value is the reflection of the starting point across the line $x = 1$. Using numerical iteration, you will never see the fixed point unless you start there, because all starting values not equal to the fixed point are caught in their own two-cycle.

    h. $k(x) = -2x + 5$: The fixed point is $\frac{5}{3}$. The graphical iteration pattern is a cobweb that spirals out; all starting values, except the fixed point itself, are pushed away from the fixed point.

6. **The definitions of attracting and repelling fixed points stated here are accurate but intuitive. The formal definitions require infinite limits. (For example, see the note after Activity 3.) Infinite limits should not be stressed with students at this time; additional work with infinite limits is undertaken in Course 4, Unit 1, "Rates of Change." Another subtle point to be aware of (in case it comes up) is that, in general, only iteration sequences that start "close" to an attracting fixed point will converge to the fixed point, but in the case of linear functions, all iteration sequences converge to an attracting fixed point, if there is one.**

    a. Activity 5 Parts a, c, and f each have an attracting fixed point. Parts b, d, and h each have a repelling fixed point; in Part h, every iteration sequence (other than the one starting at the fixed point) eventually alternates between large positive and negative numbers, while in Parts b and d, starting values greater than the fixed point are repelled to positive infinity and starting values less than the fixed point are repelled to negative infinity. Part g has two-cycle behavior, with a different two-cycle for each starting value (except for the fixed point), and the fixed point is not considered repelling or attracting since iteration sequences do not get further or closer to the fixed point. Part e is the only one that does not have a fixed point at all.

    b. If $|\, slope\, | > 1$, then the linear function has a repelling fixed point.
    If $|\, slope\, | < 1$, then the linear function has an attracting fixed point.
    If the slope is equal to 1 (and the y-intercept is not 0), then the linear function has no fixed point.
    If the slope is equal to -1, then the linear function has two-cycles and the fixed point is neither attracting nor repelling.
    A function with a positive slope will have a stair step pattern, and one with a negative slope will have a cobweb or spiral pattern.

CONSTRUCTING A MATH TOOLKIT: After the Checkpoint discussion, have students illustrate graphical function iteration and write a description of how it is done. Also, have them describe what a fixed point is, how to find it, and how to determine whether it is attracting, repelling, or neither.

See additional Teaching Notes on page T549G.

Unit 7

▶On Your Own

a.　$P_n = 0.8P_{n-1} + 1,000$

b.　Iterate $f(x) = 0.8x + 1,000$, starting with $x = 3,000$.

c.　The long-term behavior of the iteration sequence is that it levels off at 5,000. This is the same as the long-term behavior of the trout population.

d.

e.　Solving $x = 0.8x + 1,000$ yields $x = 5,000$ as the fixed point. The fixed point is attracting: The slope of the line is 0.8, and $|\,0.8\,| < 1$. Whenever the absolute value of the slope is less than 1, the fixed point is attracting.

f.　The fact that the iterated function modeling the fish-population problem has an attracting fixed point at 5,000 tells us that the population will level off over time at 5,000, regardless of where it starts.

MORE　ASSIGNMENT　*pp. 537–545*

Modeling:　4 and choice of one*

Organizing:　2 and choice of one*

Reflecting:　2 and choice of one*

Extending:　Choose one*

*When choice is indicated, it is important to leave the choice to the student.

NOTE: *It is best if Organizing tasks are discussed as a whole class after they have been assigned as homework.*

MORE　independent assignment

Modeling

1.　a.　■ The iterated values are always 1.

　　　■ The iterated values are attracted to 1.

　　　■ The iterated values are repelled to positive infinity.

　　b.　A fixed point for $f(x)$ is 1. It is a combination of attracting and repelling. It is attracting when you start with x slightly less than 1 and repelling when you start with x slightly greater than 1.

On Your Own

At the beginning of this unit, you modeled the trout population of a fishing pond. The pond had an initial population of 3,000 trout. There were 1,000 trout added at the end of each year, and regardless of restocking, the population decreased by 20% each year due to the combined effect of several causes. One of the equations that models this situation is

$$NEXT = 0.8NOW + 1,000.$$

a. Rewrite this equation as a recursive formula.

b. What function can be iterated to produce the same sequence of population numbers generated by the recursive formula? With what value should you start the function iteration?

c. Iterate the function in Part b and describe the long-term behavior of the iteration sequence. Compare this behavior to the long-term behavior of the trout population that you discovered in Investigation 1 of Lesson 1, page 489.

d. Graphically iterate this function, starting with $x = 3,000$.

e. Find the fixed point by solving an equation. Is the fixed point attracting or repelling? How can you tell by examining the slope of the function's graph?

f. Explain what the fixed point and its attracting or repelling property tell you about the changing trout population.

MORE

Modeling • Organizing • Reflecting • Extending

Modeling

1. Experiment with iterating the function $f(x) = x^3 - x^2 + 1$.

   a. Describe the behavior of the iteration sequence when you iterate $f(x)$ with the following beginning values.

   - Begin with $x = 1$.
   - Begin with $x = 0.8$.
   - Begin with $x = 1.2$.

   b. Find a fixed point for $f(x)$. Is this fixed point repelling, attracting, some combination of repelling and attracting, or none of these? Explain.

2. Experiment with iterating $g(x) = 3.7x - 3.7x^2$.

   a. Find the fixed points of $g(x)$ by writing and solving an appropriate equation.

   b. Iterate $g(x)$ starting with $x = 0.74$, which is close to a fixed point. Carefully examine the iteration sequence by listing these iterations:

   ■ List iterations 1 through 6.

   ■ List iterations 16 through 20.

   ■ List iterations 50 through 55.

   ■ List iterations 64 through 68.

   c. Describe any patterns you see in the iteration sequence. Does the iteration sequence get attracted to the fixed point? Does it get steadily repelled? A fixed point is called repelling if iteration sequences that begin near it get pushed away from the fixed point at some time, even if such sequences occasionally come back close to the fixed point. Is the fixed point at about 0.73 repelling?

3. Consider iterating $h(x) = 3.2x - 0.8x^2$.

   a. The fixed points of $h(x)$ are repelling. Do you think you will find them by numerical iteration? Explain your reasoning.

   b. Find the fixed points of $h(x)$ using symbolic reasoning.

   c. Experiment with iterating $h(x)$, starting with initial values just above and below each fixed point. Carefully describe the characteristics of each fixed point.

4. Function iteration can be used to model population change. Consider, for example, the bowhead whale population described in Modeling Task 2 of Lesson 1, page 495. A status report on the bowhead whales of Alaska estimated that the 1993 population of this stock was between 6,900 and 9,200 and that the difference between births and deaths yielded an annual growth rate of about 3.1%. No hunting of bowhead whales is allowed, except that Alaskan Inuit are allowed to take, or harvest, about 50 bowhead whales each year for their livelihood. (Source: nmml.afsc.noaa.gov/CetaceanAssessment/bowhead/bmsos.htm)

   a. Write a recursive formula and an equivalent function that can be iterated to model this situation.

2. **The point of this task and the next one is to illustrate the variety of behavior that is possible for repelling fixed points. An attracting fixed point always behaves in the same way in that iteration sequences that start close to it converge to it. In contrast, there are many ways that repelling behavior can occur. For example, iteration sequences may "blow up" and tend to positive or negative infinity; they may oscillate and become unbounded; or they may get pushed away from a repelling fixed point and toward an attracting fixed point. This task illustrates another type of behavior, in which iteration sequences get pushed away, then bounce back close, get pushed away again, bounce back, and so on. In Modeling Task 3, students will see an example of how iteration sequences can be pushed away to a two-cycle.**

   a. Solving $x = 3.7x - 3.7x^2$ produces $x = 0$ or $x = \frac{27}{37} = 0.\overline{729}$.

   b. Student responses may vary. The following uses the suggested initial value, 0.74.
      - 0.71188, 0.75890, 0.67700, 0.80908, 0.57153, 0.90607
      - 0.72825, 0.73224, 0.72544, 0.73695, 0.71725
      - 0.87707, 0.39892, 0.88719, 0.37030, 0.86276, 0.43810
      - 0.73218, 0.72555, 0.73677, 0.71757, 0.74985

   c. The iterated values seem to oscillate above and below 0.73. More interesting, they seem to move away from 0.73, then come back close, then move away, and then come back close, and it seems that this pattern continues. The iterated values do not get attracted to the fixed point, and they are not steadily repelled. But since the iterated values do get repelled at times, we classify the fixed point as repelling.

      (A more detailed analysis of this iterated function behavior is the following. There are two fixed points, $x = 0$ and $x = 0.\overline{729} \approx 0.73$. Below 0, iteration sequences are repelled toward negative infinity. Above 1, iteration sequences also tend toward negative infinity. Between 0 and 1 (except at $x = 0.\overline{729}$), there is the pattern seen above: Iteration sequences are pushed away and then at some time jump back toward $0.\overline{729}$. Iteration sequences that begin in this range are not attracted to $0.\overline{729}$. Whenever a sequence gets close to $0.\overline{729}$, either slightly larger or slightly smaller, it is then pushed away. Thus, $x = 0.\overline{729}$ is a repelling fixed point.)

3. **This task provides another example of repelling fixed point behavior. See also Modeling Task 2.**

   a. Since the fixed points are repelling, iteration sequences are pushed away from them. Thus, it would be virtually impossible to find them by trial-and-error iteration, since you would not be pulled into them by the iteration.

   b. Solving $x = 3.2x - 0.8x^2$ produces $x = 0$ or $x = 2.75$.

   c. Initial values below 0 repel to negative infinity; initial values just above 0 are repelled from 0 and then attracted to a two-cycle oscillating between about 2.05 and 3.20. Initial values just above and just below 2.75 are repelled from 2.75 and attracted to the same two-cycle. So the fixed points are both repelling (and the two-cycle is attracting).

4. a. $U_n = 1.031U_{n-1} - 50$
      $f(x) = 1.031x - 50$

Unit 7

4. b. The long-term behavior is that the iterated values are always increasing. This is not a good model for predicting the population hundreds of years from now. It is not realistic to predict that the whale population will increase without bound. There would be too many possible outside interferences that could cause changes in the population.

c. The fixed point is $\frac{50}{0.031} \approx 1{,}612.9$. The fixed point is repelling since the slope of the iterated function is 1.031, which is greater than 1.

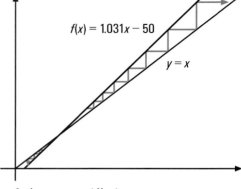

$f(x) = 1.031x - 50$

$y = x$

d. If the initial population is greater than the fixed point (1,613 whales), then the population will continue to grow without bound. If the population gets below the fixed point, the population will die out. The farther you get beyond the fixed point, the faster the population grows (dies).

Organizing

1. a. One method is to graph $y = x - 3$ and $y = 0.5x$. Then find the point of intersection; the x value is the solution. A second method is to solve the equation algebraically. The solution is 6.

b. ■ We can add 3 to both sides of the original equation and get the equivalent equation $x = 0.5x + 3$.
   ■ $f(x) = 0.5x + 3$

c. Regardless of the starting value, the iterated values are attracted to 6, which is the solution to the original equation. This long-term behavior provides a solution to the equation because the fixed point is attracting, and, by definition, the fixed point is the value of x such that $x = f(x)$. So in this case, the iteration method will generate the solution to the equation.

d. Rewrite the equation as $x = \frac{1}{3}x + 2$ and iterate. The long-term behavior of the sequence will be attracted to the fixed point, 3, which is the solution. Note that this iteration does approach the fixed point because the slope has absolute value less than 1, so the fixed point is attracting. If the equation is reformulated in a way such that the slope is greater than 1 (for example, $x = 3x - 6$), then the fixed point is repelling and cannot be found by iteration.

e. First, rewrite the equation in the form $x = rx + b$, where $|r| < 1$. Then iterate the function $f(x) = rx + b$. Rewriting the equation in this form forces the iterated function to have an attracting fixed point, which is the solution to the original equation.

2. a. Setting $x = f(x)$ and solving for x gives $x = \frac{b}{1-r}$.

b. The fixed point is $\frac{b}{1-r}$, in this case, $\frac{-4}{1-0.75}$ or -16.

c. ■ The function will have an attracting fixed point if and only if $|slope| < 1$.
   ■ The fixed point found by iterating is -16. This is the same point found using the formula.

b. Using the low population estimate as the initial value, iterate and describe the long-term behavior of the population. Do you think this model is a good one to use for predicting the bowhead whale population hundreds of years from now? Why or why not?

c. Find the fixed point. By examining the slope of the graph of the iterated function, decide if the fixed point is attracting or repelling. Confirm your conclusions by graphically iterating the function.

d. Write a brief analysis of the changing bowhead whale population, as described by your model. As part of your analysis, describe the role played by the fixed point and make some long-term predictions based on different initial whale populations.

Organizing

1. It is possible to use function iteration to solve equations. Consider the equation $x - 3 = 0.5x$.

   a. Before solving the equation by using function iteration, solve it using at least two other methods. In each case, explain your method.

   b. To solve $x - 3 = 0.5x$ by function iteration, you will make use of fixed points. Consider the equation written in an equivalent form: $x = 0.5x + 3$.

   - Explain why this form is equivalent to the original form.

   - For what function does this equation define a fixed point?

   c. Iterate the function you identified in Part b for some initial value. Describe the long-term behavior. Explain why the observed long-term behavior gives you a solution to the original equation. Compare the solution you obtained to what you found in Part a.

   d. Use the method of function iteration to solve $2x + 5 = 6x - 7$. (If at first you do not succeed, try rewriting the equation in an equivalent form.)

   e. Summarize the method of function iteration to solve linear equations.

2. In this task, you will find and use a general formula for the fixed point of a linear function.

   a. Use the algebraic method for finding fixed points to derive a general formula for the fixed point of the linear function $f(x) = rx + b$.

   b. Use the general formula to find the fixed point for $h(x) = 0.75x - 4$.

   c. If the fixed point is attracting, then you can find it by iteration.

   - How can you tell from the formula for $h(x)$ that this function has an attracting fixed point?

   - Iterate $h(x)$ to find the fixed point and compare it to what you found using the general formula in Part b.

Unit 7

3. In Lesson 1, you investigated recursive formulas of the form $A_n = rA_{n-1} + b$. Suppose such a recursive formula represents year-to-year change in some population. Assume that r is a positive number less than 1.

a. Explain why the long-term population in this situation can be found by finding the fixed point of the function $f(x) = rx + b$.

b. Use the general fixed point formula from Part a of Organizing Task 2 to explain the following patterns you previously discovered about the trout-population problem in Lesson 1.

■ Changing the initial population does not change the long-term population.

■ Doubling the restocking amount doubles the long-term population.

■ Doubling the population-decrease rate cuts the long-term population in half.

4. Consider iteration of an arbitrary function, $y = f(x)$.

a. Represent the process of iterating $f(x)$ by an equation using the words *NOW* and *NEXT*.

b. Represent the process of iterating $f(x)$ by a recursive formula.

5. In Activity 7 of Investigation 1, page 532, you investigated the logistic equation, $f(x) = rx(1 - x)$. You found that different values of r produce different long-term iteration behavior. You can program a computer to play "music" that corresponds to the long-term behavior. For example, consider the BASIC program below.

```
10  volume = 50
20  duration = 0.5
30  input "r = "; r
40  x = 0.02
50  print x
60  pitch = 220*4^x
70  sound pitch,duration,volume
80  x = r*x*(1-x)
90  goto 50
```

a. Explain the purpose of each step of this program.

b. Enter this program, or an equivalent program, into a computer. Run the program using the values 2.7, 3.2, 3.5, and 3.83 for r. Describe the results. Explain how the patterns in sound generated by the computer program compare to the numerical patterns you found in Activity 7 of Investigation 1.

3. a. To find the long-term population, you must find A_n for very large values of n. Thus, you need to evaluate many values of A_n, which is the same as iterating $f(x)$. Since $|r| < 1$, the fixed point of $f(x)$ is attracting. Thus, the fixed point of $f(x)$ will give the long-term population.

b. From Organizing Task 2, we know that the fixed point, and thus the long-term population in this case, is $\frac{b}{1-r}$.

■ The initial population is not part of this formula, so changing the initial population will not affect the long-term population.

■ Doubling the restocking amount means doubling b, which will double the numerator in the formula for the long-term population. Thus, the long-term population is doubled.

■ r is the population growth rate, so $1 - r$ is the population decrease rate. Thus, doubling the population decrease rate will double $1 - r$, which doubles the denominator in the formula for long-term population. So the long-term population is cut in half.

4. a. $NEXT = f(NOW)$

b. $U_n = f(U_{n-1})$

5. a. 10 Set the volume level for the tones.

20 Play a tone for a duration corresponding to 0.5.

30 Ask the user to input a number that will be the value for r.

40 Set the initial value at 0.02.

50 Print the current value of x (the current term of the iteration sequence).

60 Set a pitch for the tone corresponding to the current value of x. (You can see from the formula that higher values of x will have higher tones.)

70 Play the tone for the current value of x for the defined duration at the defined volume.

80 Generate the next term in the iteration sequence for this function.

90 Repeat the process of printing the current term in the sequence and playing a tone corresponding to the term.

b. How to run the program depends on your system. The program will ask the user to input a value for r. Then it will play tones for each term in the iteration sequence corresponding to that value of r. The tones will indicate the different patterns seen in the lesson activity. That is, you will hear an attracting fixed point, two-cycle, four-cycle, three-cycle, and "chaos." Note that to stop one iteration sequence and start another using a different value of r, you must interrupt the program. Again, how to interrupt depends on your system.

Reflecting

1. Recursion seems like a self-referral process because, for example, an iterated function must refer back to itself in order to produce the next values. With population, you need to know the population now before you can know the next population; thus, population refers back to population. Likewise, amount of money saved now refers back to amount of money saved previously.

2. By definition, a fixed point for a function $f(x)$ is a number x such that $x = f(x)$. To graphically find a number such that $x = f(x)$, you must look for the points of intersection of the graphs of $y = x$ and $y = f(x)$.

3. Iteration sequences will not converge to a repelling fixed point, so you will never see them by experimental iteration unless you get unbelievably lucky and choose the fixed point itself to begin your iteration.

4. **a.** With minor changes in the value of r, different things happen. The iterated values get attracted, cycle, get repelled, or follow no observable pattern at all. It is difficult to predict what will happen with different values of r. More to the point, the long-term behavior for $r = 4$ showed no discernible pattern, that is, chaos. In this case, with $r = 4$, not all calculator and computer outputs will agree on the iteration, not only because of round-off errors but also, and more importantly, because of the nature of the chaotic behavior, in particular, the property of chaos to have "sensitive dependence on initial conditions." This means even a very small difference in initial conditions can result in wildly different long-term behavior. Thus, if at any given point in the iteration two calculators disagree slightly (due to round-off), then they are liable to disagree considerably later.

   b. Responses will vary. Robert May was probably referring to the incredibly rich and complex behavior of this simple equation when it is iterated. Experimenting with this equation and seeing the rich tapestry of patterns that emerge might, at least it seemed to May, create a sense of wonder about and appreciation for the complexity that resides in even mundane-looking mathematical equations. Perhaps people gaining this perspective would, in May's mind, contribute to a better world.

   c. Reports will vary.

5. **You may want to suggest that students read the chapter mentioned in Part c of Reflecting Task 4 in preparation for doing this task. Chaos is characterized in the newspaper article in several ways. Each is mentioned on page T542 and related to the behavior of the logistic equation that students studied in the lesson.**

Reflecting

1. In this unit, you have studied recursion in several contexts, for example recursive formulas and function iteration. Recursion is sometimes described as a "self-referral" process. Explain why this is a reasonable description of recursion.

2. Explain why the fixed points for a function $f(x)$ correspond to the points of intersection of the graphs of $y = f(x)$ and $y = x$.

3. Why do you think it is sometimes said that you can never "see" a repelling fixed point?

4. In this lesson, you briefly explored a famous equation in mathematics and science: the logistic equation, $f(x) = rx(1 - x)$. This equation was first studied extensively in the 1970s. Some of the first discoveries about the behavior of the iterated equation came from trying to apply it as a model in biology and ecology. Its behavior turned out to be surprisingly complex and profound, giving rise to what is sometimes called the science of *chaos*.

   a. Review what you found out about the iterated behavior of the logistic equation in Activity 7 of Investigation 1, page 532. Why do you think the term *chaos* has been used to describe certain long-term behavior of the logistic equation?

   b. One of the first investigators of the logistic equation was an Australian biologist named Robert May. May argued that the world would be a better place if every student were given a pocket calculator and encouraged to play with the logistic equation. What do you think May meant?

   c. *Optional:* Obtain a copy of the book *Chaos: Making a New Science* by James Gleick (New York: Viking, 1987) and read Chapter 3, entitled "Life's Ups and Downs." This chapter is an entertaining account of some of the history of the logistic equation. Write a two-page report summarizing the chapter.

5. The idea of chaos in mathematics comes from a new area of mathematics that is sometimes called *chaos theory*. Chaos theory is related to certain long-term behavior of the logistic equation, which you examined in Activity 7 of Investigation 1, page 532. Read the article on the next page, which attempts to apply chaos theory to politics. Summarize the description of chaos given in the article. How does this description relate to the long-term behavior of the logistic equation? Do you think the conclusions in the article are valid? Why or why not?

Unit 7

Counting on Chaos to Save Day for Dole
by Al Kamen

It's come to this. Robert J. Dole's poll numbers are so bad that Rich Galen, director of political communications for House Speaker Newt Gingrich (R-Ga.), is touting "Chaos Theory" to inspire the GOP faithful.

"Stay with me, here," Galen began in a memo written last week "For Distribution to Talk Show Hosts," a regular salvo he sends out to about 100 or so conservative radio folks.

"There is a relatively new branch of science which is called Chaos Theory," he explained. It talks about a "butterfly fluttering its wings in Argentina which ultimately leads to a thunderstorm in New Jersey."

But "you will not be able to predict, with any degree of precision, when lightning will form and strike … One second there is no lightning, and the next second the sky is bright. Chaos."

He went on: "Take another example. Suppose you take a wineglass and begin to squeeze it at its upper rim. If you continue to apply pressure, at some point the glass will break. The system will collapse entirely and instantaneously. Until the moment it breaks, it will be a perfectly usable glass. After the glass breaks, it will be nothing but a pile of shards."

"What does this have to do with the presidential campaign?" Galen asked, which seems like a pretty good question.

"My strong impression is there will come a time … when the Clinton campaign, like the glass, will entirely and instantaneously collapse. One moment it will be a campaign, the next moment it will be unrecognizable."

"That's why we don't have to be frightened by the current Dole-Clinton polling numbers," he said. Chaos theory will save the day, or at least win New Jersey.

"What we must do, however, is to continue to keep the pressure on. If we get discouraged [and] stop squeezing the rim of the glass, then the glass will never break."

Now we know why the Republicans are infinitely more interesting than the Democrats. The Republicans look to science. All the Democrats can say is: "It's the economy, stupid."

Source: *The Washington Post*, September 16, 1996.

Extending

1. The recursive formula for a geometric sequence looks like a combined recursive formula of the form $A_n = rA_{n-1} + b$ without the added b. This connection can be used to find a function formula for such combined recursive formulas. The strategy involves building from a function formula for a geometric sequence.

   a. What is the function formula for a geometric sequence with recursive formula $A_n = rA_{n-1}$ and initial value A_0?

   b. As the next step, think about the long-term behavior of $A_n = r^n A_0$ and compare it to the long-term behavior of $A_n = rA_{n-1} + b$. Consider the situation when $|r| < 1$.

   ■ Explain why the long-term behavior of $A_n = rA_{n-1} + b$ is attracted to its fixed point.

   ■ What is the long-term behavior of $A_n = r^n A_0$?

5.

■ ... "butterfly fluttering its wings in Argentina which ultimately leads to a thunderstorm in New Jersey." This relates to the idea that a small change in initial conditions (butterfly wing flutterings) can cause big changes in the long-term behavior (thunderstorm in New Jersey). The author of the article is probably referring to a property of chaos called "sensitive dependence on initial conditions."

■ ... "you will not be able to predict, with any degree of precision, when lightning will form and strike ... ." This relates to the fact that the chaotic behavior seen when iterating the logistic equation when $r = 4$ is completely deterministic in that there is a specific formula (the logistic equation) that determines what the iteration values will be. Yet it is unpredictable in that you cannot predict what the exact pattern of the iteration sequence will be.

■ The article talks about gradually squeezing a wineglass until, suddenly, it breaks. The author may be referring here to the sudden onset of chaos that is evident when iterating the logistic equation with different values of r. As you gradually increase r, the long-term behavior changes, but it is stable in the sense that it is characterized by attraction toward fixed points or cycles. Then, suddenly, somewhere between $r = 3.83$ and $r = 4$, chaos sets in, and there is no discernible pattern in the long-term behavior.

It is interesting that this new branch of mathematical analysis has attracted so much attention that it appears even in articles such as this. However, the analogy made in the article is nothing more than an analogy; the points made are rather superficial. To really apply chaos theory to politics would require a much more careful analysis.

Extending

1. a. $A_n = r^n A_0$

b. ■ The long-term behavior of $A_n = rA_{n-1} + b$ is the same as the long-term behavior when iterating $f(x) = rx + b$. We know that since $|r| < 1$, the fixed point of this iterated function is attracting.

■ When the absolute value of r is less than one and you raise r to bigger values of n, the result gets closer and closer to zero. Thus, the product $r^n A_0$ is getting closer and closer to zero; that is, it has long-term behavior of convergence to zero.

Unit 7

1. **c.** If $|r| < 1$, then r^n will converge to 0 as n gets very large (long-term behavior). Thus, $r^n A_0$ will converge to 0, so $r^n A_0 + FIX$ will converge to FIX.

d. ■ When looking for the initial value, set $n = 0$. This will give you $r^0 A_0 + FIX$. Since $r^0 = 1$ ($r \neq 0$), the initial value is $A_0 + FIX$.

■ Substituting $n = 0$ gives $A_0 = r^0(A_0 - FIX) + FIX = 1(A_0 - FIX) + FIX = A_0$.

e. The fixed point of $y = 2x + 1$ is -1, so $A_n = 2^n(3 + 1) - 1 = 4(2^n) - 1$.
$A_5 = 4(2^5) - 1 = 127$
Using the recursive formula:
$A_0 = 3; A_1 = 7; A_2 = 15; A_3 = 31; A_4 = 63; A_5 = 127$.
They are the same value.

f. The function formula derived in Organizing Task 5 of Lesson 2, on page 523, is $A_n = r^n A_0 + b\left(\dfrac{r^n - 1}{r - 1}\right)$. The fixed point of $A_n = rA_{n-1} + b$ can be found by solving $x = rx + b$. This yields $\dfrac{b}{1 - r}$. Substituting $\dfrac{b}{1 - r}$ for FIX in the formula $A_n = r^n(A_0 - FIX) + FIX$ produces the following:

$$A_n = r^n\left(A_0 - \frac{b}{1 - r}\right) + \frac{b}{1 - r}$$
$$= r^n A_0 - r^n\left(\frac{b}{1 - r}\right) + \frac{b}{1 - r}$$
$$= r^n A_0 - b\left(\frac{r^n - 1}{1 - r}\right)$$

This algebraic reformulating shows that the two formulas are equivalent.

2. **a.** To find a function to iterate, you need to solve the given equation for x so that it is in the form $x = f(x)$. There are several ways to do this. One way will be illustrated here. Others may be more or less complicated, but the reasoning will be similar. By factoring the left-hand side of the given equation and dividing by $(2x + 5)$, we get $x = \dfrac{3}{2x + 5}$. Iterating $f(x) = \dfrac{3}{2x + 5}$ starting anywhere except $x = -3$ or $x = -2.5$ will go to the fixed point of $x = 0.5$.

b. Algebraic or graphical methods can be used to obtain the two solutions $x = 0.5$ and $x = -3$.

c. The fixed points in the method of function iteration are the solutions to the equation. You will probably find a fixed point by iteration if it is attracting. You will probably not find it by iteration if it is repelling.

d. The fixed points are shown by the intersection of the graphs of $y = x$ and $y = \dfrac{3}{2x + 5}$.

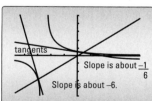

At the fixed point -3, the absolute value of the slope of the tangent is 6, greater than 1. The absolute value of the slope of the tangent at 0.5 is $\frac{1}{6}$, less than 1.

e. If the absolute value of the slope of the tangent at the fixed point is less than 1, then it will be an attracting fixed point. If the absolute value of the slope of the tangent at the fixed point is greater than 1, then it will be a repelling fixed point. If there is an attracting fixed point when solving a nonlinear equation by function iteration, then that fixed point, which is a solution to the equation, will probably be found; if the fixed point is repelling, then it is highly unlikely that you will find it by iteration.

c. Now modify the formula $A_n = r^n A_0$ so that it has the same long-term behavior as $A_n = rA_{n-1} + b$: Begin by adding the fixed point, denoted *FIX*, to the function formula $A_n = r^n A_0$ so that the new function will have the same long-term behavior as $A_n = rA_{n-1} + b$. Explain why $A_n = r^n A_0 + FIX$ has long-term behavior converging to *FIX*, if $|r| < 1$.

d. Finally, modify the formula $A_n = r^n A_0 + FIX$ so that it has the same initial value A_0 as $A_n = rA_{n-1} + b$:

- Explain why the initial value of $A_n = r^n A_0 + FIX$ is equal to $A_0 + FIX$.

- Explain why the initial value of $A_n = r^n(A_0 - FIX) + FIX$ is equal to A_0.

e. The function formula $A_n = r^n(A_0 - FIX) + FIX$ has the same long-term behavior and the same initial value as the combined recursion equation $A_n = rA_{n-1} + b$. Use this formula to find A_5 for the recursion equation $A_n = 2A_{n-1} + 1$, with $A_0 = 3$. Then compute A_5 by successively evaluating $A_n = 2A_{n-1} + 1$; compare your result to what you calculated with the function formula.

f. Compare the function formula in Part e to the function formula you derived in Organizing Task 5 of Lesson 2, page 523. Resolve any apparent differences.

2. In Organizing Task 1, page 539, you investigated the method of function iteration to solve linear equations. Investigate if this method will work for quadratic equations. Consider the quadratic equation $2x^2 + 5x = 3$.

a. Which function should you iterate in order to use the method of function iteration to solve this equation? Iterate with several different initial values and describe the results in each case.

b. Solve this equation using another method. How many solutions are there?

c. What properties of fixed points allow you to either find or not find a solution when using the method of function iteration?

d. Use your calculator or computer software to help you sketch graphs of the iterated function and $y = x$ on the same set of axes. Locate the fixed points on this graph. At each of the fixed points, visualize a line drawn tangent to the graph of the iterated function at the fixed point. Estimate the slope of each of these tangent lines. For which fixed point is the absolute value of the slope of the tangent line greater than 1? For which tangent line is the absolute value of the slope less than 1?

e. Recall the connection between iterating linear functions and slope. For this task, explain how the slope of the tangent line at a fixed point tells you if the fixed point is attracting or repelling. Explain what attracting or repelling fixed points have to do with solving nonlinear equations using the method of function iteration.

3. Although it is relatively easy to iterate linear functions graphically with a fair degree of accuracy, it is quite difficult to iterate nonlinear functions graphically. This is because, as you have seen, the shape of a graphical iteration is determined by the slope of the graph of the iterated function. And while lines have constant slopes, graphs of nonlinear functions have changing slopes. Thus, it is usually necessary to use a computer or graphing calculator to accurately iterate nonlinear functions graphically. A graphical iteration tool is built into many calculators and computer graphing packages, or such a tool can be quickly programmed.

a. Consult a manual, if necessary, to find how to use your calculator or computer to iterate graphically. Practice by graphically iterating $f(x) = -0.8x + 6$. You should get a graph that looks like the one below.

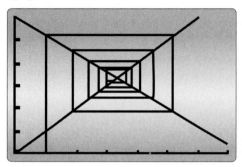

b. In Modeling Task 3, page 538, you were asked to iterate the function $h(x) = 3.2x - 0.8x^2$. Use a graphing calculator or computer to iterate $h(x)$ graphically, starting with $x = 2.6$. Compare the graphical iteration pattern to the numerical iteration results.

c. In Modeling Task 1, page 537, you were asked to iterate the function $f(x) = x^3 - x^2 + 1$. Graphically iterate $f(x)$ to illustrate each of your results in Modeling Task 1.

4. In this lesson, you iterated algebraic functions. It is also possible to iterate geometric transformations. As an example, play the following Chaos Game.

a. On a clean sheet of paper, draw the vertices of a large triangle. Any type of triangle will work, but for your first time playing the game, use an isosceles triangle. Label the vertices with the numbers 1, 2, and 3.

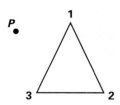

3. **a.** Since this is an Extending task, students should read a manual to determine how to graphically iterate a function using a calculator or computer. On the TI-82, TI-83, and TI-92, the mode must be set to **Seq**, and the graphing format must be set to **Web**. After entering the function and setting the starting point and the window, using the trace command and arrow buttons will draw the graphical iteration.

b. Student graphs should look like the one below.

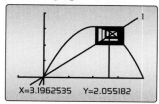

After several iterations, the cobweb graph "cycles" over and over in the same rectangle. The values that it cycles between are the same values found by numerical iteration in Modeling Task 3 on page 538, that is, about 3.20 and 2.05.

c.

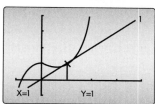

When the initial value is 1, the fixed point stays at 1.

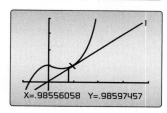

When the initial value is 0.8, the fixed point is attracted to 1.

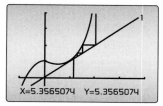

When the initial value is 1.2, the fixed point is repelled.

4. **a–b.** See students' work. Students should have six points plotted from their Chaos Game.

Unit 7

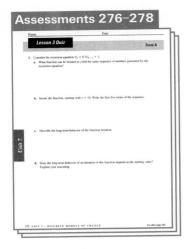

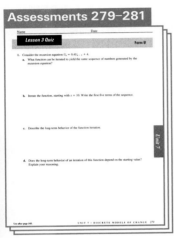

Unit 7

4. **c.** It is unlikely that students will conjecture the correct pattern.

d. Sample programs are in the manuals for the TI-82 calculator (p. 14-9) and the TI-83 calculator (p. 17-7).

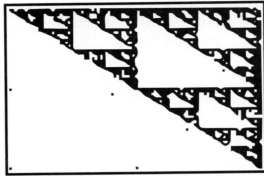

This is an example created using a TI-82.

e. For the same starting triangle, you will always get the same general pattern, no matter what initial point is used.

f. The scale factor is $\frac{1}{2}$. Each triangle has sides $\frac{1}{2}$ the length of the next larger triangle.

g. An alternative way to get a Sierpinski triangle is to successively remove triangles formed by joining the midpoints of sides of existing triangles. (See Modeling Task 5 on page 520.)

Now, suppose one of the early iteration points is in one of the removed triangles. In the next iteration, it will move half the distance to some vertex. This will put the next point in one of the removed triangles at the next level, since the removed triangles at a given level consist of all the points that are half the distance to the three vertices from points in the previous-level (larger) removed triangle. Thus, as the iteration continues, points will move from a removed triangle at one level to a removed triangle at the next (smaller) level. After a few iterations, the point will be in a removed triangle that is too small to see, so it will appear to be in one of the infinitely chopped-up regions that make up the Sierpinski triangle.

Note that the resulting figure is a Sierpinski *triangle* because we started with a triangle. Starting with 5 points at the vertices of a pentagon or 6 points at the vertices of a hexagon will result in a Sierpinski pentagon or hexagon, respectively. However, starting with a square will not yield a "Sierpinski square." Instead, the entire square will be filled.

See Assessment Resources pages 276–281.

b. Start with a point anywhere on the sheet of paper. This is your initial input. Randomly choose one of the vertices (for example, use a random number generator to choose one of the numbers 1, 2, or 3), and mark a new point one-half of the distance between your input and that vertex. This is your first output and also your new input. Then randomly choose another vertex and mark the next point, half the distance from the new input to that vertex. Repeat this process until you have plotted six points.

c. The goal of the Chaos Game is to see what happens in the long term. What do you think the pattern of plotted points will look like if you plot 300 points? Make a conjecture.

d. Program a calculator or computer to play the Chaos Game and then carry out several hundred iterations. Since you are interested only in the long-term behavior, you might carry out the first 10 iterations without plotting the resulting points and then plot all points thereafter.

e. Repeat the game for several other initial points. Do you think you will always get the same resulting figure? Try it.

f. The figure that results from the Chaos Game is an example of a familiar *fractal*. One of the most important characteristics of fractals is that they are *self-similar*, which means that if you zoom in, you keep seeing figures just like the original figure. What is the scale factor of successively smaller triangles in the fractal you produced?

g. Give a geometrical explanation for why the Chaos Game will always generate a Sierpinski triangle. (For more about Sierpinski triangles, see Modeling Task 5, page 520.)

Unit 7

Lesson 4 *Looking Back*

In this unit, you have investigated sequential change in a variety of contexts using the tools of recursion and iteration. You have extended the idea of using *NOW* and *NEXT* to model sequential change; you have studied recursive formulas, function iteration, and sequences; and you have made connections to previous work with linear, exponential, and polynomial models. In this final lesson, you will pull together and review all the ideas in the unit.

1. In Lesson 1, you modeled a variety of situations with combined recursive formulas of the form $A_n = rA_{n-1} + b$. In Lesson 3, you iterated linear functions. These two topics are closely connected. In this activity, you will summarize key features of that connection.

   By using different values for r and b in the combined recursion equation $A_n = rA_{n-1} + b$, you can build models for different situations. Four different possibilities are indicated by the table below. One recursive formula has already been entered into the table.

Four Different Versions of the Recursive Formula $A_n = rA_{n-1} + b$		
	$0 < r < 1$	$r > 1$
$b < 0$		
$b > 0$	$A_n = 0.8A_{n-1} + 1{,}000$	

   Choose *two* of the empty table entries. For each entry, write an appropriate recursive formula and prepare two reports. Title each report with the particular recursive formula on which you are reporting. Each report should include the following analysis of the chosen recursive formula and its use as a mathematical model.

   a. Briefly describe a real-world situation that can be modeled by the recursive formula along with a chosen initial value.

   b. Rewrite the recursive formula as an equation using *NOW* and *NEXT*.

   c. Write a linear function that can be iterated to yield the same sequence as the successive values of the recursive formula. Choose an initial value.

   - Iterate the function and describe the long-term behavior.
   - Find the fixed point and decide whether it is attracting, repelling, or neither. Explain in terms of slope.
   - Sketch a graph showing graphical iteration of the function for the initial value previously chosen.

Lesson 4 *Looking Back*

SYNTHESIZE UNIT IDEAS small-group activity

1. Responses will vary. Possible recursive formulas and appropriate responses are given below.

NOTE: To help clarify what students are expected to do here, you might want to refer them to their work on Organizing Task 1 of Lesson 1, page 498.

Four Different Versions of the Recursive Formula $A_n = rA_{n-1} + b$

	$0 < r < 1$	$r > 1$
$b < 0$	$A_n = 0.9A_{n-1} - 100$	$A_n = 1.06A_{n-1} - 350$
$b > 0$	$A_n = 0.8A_{n-1} + 1{,}000$	$A_n = 1.01A_{n-1} + 35$

$A_n = 0.9A_{n-1} - 100$

a. Whale population has a death rate higher than birthrate with a net result of 10% decrease in population each year. In addition, 100 whales are harvested each year. Suppose the initial population is 2,000 whales.

b. $NEXT = 0.9NOW - 100$, starting at 2,000

c. $f(x) = 0.9x - 100$
- Long-term behavior is convergence to $-1{,}000$ (whales die out at 0).
- The fixed point is $-1{,}000$. It is attracting because $|\,slope\,| = 0.9 < 1$.
- See the first graph in the margin.

d. See the second graph in the margin.

e. All initial values yield iteration sequences that converge to the fixed point at $x = -1{,}000$. For the whale population, the sequence will steadily decrease toward the fixed point of $x = -1{,}000$. But since population cannot be negative, the population will die out, corresponding to $f(x) = 0$. This will happen after about 10 or 11 years. Even if the initial count was incorrect and there are more or fewer whales initially, the population will still tend toward the fixed point of $-1{,}000$. The population will still die out, although it may take a greater or lesser amount of time for that to happen.

$A_n = 0.9A_{n-1} - 100$, Part c

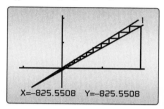

$A_n = 0.9A_{n-1} - 100$, Part d

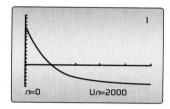

$A_n = 1.06A_{n-1} - 350$

a. Money is invested in a savings account at 6% interest compounded annually, but every year $350 is withdrawn. Suppose the initial deposit is $6,000. (For this problem, the fixed point is approximately 5,833.33, and it is repelling; thus, behavior will be quite different depending on whether the initial value is greater than, less than, or equal to 5,833.33.)

b. $NEXT = 1.06NOW - 350$

c. $f(x) = 1.06x - 350$
- Long-term behavior is for the money to grow without bound, but rather slowly.
- The fixed point is approximately 5,833.33. It is a repelling fixed point since $|\,slope\,| = 1.06 > 1$.
- See the graph in the margin.

$A_n = 1.06A_{n-1} - 350$, Part c

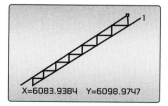

Unit 7

See additional Teaching Notes on page T549H.

2. **a.** The first several terms of the sequence are 1, 2, 4, 8, ...

   Recursive formula: $a_n = 2a_{n-1}$, $a_0 = 1$

   Function formula: $a_n = 2^n$

   There are 2^{12} or 4,096 new branches at Stage 12.

   b. The total number of branches at Stage 12 is S_{12}, the sum of the terms a_0 through a_{12} of the geometric sequence in Part a.

   $$S_{12} = 1\left(\frac{2^{13} - 1}{2 - 1}\right) = 2^{13} - 1 = 8,191 \text{ branches}$$

   c. ■ The first several terms of the sequence of the total length of all branches at each stage are 1, 2, 3, 4, ...

   ■ This is an arithmetic sequence with $a_n = 1 + n$ and $a_0 = 1$. So $a_{15} = 16$. The total length of all the branches at Stage 15 is 16 units.

Unit 7

d. Sketch a graph of n versus A_n, using the same initial value you chose in Part c.

e. Describe the long-term behavior of the real-world situation being modeled, for different initial values. Refer to the fixed point and its properties, but keep your description in the context of the particular situation being modeled.

2. Many irregular shapes found in the natural world can be modeled by fractals. Study the first few stages of the fractal tree shown below.

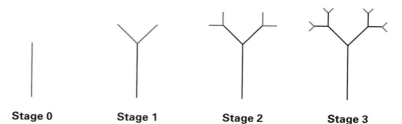

Stage 0   **Stage 1**   **Stage 2**   **Stage 3**

a. Write the number of new branches at each stage for the first several stages. Then write recursive and function formulas that describe this sequence. Use one of the formulas to predict the number of new branches at Stage 12. Check your prediction using the other formula.

b. Find the total number of branches at Stage 12.

c. Suppose that the length of the initial branch is 1 unit and that the branches at each successive stage of the fractal tree are half the length of the branches at the previous stage.

- Write the total length of all the branches at each stage for the first several stages.

- Find the total length of all the branches at Stage 15.

3. When you attend a movie, concert, or theater production, you may notice that the number of seats in a row increases as you move from the front of the theater to the back. This permits the seats in consecutive rows to be offset from one another so that you have a less obstructed view of the stage.

Unit 7

The center section of the orchestra level of Laser Auditorium is arranged so that there are 42 seats in the first row, 44 seats in the second row, 46 seats in the third row, and so on for a total of 25 rows.

a. Determine the number of seats in the last row in two different ways. Compare your result and your methods to those of another group and resolve any differences.

b. Determine the total number of seats in the center section of the orchestra level in at least two different ways. One method should involve using a rule showing the total number of seats as a function of number of rows n.

4. Nicole was investigating the maximum number of regions into which a plane is separated by n lines, no two of which are parallel and no three of which intersect at a point. For example, the diagram below shows the maximum number of regions for 3 lines.

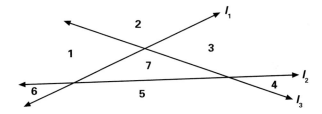

Nicole gathered the data shown in the table below.

Number of Lines	0	1	2	3	4
Number of Regions	1	2	4	7	11

a. Verify the entries in the table.

b. Find a function formula for the maximum number of regions formed by n lines using the method of finite differences.

c. Write a recursive formula for this relationship.

5. Find recursive and function formulas for each of the sequences below. Then find the sum of the terms up through the term with subscript 15.

a.

n	0	1	2	3	4	5	6	...	15	...
P_n	-3	2	7	12	17			...		...

b.

n	0	1	2	3	4	5	6	...	15	...
L_n	600	300	150	75	37.5			...		...

3. a. The 25th row will have 90 seats in it.

Students can find this recursively using $r_n = r_{n-1} + 2$, with $r_0 = 42$ and r_{24} representing the 25th row, or with $r_1 = 24$ and r_{25} representing the 25th row.

The function formula is $r_n = 42 + 2(n - 1)$, where n is the row number.

b. Unless students have completed Organizing Task 2 on page 522, they will need to write the recursive formula using r_0 as the first term in order to use $S_n = \frac{(n+1)(a_0 + a_n)}{2}$. Thus, $S_{24} = \frac{25(42 + 90)}{2} = 1{,}650$ seats. (If students have done Organizing Task 2, they might use $T_n = \frac{n(a_1 + a_n)}{2}$ and $T_{25} = \frac{25(42 + 90)}{2} = 1{,}650$ seats.) Students could also use a data list to produce the first 25 terms of the sequence and then find the sum of the list.

4. a. Students should verify the entries in the table. The diagram at the right shows eleven regions that can be formed using four lines.

b.

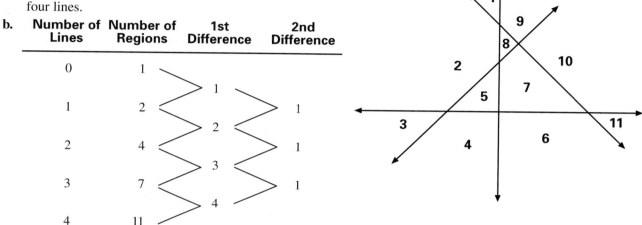

Number of Lines	Number of Regions	1st Difference	2nd Difference
0	1		
		1	
1	2		1
		2	
2	4		1
		3	
3	7		1
		4	
4	11		

Since the 2nd differences are constant, the function formula will be of the form $A_n = an^2 + bn + c$. Solving the matrix equation

$$\begin{bmatrix} 1 & 1 & 1 \\ 4 & 2 & 1 \\ 9 & 3 & 1 \end{bmatrix} \begin{bmatrix} a \\ b \\ c \end{bmatrix} = \begin{bmatrix} 2 \\ 4 \\ 7 \end{bmatrix}$$

gives $a = 0.5$, $b = 0.5$, and $c = 1$. So the function formula is
$$A_n = 0.5n^2 + 0.5n + 1.$$

c. $A_n = A_{n-1} + n$

5. a. This is an arithmetic sequence with common difference $d = 5$.

$P_n = P_{n-1} + 5$

$P_n = -3 + 5n$

$P_{15} = -3 + 5(15) = 72$

$S_{15} = \frac{16(-3 + 72)}{2} = 552$

b. This is a geometric sequence with common multiplier $r = 0.5$.

$L_n = (0.5)L_{n-1}$

$L_n = (600)(0.5^n)$

$L_{15} \approx 0.0183$

$S_{15} = 600\left(\frac{0.5^{16} - 1}{-0.5}\right) \approx 1{,}199.98$

Unit 7

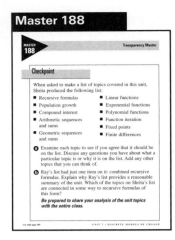

Master 188

Unit 7 Summary

Assessments 282–302

Checkpoint

See Teaching Master 188.

ⓐ Other topics that could be added to the list include subscript notation, recursion, sequential change, long-term behavior, repelling, attracting, and cycles. Students may think of others as well.

ⓑ It is reasonably accurate to say that this unit is about combined recursive formulas, that is, recursive formulas of the form $A_n = rA_{n-1} - b$. In Lesson 1, combined recursive formulas are used as models for real-world situations (like population growth, medicine absorption, and compound interest), and subscript notation is used to help analyze them. In Lesson 2, the recursive formulas for arithmetic and geometric sequences are special cases of combined recursive formulas. In Lesson 3, iterating linear functions is just another way of thinking about successively evaluating combined recursive formulas. The only major topics in the unit that are not directly connected to combined recursive formulas are finite differences in Lesson 2 and some of the more general function iteration in Lesson 3. All of the items on Shrita's list are connected in some way to combined recursive formulas. (The connections to finite differences and polynomial functions are weak, but a possible connection can be made if one thinks of a linear function as a special case of a polynomial function.)

▶On Your Own

See Unit 7 Summary Masters.

Responses will vary. Above all, preparation of this unit summary should be something that is useful to the individual student. You may wish to have students use the unit summary masters for "Discrete Models of Change" to help them organize the information.

See Assessment Resources pages 282–302.

Checkpoint

When asked to make a list of topics covered in this unit, Shrita produced the following list:

- Recursive formulas
- Population growth
- Compound interest
- Arithmetic sequences and sums
- Geometric sequences and sums
- Finite differences

- Linear functions
- Exponential functions
- Polynomial functions
- Function iteration
- Fixed points

a Examine each topic to see if you agree that it should be on the list. Discuss any questions you have about what a particular topic is or why it is on the list. Add any other topics that you can think of.

b Ray's list had just one item on it: combined recursive formulas. Explain why Ray's list provides a reasonable summary of the unit. Which of the topics on Shrita's list are connected in some way to recursive formulas of this form?

Be prepared to share your analysis of the unit topics with the entire class.

On Your Own

Write, in outline form, a summary of the important mathematical concepts and methods developed in this unit. Organize your summary so that it can be used as a quick reference in future work and courses.

Looking Back, Looking Ahead

▶ Reflecting on Mathematical Content

This unit has accomplished several goals. Students (a) refined their skills in mathematical modeling as they modeled processes of sequential change using recursion, (b) formalized the informal *NOW-NEXT* representation of recursion using subscript notation and recursive formulas, (c) studied and applied arithmetic and geometric sequences and series, (d) studied and applied the method of finite differences as related to sequences, (e) reviewed linear, exponential, and polynomial functions from a discrete viewpoint, (f) studied and applied function iteration, and (g) previewed function composition, specifically by composing a function with itself.

Several topics from this unit will be further developed in Course 4 of the *Contemporary Mathematics in Context* curriculum. The concept of recursion will continue to be developed and applied throughout Course 4, particularly in units and lessons involving spreadsheets and proof by mathematical induction. The ideas of geometric growth, accumulated amount, and additional amount will be revisited, and function composition will be carefully studied. Thus, this unit at the end of Course 3 has included important ideas from previous units and courses, developed several new ideas, and previewed ideas yet to come in Course 4.

▶ Reflecting on Teaching

By this time, you will have likely taught all three years of the CMIC curriculum. In your conversations with colleagues as you have implemented this curriculum, you may have already engaged in discussions about mathematics reform and implementation issues. If not, you and your colleagues might find it helpful to plan some time for discussion around questions such as the ones listed below.

How does technology affect the content and instruction of mathematics?

How do I create a classroom climate that encourages student ownership of learning?

How do I stimulate students to make connections and develop a coherent framework for mathematical ideas?

How do I promote problem posing by students?

What specific methods do I use to facilitate classroom discourse?

What does it mean to assess student learning?

You may wish to form study groups around sections from *The Professional Standards for Teaching Mathematics* published by the National Council of Teachers of Mathematics.

Unit 7 Assessment

Teaching Notes continued

Notes continued from page T489

2. **a.** The results of the long-term analysis can be surprising. Students should make conjectures based on their current computations and their intuition. You will probably have students who think the population will grow without bound and others who think it will level off. It is not possible for the pond to have no fish in it since 1,000 fish are added each year.

   b. The long-term population is 5,000. Students can determine this population by repeating the necessary calculations (preferably using "last answer"). The fish population doesn't grow without bound, and it doesn't die out. This seems reasonable in terms of reaching a point at which the pond ecology is in balance (for example, neither too much nor too little food).

   c. The fish population changes faster around year 5 than around year 25. It changes most quickly in the beginning, and then it levels off and has small changes when the population gets close to 5,000. Students should explain how they see this growth in their calculations. They may refer to rate of change. They may even sketch a graph or use a table at this point, although they have not been asked to do so yet.

3. Students may conjecture that the long-term population will be different if the initial population is different. Surprisingly, this is not the case! The long-term population will always be 5,000, no matter what the initial population is. If the initial population is smaller than 5,000, the population will increase (more rapidly at the beginning) to 5,000. If the initial population is greater than 5,000, the population will decrease (more rapidly at the beginning) to 5,000.

Notes continued from page T492

4. To begin this activity, students are asked to determine how loan balances are computed (see Part a). Most students will be able to figure this problem out, and by doing so they will have a better understanding of the rest of the activity and of how loans work. Depending on your particular situation and your particular students, you may need to provide guidance on how to get started, but as much as possible it is beneficial to let students figure the problem out themselves.

   In this activity, the *r* value (1.01) increases what is owed (*NOW*), and the *b* value decreases this amount. Ask students what this equation would represent in the context of the trout problem. (The trout population increases by 1% and, instead of restocking, fish are removed.) This equation behaves in different ways from the equation in which *r* < 1. This type of problem will be investigated further in Organizing Task 1, page 498, so your students do not have to completely investigate the impact of *r* at this time. However, you may want to challenge students who easily complete this activity to try different repayment amounts, as well as different starting amounts. This time, the starting amount *does* have an impact on the long-term value of U_n. This is practical; even for loans that increase at the same rate of interest, a particular payment amount will not reduce *any* starting debt to zero. A large debt may cause the interest to exceed the fixed payment.

Teaching Notes *continued*

Notes continued from page T495

2. d. In the table and graph that follow, year 0 corresponds to 1993.

Year	Population
0	8,050.0
1	8,249.6
2	8,455.3
3	8,667.4
4	8,886.1
5	9,111.6
6	9,344.0
7	9,583.7
8	9,830.8
9	10,086

Year	Population
10	10,348
11	10,619
12	10,898
13	11,186
14	11,483
15	11,789
16	12,104
17	12,429
18	12,765

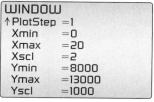

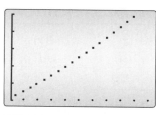

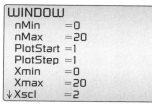

```
WINDOW
 nMin    =0
 nMax    =20
 PlotStart =1
 PlotStep  =1
 Xmin    =0
 Xmax    =20
↓Xscl    =2
```

```
WINDOW
↑PlotStep =1
 Xmin    =0
 Xmax    =20
 Xscl    =2
 Ymin    =8000
 Ymax    =13000
 Yscl    =1000
```

Again, the trend in the short term may appear to be linear, but in fact the population change is nonlinear, which is seen in a longer-term graph. The long-term trend is to grow without bound.

e. The population will slowly die off. (Because the multiplier in this equation is greater than 1, the initial population will affect long-term population—See Lesson 3.) In this case, each year there are more whales being harvested than are replaced due to the growth rate.

Notes continued from page T518

c The most direct use of finite differences tables, and the only one investigated in this lesson, occurs when a column of differences becomes constant; for example, the rth differences are constant. In this case, the function formula is a polynomial of degree r. (It is possible to use finite differences tables in creative ways to find function formulas for a variety of sequences.)

APPLY   individual task

▶On Your Own

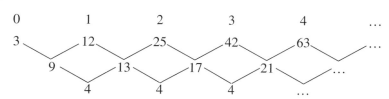

n	0	1	2	3	4	...
A_n	3	12	25	42	63	...
1st Difference		9	13	17	21	...
2nd Difference			4	4	4	...

The 2nd differences are constant, so the function formula is a quadratic function of the form $A_n = an^2 + bn + c$. Find the coefficients by solving the following system of three equations.

$$
\begin{aligned}
a + b + c &= 12 \\
4a + 2b + c &= 25 \\
9a + 3b + c &= 42
\end{aligned}
\qquad
\begin{bmatrix} 1 & 1 & 1 \\ 4 & 2 & 1 \\ 9 & 3 & 1 \end{bmatrix}
\begin{bmatrix} a \\ b \\ c \end{bmatrix}
=
\begin{bmatrix} 12 \\ 25 \\ 42 \end{bmatrix}
$$

$a = 2$, $b = 7$, and $c = 3$. Thus, the function formula is $A_n = 2n^2 + 7n + 3$.

Teaching Notes continued

Notes continued from page T531

2. **a.** For their tables, students do not need to include arrows as shown in the student book.

Iterating $f(x) = 3x + 1$

x IN	$f(x)$ OUT
2	7
7	22
22	67
67	202
202	607

b. The table with initial value 0 is shown below. Although the numbers are different from those in Part a, the table values are still growing quickly.

Iterating $f(x) = 3x + 1$

x IN	$f(x)$ OUT
0	1
1	4
4	13
13	40
40	121

Notes continued from page T532

7. **b.** Converges to a "two-cycle"; that is, it oscillates between approximately 0.5130445 and 0.7994555.

c. Converges to a "four-cycle"; that is, it oscillates among approximately 0.8749973, 0.3828197, 0.8269407, and 0.5008842.

d. Converges to a "three-cycle"; that is, it oscillates among approximately 0.9574166, 0.1561493, and 0.5046665.

e. There is no discernible pattern ("chaos"). Note that not all calculator and computer outputs will agree for this iteration, not only because of round-off errors but also, and more importantly, because of the nature of chaotic behavior, in particular, the property of chaos to have "sensitive dependence on initial conditions." This means even a very small difference in initial conditions can result in wildly different long-term behavior. Thus, if at any given point in the iteration two calculators disagree slightly (due to round-off), then they are liable to vary considerably later.

Teaching Notes *continued*

Notes continued from page T535

3. a. The fixed point is $x = 4$. Note that the fixed point is a limiting value; it is only the round-off of the calculator or computer making it seem that you actually get to the fixed point.

b. By iterating, you can estimate that the fixed point is approximately 3.529. Students will probably find the fixed point by iterating since that is the only technique discussed so far. (The exact value is $\frac{6}{1.7}$.)

c. You might think of the equation $x = f(x)$ as saying *input = output*. Thus, if $x = f(x)$, then the outputs and inputs never change as you iterate $f(x)$ starting from x. So, in the iteration process, once you get to x you will never get anything different; that is, "if you reach that value, you never leave it."

NOTE: When we talk here about "reaching" a fixed point, we are technically referring to attracting fixed points and infinite limits. Attracting fixed points will be investigated explicitly in Activity 6. Infinite limits are not dealt with except in an intuitive and implicit manner. This is not something you should stress with students, but it may come up. It is always the case that if you start at a fixed point, then you will never leave it. But "reaching a fixed point" happens only with attracting fixed points, and then only at the limit. That is, $f^n(x_0) \to$ (fixed point) as $n \to \infty$. Round-off error on a calculator or computer makes it seem that a fixed point is actually reached after finitely many iterations.

---

4. Setting $x = f(x)$ yields $x = 0.5x + 2$. Solving this gives $x = 4$ for the fixed point. This is the same result you get if you numerically or graphically iterate to find the fixed point.

Unit 7

Teaching Notes continued

Notes continued
from page T536

SHARE AND SUMMARIZE   full-class discussion

Checkpoint

See Teaching Master 187.

This Checkpoint overlaps somewhat with Activity 6, but there are more behaviors to be described in the Checkpoint, and those in Activity 6 are important enough to warrant a second systematic look.

ⓐ By definition, a fixed point is a number x such that $x = f(x)$. In terms of graphs, one important way to think about fixed points that has not been explicitly mentioned so far is that a fixed point is the point of intersection of the graphs for $y = x$ and $y = f(x)$. (Students should have recognized this fact by now, and they should be encouraged to articulate it.) In terms of iteration sequences, a fixed point is a number in a function iteration sequence such that if you ever get to it, it will be repeated forever. This interpretation arises since the equation $x = f(x)$ in effect says that *input = output*, so feeding outputs back in as inputs will result in generating the same number over and over again.

A fixed point can be attracting, repelling, or neither. An attracting fixed point has the property that iteration sequences converge to it. (In general, only iteration sequences that start "close" to an attracting fixed point will converge to the fixed point, but in the case of linear functions, all iteration sequences converge to an attracting fixed point, if one exists.) In contrast, iteration sequences move away from a repelling fixed point. A fixed point might be neither attracting nor repelling, as when there are two-cycles with linear functions.

Methods for finding fixed points include numerical or graphical iteration, if the fixed point is attracting; solving the equation $x = f(x)$; or finding the point of intersection of the graphs for $y = x$ and $y = f(x)$.

ⓑ It is always the case that if you start at a fixed point, then you will never leave it. But "reaching a fixed point" happens only with attracting fixed points, and then only in the limit. That is,

$$f^n(x_0) \to \text{(fixed point) as } n \to \infty.$$

(See the note after Activity 3 Part c, page T549F.)

ⓒ Some of the behaviors that students might describe and characterize follow.

- Sequence approaches an attracting fixed point. ($|\,slope\,| < 1$)
- Sequence moves away from a repelling fixed point. ($|\,slope\,| > 1$)
- There is no fixed point (*slope* $= 1$ and the *y*-intercept is not 0).
- Sequence is a two-cycle. Fixed point is not attracting or repelling. (*slope* $= -1$)
- Stair step pattern of iteration (positive slope)
- Cobweb/spiral pattern of iteration (negative slope)
- Sequence tends to positive infinity. (*slope* $= 1$ with positive *y*-intercept, or *slope* > 1 and starting value greater than fixed point)
- Sequence tends to negative infinity. (*slope* $= 1$ and negative *y*-intercept, or *slope* > 1 and starting value less than fixed point)
- Sequence oscillates. (negative slope)

ⓓ Successively evaluating recursive formulas of the form $A_n = rA_{n-1} + b$ is the same as iterating linear functions, as long as the starting point for each process is the same.

Teaching Notes *continued*

◄ **Notes continued from page T546**

d. See the first graph in the margin.

e. The fixed point is about \$5,833.33, and it is repelling. If the starting value is above \$5,833.33, the long-term behavior is unbounded, tending to positive infinity. If the starting value is below \$5,833.33, the long-term behavior is also unbounded, but this time tending to negative infinity. Thus, it makes a big difference what the initial deposit is. If the initial deposit is \$5,833.33, then \$350 can be withdrawn each year and the principal will stay fixed at \$5,833.33. If the starting balance is more than \$5,833.33, then \$350 can be withdrawn each year and the principal will grow forever. If the starting balance is less than \$5,833.33, then withdrawing \$350 each year will eventually deplete the account.

$A_n = 1.06A_{n-1} - 350$, Part d

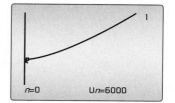

$A_n = 1.01A_{n-1} + 35$

a. Invest, for example, \$500 at 12% annual interest, compounded monthly, and add \$35 each month.

b. $NEXT = 1.01NOW + 35$

c. $f(x) = 1.01x + 35$
- ■ The long-term behavior is to grow without bound.
- ■ The fixed point is at $-3,500$, and it is repelling since $|\ slope\ | = 1.01 > 1$.
- ■ See the second graph in the margin.

d. See the third graph in the margin.

e. The fixed point at $-3,500$ is repelling. Initial values greater than $-3,500$ lead to iteration sequences that go to positive infinity, and initial values less than $-3,500$ generate iteration sequences that go to negative infinity.

    Since negative initial deposits don't make sense and since only initial values less than or equal to $-3,500$ do not yield long-term behavior that tends to positive infinity, we can say that all initial deposits will grow without bound.

$A_n = 1.01A_{n-1} + 35$, Part c

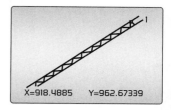

$A_n = 1.01A_{n-1} + 35$, Part d

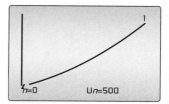

Unit 7

Capstone ▶ Looking Back at Course 3

CAPSTONE OVERVIEW The five investigations in this Capstone are comprised of applications of mathematics from all content strands over Courses 1, 2, and 3, as well as some new ideas. Students will probably recall the broad outlines of the mathematical ideas presented but maybe not all the details. This Capstone will help them review and remember many big ideas and important details.

Optimization can be viewed either as a separate area of mathematics, or as a broad application of mathematics that spans all mathematical strands. In either case, optimization pervades mathematics and life. By exploring optimization in this Capstone, students will learn about this important area of mathematics and will apply and review much of the mathematics they have learned. (Note that Investigation 1 is much shorter than the other investigations. It is recommended that all students work Investigation 1, and then each group should choose two of the remaining investigations to complete.)

■ Investigation 1 considers the idea of optimization by looking at honeycombs. This investigation reviews regular polygons, area, and sequences, and it requires students to reason symbolically about geometry and trigonometry.

■ Investigation 2 concentrates on the concepts of perimeter and area. The ideas reviewed are primarily geometric and trigonometric, but students have to analyze multivariate expressions and use algebraic reasoning and proof to obtain general results. Two new ideas are introduced: the Isoperimetric Theorem and the Double-Bubble Conjecture.

■ Investigation 3 focuses on minimizing distance. The ideas reviewed include slope, equations of lines, statistical regression, the distance formula, transformations, the Triangle Inequality Theorem, the Law of Cosines, and proof. The new idea introduced in the "On Your Own" task is a Steiner tree.

■ At the center of Investigation 4 is the idea of regression. Students review the least squares regression line, correlation, other regression curves, the meaning of residuals, and the general idea of sums of squared errors. The new idea is root mean squared error, which students connect to their work with control charts and families of functions.

■ In Investigation 5, students review and apply the following ideas: voting methods, samples and surveys, confidence intervals, linear programming, and quadratic functions.

See additional Teaching Notes on page T568A.

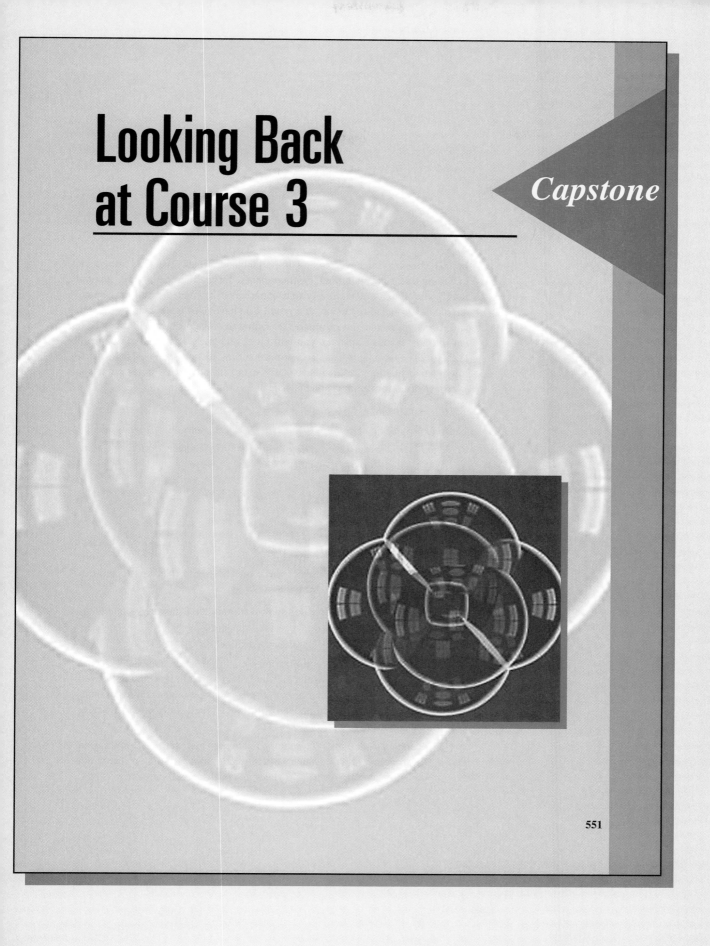

Looking Back at Course 3

551

Making the Best of It:
Optimal Forms and Strategies

In this course, you have studied important and broadly useful mathematics, including linear programming, election theory, surveys and confidence intervals, families of functions, similarity and congruence, normal distributions, control charts, iteration and recursion, and proof. You have used mathematical modeling and formal algebraic and geometric reasoning to solve problems in many different settings. In this Capstone, you will focus on a very important class of problems: *optimization problems*. To optimize means to find the "best." In the following investigations, you will use mathematics from units in this course to solve a variety of optimization problems. The units are listed below.

1. *Multiple-Variable Models*   5. *Patterns in Variation*

2. *Modeling Public Opinion*   6. *Families of Functions*

3. *Symbol Sense and Algebraic Reasoning*   7. *Discrete Models of Change*

4. *Shapes and Geometric Reasoning*

Think About This Situation

Most people want to make the best choices they can. That's why understanding optimization problems and strategies is so important. As a group, brainstorm possible responses to these questions and then be prepared to share your ideas with the entire class.

a What are some examples of optimization in the following contexts?
- Business and industry   ■ Education
- Your daily life   ■ Nature

b Describe at least one optimization situation from the Course 3 algebra and functions strand (Units 1, 3, and 6) and explain how you optimized it. Do the same for each of the other stands: geometry and trigonometry (Unit 4), statistics and probability (Units 2 and 5), and discrete mathematics (Units 2 and 7).

c Leonhard Euler, an 18th-century mathematician, said, "… nothing in all of the world will occur in which maximum or minimum rule is not somehow shining forth." Do you agree or disagree? Explain.

Capstone

Making the Best of It: Optimal Forms and Strategies

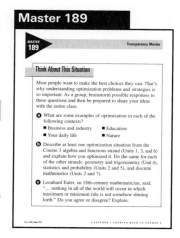

LAUNCH full-class discussion

Think About This Situation

See Teaching Master 189.

As students are thinking and talking about these examples, be sure to discuss how optimization can mean finding the best, most, least, fastest, slowest, highest, lowest, and so on.

a ■ Examples in business and industry include maximizing profit, minimizing cost, minimizing on-the-job accidents, producing the best product, maximizing customer satisfaction, minimizing equipment breakdowns, and designing the most efficient delivery route.

■ Examples in education include minimizing absences or tardiness, maximizing learning, producing the best textbooks, getting the best grades, and offering the most nutritious lunch menus.

■ Examples in daily life include getting the best parking place, waiting in line for the least amount of time, getting the best concert seats, making the most money, and finding the most efficient route from home to school.

■ Examples in nature include migrating birds choose the optimal route, light (in usual situations) travels in a straight line, and bees' honeycombs are the optimal shape for storing honey (see Investigation 1).

b This activity provides an opportunity for students to review the specific units of Course 3. You may wish to have students record their ideas on Teaching Master 190.

In the algebra and functions strands, students encountered several optimization situations: choosing the best lease plan; choosing a ticket price to maximize profit; using linear programming to maximize profit (minimize cost), subject to a variety of production constraints; and finding the best modeling equation for a given situation.

In the geometry and trigonometry strand, students considered the "best" proof of a geometric conjecture. "Best" might mean shortest, most aesthetically pleasing, or most efficient. For example, when considering a proof involving the lengths of sides of a triangle, choose the best tool from among the Law of Cosines, the Law of Sines, and the Pythagorean Theorem.

In the statistics and probability strand, students looked at how to design surveys and conduct polls so the best results could be obtained. They also used 90% box plot charts to help them get the best estimates of true population percents. In the "Patterns in Variation" unit, students used control charts to determine whether a process was going out of control in order to optimize the process.

In the discrete mathematics strand, students used a recursion equation to find the maximum population over time (long-term population). They chose whether a function formula or a recursive formula was better to use in a given situation. They also considered "best" vote-analysis methods.

c Responses may vary.

Capstone

INVESTIGATION ▶ 1 Do Bees Build It Best?

In this investigation, students revisit concepts from geometry and trigonometry related to regular polygons that tile the plane in the context of maximizing volume in honeycombs. Students determine that the (*number of sides, measure of one angle*) table is not an arithmetic or a geometric sequence.

In this investigation, students are expected to:

■ find the measures of angles of regular polygons;

■ write an algebraic rule for the relationship between the number of sides and the measure of one angle of a polygon;

■ find cross-sectional area, surface area, and volume; and

■ use symbolic reasoning to analyze a complex equation for maximum and minimum values.

1. **a.** The measure of each angle of a regular polygon must be a factor of 360 if the polygon is to tile a plane. The measure of each angle of an equilateral triangle is 60°. The measure of each angle of a square is 90°. The measure of each angle of a regular hexagon is 120°. All three of these measures are factors of 360.

b. ■ **Equilateral Triangle** If the perimeter is 24 mm, each side has length 8 mm. The altitude of the triangle has length $\sqrt{8^2 - 4^2}$ or approximately 6.93 mm. So, the area of the triangle is 0.5(8)(6.93) or approximately 27.71 square mm.

■ **Square** If the perimeter is 24 mm, the length of each edge is 6 mm. Thus, the area is 36 square mm.

■ **Hexagon** If the perimeter is 24 mm, then each side of the hexagon is 4 mm long. The hexagon can be divided into six equilateral triangles as shown in the diagram at the left. Each triangle has area $(0.5)(4)(2\sqrt{3})$ square mm. Thus, the total area is $6(0.5)(4)(2\sqrt{3})$ or approximately 41.57 square mm.

c. The hexagon has the greatest cross-sectional area for a fixed perimeter of 24 mm. As the number of sides increases, the area increases. However, the rate of increase is not constant. Rather, the area is increasing at a decreasing rate. (Note: It is approaching the area of a circle with circumference 24 mm, which is approximately 45.84 square mm. Students will learn about this area-maximizing property of a circle in the next investigation.)

d. The cell with the greatest cross-sectional area will have the greatest volume. So the cell with a hexagonal base will have the greatest volume. It is not necessary to compute the volumes, but they are as follows.

Equilateral triangle base: 20(27.71) = 554.2 cubic mm

Square base: 20(36) = 720 cubic mm

Regular hexagon base: 20(41.57) = 831.4 cubic mm

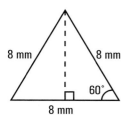

8 mm 8 mm

8 mm

60°

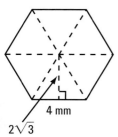

4 mm

$2\sqrt{3}$

Capstone

You will now pull together much of the mathematics you have been learning to analyze several new optimization situations. Each group should complete Investigation 1 and any two of Investigations 2 through 5. You will prepare a report on one of the investigations that you choose. Guidelines for the report are given on page 567. Verify your choices with your teacher before you begin.

Investigations 1 through 4 include optional "On Your Own" tasks. Individually, each group member should select and complete one of these tasks.

INVESTIGATION 1 ▶ Do Bees Build It Best?

As you brainstormed about possible examples of optimization in nature, you may have considered the honeycombs that bees make for storing honey. They appear to be three-dimensional tilings of regular hexagonal prisms.

1. In Course 1, you experimented with regular polygon shapes and discovered that equilateral triangles, squares, and regular hexagons will tile a plane. Portions of these tilings are shown below. You will investigate why bees build hexagonal tilings.

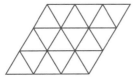 

a. What must be true of the measure of each angle of a regular polygon if the polygon is to tile a plane? Verify that the shapes above satisfy this criterion.

b. Now suppose the perimeter of one cell of a honeycomb is 24 mm. Find the cross-sectional area of a cell, assuming the cell has the following shapes.

   ■ An equilateral triangle

   ■ A square

   ■ A regular hexagon

c. Which cell has the greatest cross-sectional area for a fixed perimeter of 24 mm? As the number of sides of a regular polygon with fixed perimeter increases, how does the corresponding area change?

d. Suppose the height of each cell is about 20 mm. Determine which of the three shapes in Part b produces the cell with the greatest volume.

Capstone

e. Explain why the *lateral surface area* (the surface area not including the area of the bases) is fixed, regardless of the shape of the base, if the height h and perimeter P of a base of a regular polygonal prism are fixed.

2. Now that you have determined which of the three shapes in Activity 1 with fixed perimeter has the greatest area, investigate whether there are other regular polygonal shapes that will tile a plane and have a greater area measure.

   a. Complete a copy of the table below, which relates the measure of each angle of a regular n-gon to the number of sides n.

Regular Polygons						
Number of Sides, n	3	4	5	6	7	8
Measure of One Angle	60°	90°	108°	120°	?	?

   b. Examine the sequence of angle measures in your completed table. Is the sequence an arithmetic sequence, a geometric sequence, or neither? Explain.

   c. Formulate an algebraic rule to predict the measure of one angle of a regular polygon. Compare your rule and strategy for discovering it to those of another group. Resolve any differences.

   d. Use your rule to predict the measure of one angle of a regular 20-gon. Could a bee form a honeycomb of regular 20-gons? Explain your reasoning.

   e. Prove that the only regular polygons that will tile a plane have 3, 4, or 6 sides.

3. In what sense are honeycombs an optimal form?

4. Make a neat copy of your work on this investigation and file it at the location designated by your teacher. Examine the work filed by other groups and compare their work to what you did. Write a question to at least one group asking its members to explain something about their work that you found interesting or that you did not understand. Answer any questions your group receives.

▶ On Your Own

The cells of a complete honeycomb are hexagonal prisms arranged in two layers so that the cell openings for the two layers face in opposite directions. This arrangement compresses the base of the cells into trihedral pyramids, as shown in the vertical cross section at the right.

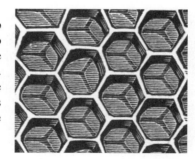

Capstone

1. **e.** The lateral surface area is found by adding the areas of all the faces of the prism. If the base of the prism is a regular n-gon, the length of each side is $\frac{P}{n}$. Thus, the area of each face of the prism is $h \cdot \frac{P}{n}$ or $\frac{hP}{n}$. Now, since there are n such faces, the total area is $n\left(\frac{hP}{n}\right)$ or hP. Thus, since h and P are fixed, the lateral surface area is fixed and is equal to hP.

Some students may prove that the lateral surface area is hP by describing the lateral surface area as a rectangle which has dimensions $P \times h$. This may be prompted by their work in Course 1 with the experiment involving weights supported by columns.

2. **a.** ### Regular Polygons

Number of Sides, n	3	4	5	6	7	8
Measure of One Angle	60°	90°	108°	120°	128.6°	135°

b. Neither. The sequence is not arithmetic because there is no common difference between consecutive terms. For example, $M_4 - M_3 = 30°$ and $M_5 - M_4 = 18°$. The sequence is not geometric because there is no common ratio between consecutive terms. For example, $\frac{M_4}{M_3} = \frac{90}{60} = 1.5$ and $\frac{M_5}{M_4} = \frac{108}{90} = 1.2$.

c. Students can use a variety of methods to find a rule to predict the measure of one angle of a regular polygon. They might try to use the method of finite differences, the regression capability of a calculator or computer software, or a combination of geometric and algebraic reasoning. If they try to use finite differences, they should soon discover that the differences will never be constant. This indicates that the rule is not polynomial. The rules that students get should be equivalent to $M_n = \frac{(n-2)(180)}{n} = 180 - \frac{360}{n}$. Be sure that they can explain why their rules make sense.

d. $M_{20} = 180 - \frac{360}{20} = 180 - 18 = 162°$. Since 162 is not a factor of 360, 162° angles will not fill without overlap around a point. So a honeycomb of regular 20-gons will have holes in it.

e. We know that regular polygons of 3, 4, and 6 sides will tile a plane. We need to prove that no others will. One proof is the following; other proofs are possible.

A regular polygon with 5 sides will not tile a plane because 108° is not a factor of 360°. For any polygon with more than 6 sides, the measure of each angle will be between 120° and 180°. But in a tiling there is a whole number of polygons meeting at each vertex. Since $2(180) = 360$ and $3(120) = 360$, it is impossible to multiply any number between 120° and 180° by a whole number to get 360°. Thus, the only regular polygons that will tile a plane have 3, 4, or 6 sides.

3. The honeycomb is an optimal form because regular hexagons tile a plane and, among the regular polygons that tile a plane, a regular hexagon has maximum area for a fixed perimeter. Thus, the regular hexagonal honeycombs that bees build will hold the greatest amount of honey for a fixed amount of wax. A single circular cross-sectional cell would hold more honey than a hexagonal cell, but there would be gaps between cells in the honeycomb. Since regular hexagons tessellate, each side of each hexagonal cell can be a wall for two cells. This further reduces the amount of wax needed for the honeycomb.

4. **This activity is an important part of each investigation. It provides a mechanism for students to talk to each other about what they have done, to compare answers, to make revisions, and to reflect more deeply upon their work. It also gives you the opportunity to monitor each group's progress and give feedback on any changes or additions that may need to be considered before the group gives its report.**

Capstone

▶**On Your Own**

a. As θ approaches approximately 54.74°, the surface area will be the smallest. Students may investigate this idea in a variety of ways. Examining the graph or table of $y = \frac{(\sqrt{3} - \cos \theta)}{\sin \theta}$ is one efficient method.

b. As θ approaches 0°, the surface area will be the largest. In the honeycomb, this corresponds to the sides of the pyramid getting steeper and steeper and thus requiring more wax to make.

c. $SA = 6sh + 1.5\frac{\sqrt{3}s^2}{\sin \theta} - 1.5s^2\frac{\cos \theta}{\sin \theta}$

This form seems to be more difficult to use since we now have two terms which vary with the angle size, one which increases and one which decreases the lateral surface area.

INVESTIGATION ▶2 From Bees to IQs

In this investigation, students explore what is considered to be the first optimization problem in history: the problem of Queen Dido. This problem leads to the famous Isoperimetric Theorem and to a recent optimization problem that is still not completely solved: finding and proving the optimal geometric properties of soap bubbles.

In this investigation, students are expected to:
- ■ find the area of a circle and a variety of polygons, given their perimeters;
- ■ find the perimeter of a circle and a variety of polygons, given their areas;
- ■ make a general comparison of areas and perimeters of similar figures;
- ■ prove statements about area and perimeter for planar shapes and statements about volume and surface area for three-dimensional shapes; and
- ■ simplify multiple-variable expressions.

1. The two main results of this activity are that, for a fixed perimeter, a square is the rectangular region with the greatest area and a circle is the general shape with maximum area.

 a. ■ All rectangles with perimeter 900 yards do not have the same area. The area varies depending on the dimensions of the rectangle. Students should experiment with a few rectangles. They might organize their results in a table and use the table to find a pattern. Using formulas, they might reason that $900 = 2l + 2w$, which means $l = 450 - w$, so $A = (450 - w)(w) = 450w - w^2$. This is a quadratic function whose graph is a concave-down parabola. By finding the vertex, students can find the dimensions of the rectangle with maximum area.

 ■ A square will give maximum area. Each side of the square will have length 225 yards. This length corresponds to the vertex of the parabola with equation $A = 450w - w^2$ and to the greatest y value in a table of values for the same equation.

Using visualization and a combination of algebraic, geometric, and trigonometric reasoning, one can prove that the surface area of a cell is given by

$$SA = 6sh + 1.5s^2\left(\frac{\sqrt{3} - \cos \theta}{\sin \theta}\right),$$

where s is the side length of the hexagon, h is the height of a cell, and θ (the Greek letter "theta") is the angle made by a line parallel to the faces of the prism through the vertex of the pyramid and one of the edges of the pyramid.

a. What value of θ will give the minimal surface area?

b. For what value of θ will the surface area be maximal?

c. Rewrite the above formula in expanded form. Is it easier or more difficult to answer Parts a and b using this equivalent symbolic form? Explain your reasoning.

INVESTIGATION 2 ▶ From Bees to IQs

In Investigation 1, you verified that when building a honeycomb, bees use the best form possible. Among all regular polygons with fixed perimeter, the regular hexagon is the one which both tessellates and encloses the largest area. Thus, when the height of the prism is fixed, the hexagonal honeycomb cell encloses the maximum volume.

In this investigation, you will further investigate shapes with fixed perimeter but without the restriction that the shapes be regular polygons.

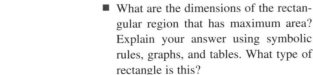

1. In *The Aeneid* by the Roman poet Vergil, a story is told about Queen Dido of Carthage. When Dido was a princess in the city of Tyre (now in Lebanon), her brother, King Pygmalion, killed her husband in order to capture her possessions. She fled by ship to a place in Africa that later became Carthage. She wanted to buy land from the local ruler, King Jarbas of Numidia. The king granted her only as much land as she could enclose in the hide of an ox. Dido was very clever in her interpretation of this decree. She had her people cut the hide into very thin strips and tie them together to form a cord of great length. She used the cord to surround the largest possible region of land. For Parts a and b that follow, suppose the length of the cord was 900 yards.

a. Suppose the shape of the region that Dido enclosed was a rectangle.

   ■ Do all rectangles with a perimeter of 900 yards have the same area? Defend your answer by sketching a few such rectangles and computing their areas.

   ■ What are the dimensions of the rectangular region that has maximum area? Explain your answer using symbolic rules, graphs, and tables. What type of rectangle is this?

MAKING THE BEST OF IT: OPTIMAL FORMS AND STRATEGIES   **555**

b. What if the region Dido enclosed was not rectangular? Experiment with some nonrectangular shapes. Compare the areas of those shapes to the maximum area of a rectangular region you found in Part a. Make a conjecture about what shape with a perimeter of 900 yards has the maximum area. Compare and discuss your conjecture with other groups. (To provide evidence for your conjecture, you should determine the area of at least two nonrectangular shapes that have perimeters of 900 yards.)

2. A useful ratio for comparing shapes with respect to area and perimeter is $\frac{4\pi A}{P^2}$, where A represents the area of a given shape and P represents the perimeter of the shape. This ratio is called the **Isoperimetric Quotient (IQ)**.

   a. Compute the IQ for an equilateral triangle that has a perimeter of 900 yards. Compute the IQ for several other equilateral triangles with different perimeters. What do you notice?

   b. Determine the IQ for several circles. What pattern do you notice? Prove what you have discovered by using algebraic reasoning with the general formulas for area and circumference of a circle.

   c. Prove that similar figures have the same IQ.

   d. You found the IQ for equilateral triangles and circles in Parts a and b. Now determine the IQ for squares.

   e. The IQ for regular pentagons is 0.865. Determine the IQs for regular hexagons and regular octagons.

   f. Organize all your IQ data in a table. Describe any patterns in the data. Compare those patterns to visual patterns in the following diagram.

3. A famous theorem, called the **Isoperimetric Theorem**, states that for a fixed perimeter, the shape with maximum area is a circle.

   a. Does this match your conjecture in Part b of Activity 1? If not, go back and reexamine that activity.

   b. Why do you suppose bees don't use cylinders in building their honeycombs?

   c. Another statement of the Isoperimetric Theorem, using the IQ, is given here:

   For every region with area A and perimeter P, the following are true.

   ■ $\frac{4\pi A}{P^2} \leq 1$

   ■ $\frac{4\pi A}{P^2} = 1$ if and only if the region is circular.

   Does this statement agree with your IQ data in Activity 2? If not, go back and reexamine that activity.

1. b. In this activity, students need to find areas of nonrectangular shapes. They can find areas of circles and triangles from their previous study of geometry. In the case of regular *n*-gons with $n > 4$, students may divide the *n*-gon up into *n* congruent triangles and then use trigonometric ratios or the Law of Sines to obtain the altitude of each triangle. See the example below for a regular decagon and the examples in Activity 2 Part e.

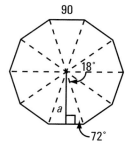

$360 \div 10 = 36$ and $\frac{180-36}{2} = 72$, so the triangles have angle measures 36°, 72°, and 72°.

$$\frac{a}{\sin 72°} = \frac{45}{\sin 18°}$$

$a \approx 138.5$

$Area = 10\left(\frac{1}{2}\right)(138.5)(90) \approx 62{,}325$

Given a perimeter of 900 yards, a square has an area of 50,625 square yards; an equilateral triangle has an area of approximately 38,971 square yards; a regular decagon has an area of approximately 62,325 square yards; and a circle has an area of approximately 64,458 square yards. Each group should find the area of at least two nonrectangular regions. If no group chooses to look at circles, you should suggest that they do. By comparing with other groups, there should be enough evidence to make a convincing case for circles as the optimal shape. This idea is formally stated in Activity 3.

Activities 2 and 3 use the Isoperimetric Quotient (IQ) to review the mathematical concepts of area, perimeter, and similarity and the mathematical process of finding patterns, making conjectures, and then proving the conjectures. An alternative aproach is to recast these activities in a way that allows students to generate the IQ, as follows.

Incorporate the present Activity 3 introduction and Part a as a new Activity 1 Part c, then recast Activity 2 to examine the effects of changing units and rescaling shapes, including the present Activity 3 Part c, as follows:

a. How would measuring the perimeters (and areas) of shapes in millimeters (and square millimeters) rather than centimeters (and square centimeters) affect the ratio of area to perimeter?

b. How would enlarging shapes (by some scaling factor) affect the ratio of area to perimeter?

c. Devise a ratio expression that can be calculated for any shape and that compares area to some function of perimeter. The ratio should have three important properties: (i) it is dimensionless; that is, it has no units, (ii) it is independent of the basic unit of measure of length adopted and invariant under rescaling of shape, and (iii) it takes the value of 1 for any circle.

d. Tabulate the values of this ratio expression for other shapes, and restate the Isoperimetric Theorem as in Activity 3 Part c.

2. The three main results of this activity are that similar figures have the same IQ, circles have an IQ of 1, and all other regions in a plane have an IQ of less than 1. The latter two results are formally stated in Activity 3.

a. The area of an equilateral triangle with perimeter of 900 is $\frac{1}{2}(300)\left(\frac{300\sqrt{3}}{2}\right)$ or approximately 38,971. So, the IQ is $\frac{4\pi(38{,}971)}{900^2}$ or approximately 0.605. Students will find that *any* equilateral triangle has an IQ of approximately 0.605.

b. All circles have an IQ of 1. This is proven by substituting the formulas for area and circumference of a circle into the IQ formula. $IQ = \frac{4\pi(\pi r^2)}{(2\pi r)^2} = \frac{4\pi^2 r^2}{4\pi^2 r^2} = 1$.

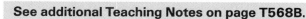

See additional Teaching Notes on page T568B.

4. The Isoperimetric Theorem can be stated equivalently in two forms: If you fix the perimeter, a certain shape will have the maximum area possible; if you fix the area, a certain shape will have the minimum perimeter possible. The optimal shape in both cases is a circle. That is, a circle is the area-maximizing shape for a given perimeter, and a circle is the shortest curve enclosing a given area in a plane. There is a similar theorem in three dimensions.

   For a square with an area of 9 square meters, the perimeter will be 12 meters. For a circle with an area of 9 square meters, the perimeter is approximately 10.635 meters. By experimenting with other regions and comparing results with other groups, students should conjecture that a circle has the minimum perimeter.

5. **a.** For any cube with side x, $IQ = \dfrac{36\pi(x^3)^2}{(6x^2)^3} = \dfrac{36\pi x^6}{216x^6} = \dfrac{\pi}{6} \approx 0.524$

   b. For any sphere with radius r, $IQ = \dfrac{36\pi\left(\frac{4}{3}\pi r^3\right)^2}{(4\pi r^2)^3} = \dfrac{64\pi^3 r^6}{64\pi^3 r^6} = 1$.

   c. The sphere will have minimum surface area for a fixed volume. Reasoning may vary. Students are not expected to prove this observation, but they will probably refer to the results in Parts a and b and possibly make an analogy to the Isoperimetric Theorem in Activity 3.

6. **This activity is an important part of each investigation. It provides a mechanism for students to talk to each other about what they have done, to compare answers, to make revisions, and to reflect more deeply upon their work. It also gives you the opportunity to monitor each group's progress and give feedback on any changes or additions that may need to be considered before the group gives its report.**

APPLY   individual task

▶On Your Own

Students need to choose only one of these optional tasks.

a. For this problem, students will most likely need to learn about the *apothem* for a regular polygon. They can learn about the apothem and the related formula for the area of a regular polygon in several ways. You might give them a book to read, tell them what they need to know, or ask them to work through the instructional sequence below. They should find that for a regular n-gon, the area is $n\left(\frac{1}{2} \cdot s \cdot \frac{s}{2} \tan \frac{180°(n-2)}{2n}\right)$ or $\frac{ns^2}{4} \tan \frac{180°(n-2)}{2n}$.

   Thus, the IQ for a regular n-gon is $\dfrac{4\pi\left(\frac{ns^2}{4}\right) \tan \frac{180°(n-2)}{2n}}{s^2 n^2}$ or $\frac{\pi}{n} \tan \frac{90°(n-2)}{n}$. By graphing and tracing this function, students can see that as n gets very large, the IQ gets very close to 1. This is consistent with the previous analysis of IQ because a very large n means that the regular n-gon is close to being a circle, which has an IQ of 1.

See additional Teaching Notes on page T568C.

In the Isoperimetric Theorem in Activity 3, you fix the perimeter, and the theorem tells you the shape with maximum area. Suppose you reverse this perspective. That is, fix the area and look for the shape with minimum perimeter. Now the problem is to find the shortest curve enclosing a given area in a plane.

4. Suppose you want to build a dog pen that has an area of 9 square meters. You want to use the least amount of fence to enclose the pen. How should you lay out the pen? Experiment with a few different regions and make a conjecture about the region with the smallest perimeter for a given area. Compare and discuss your conjecture with other groups. Resolve any differences.

5. Consider what happens in three dimensions. The IQ for three-dimensional shapes is $\frac{36\pi V^2}{S^3}$, where V represents volume and S represents surface area.

   a. Determine the IQ for cubes.

   b. Prove that the IQ for every sphere is 1. (Recall that the volume of a sphere is given by $V = \frac{4}{3}\pi r^3$ and the surface area of a sphere is given by $S = 4\pi r^2$.)

   c. For a fixed volume, what enclosing shape do you think will have minimum surface area? Explain your reasoning.

6. Make a neat copy of your work on this investigation and file it at the location designated by your teacher. Examine the work filed by other groups and compare their work to what you did. Write a question to at least one group asking its members to explain something about their work that you found interesting or that you did not understand. Answer any questions your group receives.

▶ On Your Own

Choose one of the following tasks to complete.

a. In Activity 2, you found the Isoperimetric Quotients of several regular polygons. Express the IQ of a regular n-gon as a function of n only. Use your function to describe what happens to the IQ as n gets very large. Give a geometric interpretation of this situation. You may find it helpful to read or ask your teacher about what's called the *apothem* of a regular polygon.

b. In Activity 3, you were given two statements of the Isoperimetric Theorem. Prove that the statement in Part c is equivalent to the statement given at the beginning of Activity 3.

c. The optimal property of spheres from Part c of Activity 5 applies to soap bubbles. A single soap bubble has the shape of a sphere and uses the least surface area to enclose a given volume of air. This could be called the Single-Bubble Theorem. A double bubble exists when two bubbles are hooked together. Do you think a double bubble uses the least possible surface area to enclose two given volumes of air? Make a conjecture. Then do some research on what is currently known about the so-called Double-Bubble Conjecture, which was still unproven at the time this book was written. Write a one-page report.

Capstone

INVESTIGATION 3 ▸ Minimizing Distance

Many situations involve minimizing distance. For example, a manufacturer may want to find the shortest route for shipping products, a robotics engineer may want to minimize the distance traveled by a robot on a computerized assembly line, or a student may wish to find the shortest route to school. In this investigation, you will consider some other situations involving minimizing distance.

1. Many large oil fields lie under the ocean. Huge offshore oil rigs are used to drill for this oil. Underwater pipelines are built to transport the oil from the rigs to refineries on shore. Suppose that two offshore oil rigs are located as shown in the following diagram. (Units are in miles.) One refinery will be built along the shoreline to process the oil from both rigs.

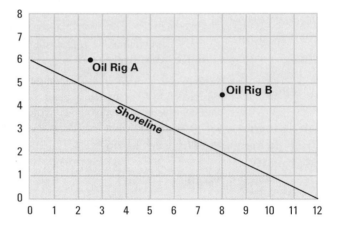

  a. Under what conditions might it be best to locate the refinery as close to Oil Rig A as possible? Assuming those conditions, determine the coordinates of the optimal refinery location and the total length of underwater pipeline needed. Explain your method.

Now suppose there are no special conditions that might suggest locating the refinery closer to one oil rig than the other. Again, assume the refinery must be connected to both oil rigs via underwater pipelines. Since it is very expensive to build underwater pipelines, the oil company would like to build the fewest number of miles of pipeline. In Parts b through e that follow, consider the following question:

  Where along the shoreline is the optimum location of the refinery?

  b. State precisely what it means for the location of the refinery to be optimum. Then brainstorm with your group about some strategies that might work to find the optimum location. Try the strategies that seem most promising. Where should the refinery be located?

Capstone

INVESTIGATION 3 Minimizing Distance

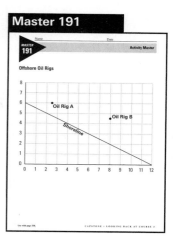

In this investigation, students explore and apply the following ideas. (1) The shortest distance from a point to a line is the perpendicular distance. (2) The smallest sum of distances from two points to a line can be found using regression methods, algebraic methods, or transformation methods. (3) The Triangle Inequality Theorem is a fundamental result which is often used in geometric optimization problems. The optional "On Your Own" task is a famous problem in mathematics, called Fermat's problem or a Steiner tree problem, in which students find a point that minimizes the sum of distances from that point to three given points.

In this investigation, students are expected to:

- find the slope and equation of a line, the slope and equation of a line perpendicular to another line, and the point of intersection of two lines;
- find the distance between two points;
- fit a curve to data using technology and make a prediction from the regression equation;
- write a general expression for the sum of distances and find the minimum value of this expression using technology;
- use reflection to create a shortest path;
- use the Triangle Inequality Theorem to solve optimization problems; and
- prove the Triangle Inequality Theorem using the Law of Cosines.

1. **See Teaching Master 191**.

   a. If Oil Rig A produces a greater amount of oil than Oil Rig B, you might want to locate the refinery as close to A as possible. Students may conjecture that (2, 5) is the optimum location, just by eye. However, students should be encouraged to think about the properties of a line segment from a point (Oil Rig A) to a line (the shoreline) such that the line segment's length is the shortest distance from the point to the line. Once they realize that they need to be looking for perpendicular distance, they might reason as follows: The slope of the shoreline is $-\frac{1}{2}$. Thus, the slope of the perpendicular segment from the point to the line is 2. (2, 5) looks like the point on the line that we want, and in fact this is verified because the slope of the line through (2, 5) and (2.5, 6) is 2. Another method students may use is to find the equation of the shoreline and then the equation of the line perpendicular to it through (2.5, 6) and then use these equations to find the point of intersection. This point of intersection has coordinates (2, 5).

   b. The optimum location of the refinery is the one that requires the least amount of connecting pipeline. That is, the one that minimizes the total distance from the refinery to the two oil rigs. Assume that the refinery will be built directly on the line representing the shoreline. Encourage students to brainstorm and try some of their own methods before they try the methods outlined in Parts c–e. However, be careful not to let them spend too much time on this activity, particularly if they are having difficulty getting started.

Capstone

1. c. Here are some distance sums for different x-coordinates:

x	3	4	5	6	7
Distance	6.58	6.53	6.70	7.11	7.94

A scatterplot of these data looks parabolic. (Actually, it isn't; see Part d.) The quadratic regression equation is $y = 0.1429x^2 - 1.0986x + 8.6077$. Using this equation yields an estimate of 3.8 for the x-coordinate of the optimum refinery location, with a total distance of about 6.5 miles.

NOTE: Students will find the exact function that describes this relationship in Part d.

---

d. $y = 6 - 0.5x$ is the equation of the shoreline. Using that substitution for y gives the following expression for the sum of distances s from the point (x, y) on the shore to the points $(2.5, 6)$ and $(8, 4.5)$:

$$s = \sqrt{(x - 2.5)^2 + 0.25x^2} + \sqrt{(x - 8)^2 + (1.5 - 0.5x)^2}$$

Using a graph or table gives a good estimate of the optimum refinery location as $x = 3.67$, with a total distance of about 6.52 miles.

e. ■ Let A be the point representing Oil Rig A, B be the point representing Oil Rig B, and l be the line representing the shore. We want to minimize the length of the path from A to l to B. Reflect B across l and call the reflected point B'. The path from A to l to B has the same length as the path from A to l to B', since reflection preserves length. Thus, we can minimize the length of the path from A to l to B by minimizing the length of the path from A to l to B'. The path from A to l to B' will be shortest when the path is a straight line, that is, when A and B' are connected by a line. So, to find the optimum location of the refinery, draw a line segment between A and B'. The intersection of this line segment with l will be the optimum location for the refinery on the shore.

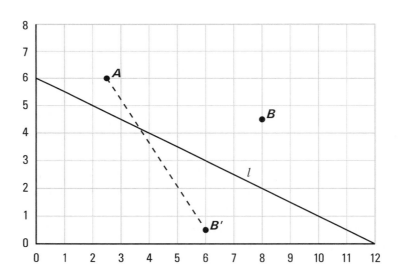

See additional Teaching Notes on page T568D.

A variety of methods can be used to find the optimum refinery location; some of which you may have used in Part b. In Parts c through e, you will investigate three possible methods, using ideas from statistics, algebra, and geometry. If you have previously used a method, go on to the next part.

c. **Statistical Regression Method:** Choose several points along the shoreline where the refinery could be located. Find the sum of the distances from each of these possible refinery locations to the two oil rigs. Make a scatterplot of the (*x-coordinate of potential refinery location, sum of distances*) data. Use the scatterplot and the statistical regression capabilities of your calculator or computer software to estimate the optimum location of the refinery. Explain your reasoning.

d. **Algebraic Reasoning Method:** Choose an arbitrary refinery location (*x, y*) on the shoreline. Write an expression showing the sum of the distances from (*x, y*) to each of the oil rigs. Find the equation of the line representing the shoreline, and use it to write the sum of distances in terms of *x* only. Use a table or graph to find the minimum value of this function. What is the optimum location of the refinery?

e. **Geometric Transformation Method:** Consider the shoreline as a line of reflection. Find the reflection image across this line of the point representing Oil Rig B. Think about paths from Oil Rig A to the shoreline to the *reflection image* of Oil Rig B, and compare those to paths from Oil Rig A to the shoreline to Oil Rig B. Using this strategy, describe a procedure for finding the optimum refinery location.

   ■ Illustrate the procedure on a copy of the oil-rigs diagram.

   ■ Find the coordinates of the optimum refinery location.

   ■ Find the minimum total distance to the two oil rigs.

2. A fundamental idea related to minimizing distance is that the shortest distance between two unobstructed points on a flat surface is a straight line. This idea is captured in a famous theorem called the Triangle Inequality Theorem. Along with the Pythagorean Theorem, the Triangle Inequality Theorem is one of the most widely used geometry theorems. You may have investigated this theorem previously in Extending Task 1 (page 323) of Unit 4, "Shapes and Geometric Reasoning."

Triangle Inequality Theorem

The sum of the lengths of two sides of a triangle is greater than the length of the third side.

---

a. Use the Law of Cosines and what you know about the range of the cosine function to prove that in $\triangle ABC$, $b + c > a$.

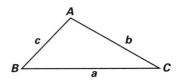

Capstone

b. The Triangle Inequality Theorem was used in the transformation method for finding the optimum refinery location in Activity 1, although you may not have noticed it. Go back and examine the transformation method in Part e of Activity 1 and explain how the Triangle Inequality Theorem was used.

c. Oil fields are found inland as well as under the ocean. Suppose the locations of four inland oil wells are represented on a coordinate system as shown below. (Units are in miles.)

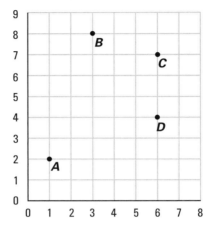

One refinery is to be built to process the oil from all four oil wells. Again, the goal is to minimize the total number of miles of pipeline needed to connect the refinery to each of the four oil wells. Find the optimum location of the refinery. Explain how you used, or could have used, the Triangle Inequality Theorem in your solution.

3. Make a neat copy of your work on this investigation and file it at the location designated by your teacher. Examine the work filed by other groups and compare their work to what you did. Write a question to at least one group asking its members to explain something about their work that you found interesting or that you did not understand. Answer any questions your group receives.

▶ **On Your Own**

Choose one of the following tasks to complete.

a. In Activity 1, you used several methods to find the optimum refinery location. Model the oil-refinery problem using a geometry drawing program that allows you to construct, measure, and move geometric figures. Demonstrate how to use the software to estimate the optimum location of the refinery.

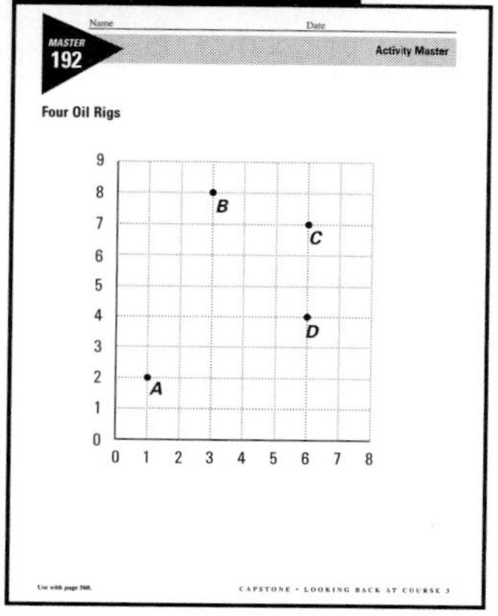

2. **b.** In Part e of Activity 1, the Triangle Inequality Theorem is used when the shortest path from A to l to B' is chosen to be the straight line from A to B'. Comparing to any other path gives a triangle, and the Triangle Inequality Theorem applies to establish that the straight line distance from A to B' is the shortest distance.

   c. **See Teaching Master 192.**

   Consider points B and D. Any point on the straight line segment between B and D will have minimum total distance to each of B and D, since any point off segment BD would form a triangle having the segment BD as one side and the Triangle Inequality Theorem would then apply. Similar reasoning applies to the points A and C. Thus, the intersection of $\overline{AC}$ and $\overline{BD}$ will be the optimum location.

   This point can be found by solving the system of equations consisting of the equations for the lines BD and AC. The equation of line BD is $y = -\frac{4}{3}x + 12$. The equation of line AC is $y = x + 1$. The point of intersection is $\left(\frac{33}{7}, \frac{40}{7}\right)$.

3. **This activity is an important part of each investigation. It provides a mechanism for students to talk to each other about what they have done, to compare answers, to make revisions, and to reflect more deeply upon their work. It also gives you the opportunity to monitor each group's progress and give feedback on any changes or additions that may need to be considered before the group gives its report.**

APPLY   individual task

On Your Own

Students need to choose only one of these optional tasks.

a. This problem could be modeled using software like the Geometer's Sketchpad® or Cabri®.

Capstone

b. The exact optimum location is a point *W* in the interior of triangle *ABC* such that the three angles *BWC*, *CWA*, and *AWB* each have measure 120°. Such a point is called a Steiner point. In the 17th century, two Italian mathematicians, Francesco Cavalieri and Evangelista Torricelli, first proved this fact. The construction they used, shown below, proceeds as follows.

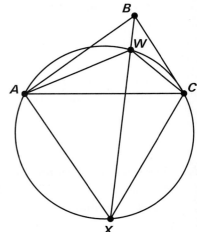

Find the longest side of △*ABC*. In this case, the longest side is $\overline{AC}$. Construct an equilateral triangle *ACX*. Construct a circle such that points *A*, *C*, and *X* are on the circle. (That is, construct a circle that circumscribes △*ACX*.) Draw the line segment *BX*. Let *W* be the point of intersection of $\overline{BX}$ and the circle (*W* ≠ *X*). Then *W* is the point such that the segments to *A*, *B*, and *C* form 120° angles, and the sum of the distances from *W* to each of *A*, *B*, and *C* is minimum. For a proof, see, for example, *Excursions in Modern Mathematics*, 2nd edition, by Tannenbaum and Arnold (Prentice-Hall, 1995, pp. 254–55).

EXPLORE small-group investigation

INVESTIGATION 4 Best-Fitting Data Models

In this investigation, students will perform some analysis of real data. In general, they will consider "best-fitting" data models and correlation. In particular, they will use and review the following topics: least squares regression line, exponential curve fitting, transforming functions, correlation, and sum of squared errors, including a new application of sum of squared errors called root mean squared error (RMS).

In this investigation, students are expected to:

- ■ choose a model that fits data;
- ■ transform a model;
- ■ determine and interpret the correlation coefficient;
- ■ apply and interpret sums of squared differences; and
- ■ create and interpret a root-mean-squared-error plot.

b. Consider a situation similar to the one in Activity 2, except with three oil wells. The three oil wells are located on a coordinate system as shown in the following diagram. (Units are in miles.)

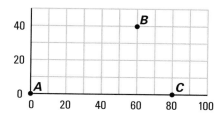

The problem, as before, is to find the optimum location of a refinery that will service all the oil wells. That is, you must find a point *R* such that the sum of the distances from *R* to each of the three points *A*, *B*, and *C* is minimum. This problem is sometimes called a *Steiner tree problem* or *Fermat's problem*. Research to find out how to solve this problem. Write a brief report on what you find.

INVESTIGATION 4 Best-Fitting Data Models

In Course 3 and in previous courses, when trying to make sense of data you often looked for the "best-fitting" model. This strategy capitalizes on the statistical regression capabilities of graphing calculators or computer software. As you have previously seen, the effectiveness of this method depends on first examining a scatterplot of the data for patterns or overall trends.

1. Information about the number of births in a country is very useful for making governmental policy decisions. For example, funding decisions for health care and education programs are influenced by birth data.

Examine the table below, which shows the number of births in Bangladesh. The entries from 1955 to 1990 are actual measurements; the entries from 1995 to 2025 are projections.

Bangladesh: Births			
Year	**Births**	**Year**	**Births**
1955	2,137,842	1995	5,368,091
1960	2,406,409	2000	5,752,499
1965	2,723,170	2005	5,971,843
1970	3,166,872	2010	5,532,962
1975	3,714,227	2015	5,074,848
1980	4,163,936	2020	4,842,618
1985	4,531,385	2025	4,699,740
1990	4,878,024		

Source: World Resources Institute Database

Capstone

a. Write a brief description of these data. Include the following.

- At least one scatterplot
- Descriptions of patterns, trends, or unusual features
- Description of the entire data set, as well as interesting parts of the data

b. Does it seem reasonable that the data for 1995 to 2025 are projected from the trend in the actual data? What are some possible reasons or assumptions that could explain the trend in the projected data?

c. When fitting models to data, it is sometimes reasonable to fit different models to different parts of the data. Where would you "break" the data in order to find two "best-fitting" models? Explain your reasoning.

d. Find a model that is a good fit for the data from 1955 to 2000.

e. Plot separately the projected data from 2005 to 2025.

- Use the statistical regression capability of your calculator or computer software to fit an exponential function to these data.
- At what birth level does the graph of the exponential model level off?
- In the data table, it looks like the data level off at about 4,000,000 births. So the graph of the calculator- or computer-based exponential model levels off at a different place from the data. Refine your exponential model so that it has an asymptote at $y = 4,000,000$.

2. The table below shows data on infant mortality and adult female literacy in 1990 in 16 countries around the world.

Literacy-Mortality Data		
Country	**Percent Adult Female Literacy**	**Percent Infant Mortality**
Nepal	13.2	12.8
Somalia	14.0	13.2
Pakistan	21.1	10.9
Angola	28.5	13.7
Egypt	33.8	6.5
Papua New Guinea	37.8	5.9
Morocco	38.0	8.2
Cameroon	42.6	9.4
Iran	43.3	5.2
Guatemala	47.1	5.9
Zimbabwe	60.3	6.6
Kuwait	66.7	1.8
Malaysia	70.4	2.4
Madagascar	72.9	12.0
Lebanon	73.1	4.8
Sri Lanka	83.5	2.8

Source: World Resources Institute Database

Capstone

1. **a.** In the margin is the scatterplot of all the data. The actual 1955–90 data are shown as boxes, and the projected 1995–2025 data are shown as crosses. The entire data set shows a steady increase and then a sharp downturn, followed by a steady decrease. This same general pattern is seen in the projected data. The actual data increase steadily, so the projected data do not fit the trend shown in the actual data. In terms of consistent trends, there are two parts of the data set: the steadily increasing part, from 1955 to 2005, and the steadily decreasing part, from 2005 to 2025.

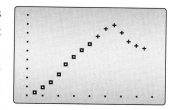

 b. The projected data clearly were not projected from the trend in the actual data. That trend, and the regression curve modeling the actual data, would predict ever-growing birth numbers rather than the sharp downturn predicted. The projections might have been due to a new governmental policy in Bangladesh. For example, maybe the projected data are based on a new program of family planning. Questions to consider include the following: Are the projections realistic? Are the new policies that the projections depend upon already approved and funded? Are these projections just political wishful thinking? One would need to research this situation carefully before basing important decisions on the projected data.

 c. The data set seems to break naturally at 2005, where the downturn occurs. It would be reasonable to try to find a regression curve and equation for each of these two parts of the data. The projected 1995–2025 data are too inconsistent to productively analyze them in terms of a single best-fitting model. (See Part b.)

 d. In the margin is a scatterplot of the 1955–2000 data, shown with the least squares regression line and the exponential regression curve, where x is the number of years after 1900 (55, 60, and so on). The linear equation is $y = -2{,}558{,}231 + 83{,}128.73x$. The exponential equation is $y = (641{,}289)1.023^x$. If students use the actual year for x (1955, 1960, and so on), their equations will not be the same. Be sure to have students explain how they entered the data to get the regression equations.

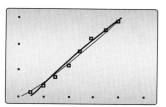

 On the one hand, both seem to fit well, and both have high values for the correlation coefficient r. The linear model might be the better model because it does not begin to stray away from the data points at the upper end. On the other hand, neither model captures the apparent **S** shape of the points. Depending on the technology available, some students might try to fit other curves, such as a logistic curve, which may be a better fit.

 e. ■ Using exponential regression, the modeling equation is $y = 21{,}281{,}672(0.9878)^x$. In the margin is the scatterplot of the data from 2005 to 2025 with this exponential regression curve.

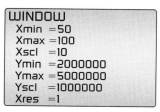

 ■ The graph of the equation above has a horizontal asymptote at $y = 0$.

 ■ An exponential curve with a horizontal asymptote at $y = 4{,}000{,}000$, is $y = (529{,}589{,}129)(0.9480)^x + 4{,}000{,}000$. One way to get this curve is to first transform the original data by subtracting 4,000,000 from each y value. Then, fit an exponential equation of the form $y = ab^x$ to the transformed data. Finally, shift the graph up by 4,000,000 by adding 4,000,000 to the equation.

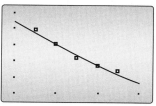

WINDOW
Xmin =50
Xmax =100
Xscl =10
Ymin =2000000
Ymax =5000000
Yscl =1000000
Xres =1

Capstone

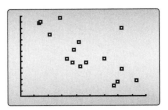

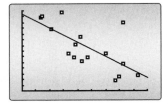

2. **a.** The scatterplot of the data is shown in the margin. It is important for the consistent continued analysis of this data that percent adult female literacy is on the horizontal axis. Some observations that students might make about the data include the following:
    - The scatterplot has a roughly linear pattern.
    - There is one prominent outlier at the top right, corresponding to Madagascar.
    - The general trend is that as percent adult female literacy goes up, percent infant mortality goes down.

    b. It is important for students to first consider whether the scatterplot looks linear before trying to model it with the least squares regression line or compute the correlation coefficient. It is inappropriate and possibly misleading to model obviously nonlinear data with a least squares regression line, even though the correlation coefficient may turn out to be reasonably high. The graph at the left shows the scatterplot with the least squares regression line. The equation of the least squares regression line is $y = 13.40 - 0.1237x$, and the value of the correlation coefficient is -0.6949. The negative correlation coefficient corresponds to the negative slope of the regression line. (Students should understand that the value of the slope is not the same as the value of the correlation coefficient.) The relatively high absolute value of the correlation coefficient is consistent with the linear trend of the data. Students should be careful not to assume a cause-and-effect relationship just because the correlation coefficient is high (in absolute value). (See Part h.)

    c. ■ Recall that the formula for the standard deviation is: $\sigma = \sqrt{\frac{\sum(x - \bar{x})^2}{n}}$. From the expression $\sum (x - \bar{x})^2$ in the formula, it is easily seen that the sum of squared differences is involved. To compute the standard deviation, find the difference between x and $\bar{x}$, square each quantity, and sum all the squares.
    - Consider the distance formula, for example, in two dimensions. Recall that the distance between two points (a, b) and (c, d) is $\sqrt{(a - c)^2 + (b - d)^2}$. This can be seen as involving the sum of squared differences.

    (Students may recall that the formula for Spearman's rank correlation coefficient also involves the sum of squared differences.)

    d. ■ For each data point (x, y), find the predicted value $\hat{y}$ by substituting x into the equation for the regression line. Then compute the difference, $(y - \hat{y})$, and square it. Next, sum all these squared differences, divide by the number of data points, and take the square root.
    - The RMS is like an average error from the regression line or average vertical distance from the regression line, taken over all data points. (Students should be encouraged to recognize that the numerator of the fraction in the formula for the RMS is just the SSE, sum of squared errors, which they used in the Course 2 Unit, "Patterns of Association," when studying the least squares regression line.)

See additional Teaching Notes on page T568D.

Capstone

a. Make a scatterplot of the (*percent adult female literacy, percent infant mortality*) data. Describe any patterns, trends, or unusual features of the data.

b. Does there appear to be a linear association between percent adult female literacy and percent infant mortality? Graph the least squares regression line along with the scatterplot for these data. What is the correlation coefficient, and what does it tell you?

c. Recall that the least squares regression line is the line that gives the smallest sum of squared errors for a set of points. The general idea of the *sum of squared differences* is important and widely used in mathematics. Explain how each of the following can be interpreted in terms of the sum of squared differences.

- The standard deviation of a distribution

- The distance formula for the distance between two points in a coordinate plane

Try to think of another topic you have studied that involves the sum of squared differences.

d. Another application of the sum-of-squared-differences idea is found in a measure of error called the **root mean squared error (RMS)**. The RMS can help you analyze the literacy-mortality data. Examine this formula for computing the RMS.

$$\text{RMS} = \sqrt{\frac{\Sigma\,(y - \hat{y})^2}{n}}$$

where y is the actual y value and $\hat{y}$ is the corresponding value predicted from the regression equation. In this activity, y is *percent infant mortality*.

- Give a verbal description of how to compute the RMS.

- Based on the above formula, describe the meaning of the RMS.

- How is the RMS different from and similar to the standard deviation?

- Use your calculator or computer software to help you compute the RMS for the literacy-mortality data.

Capstone

e. In some ways, the RMS is to the least squares regression line as the standard deviation is to the mean in a normal distribution. For example, about 68% of the data will typically be within one RMS of the least squares regression line, and about 95% will be within two RMSs. Let $y = f(x)$ represent the regression line. Graph the following on the same set of axes:

- Scatterplot of literacy-mortality data, with *literacy* on the horizontal axis
- $y = f(x)$
- $y = f(x) + \text{RMS}$
- $y = f(x) + 2(\text{RMS})$
- $y = f(x) - \text{RMS}$
- $y = f(x) - 2(\text{RMS})$

f. Identify any data points that lie outside the range of $y = f(x) \pm 2(\text{RMS})$. It is reasonable to consider such data points as outliers. Describe how the "RMS-plot" in Part e is like the *control charts* you studied in Unit 5, "Patterns in Variation."

g. Remove any outliers you found in Part f and recompute the regression line and the correlation coefficient. Is the fit better for the remaining data?

h. Can you conclude from your analysis so far that there is a cause-and-effect relationship between percent adult female literacy and percent infant mortality? Explain your reasoning and include a reasonable argument for why a country, such as Madagascar, could have a relatively high adult female literacy rate and yet also have a surprisingly high infant mortality rate.

i. The World Resources Institute Database contains literacy-mortality data for 1970 and 1990 on 86 countries, not just the 16 you have been analyzing. The table below shows some of the statistics computed for all 86 countries.

Literacy-Mortality Data for 86 Countries

	1970	1990
Correlation Coefficient (r)	0.853	0.847
RMS	2.479	2.340
Least Squares Regression Line	$y = -0.13x + 17.03$	$y = -0.13x + 15.23$

A separate analysis shows that there was a general increase in the literacy level of women from 1970 to 1990. As the literacy of adult women increased, did the association between adult female literacy and infant mortality get stronger? Explain your answer using the information in the table.

3. Make a neat copy of your work on this investigation and file it at the location designated by your teacher. Examine the work filed by other groups and compare their work to what you did. Write a question to at least one group asking its members to explain something about their work that you found interesting or that you did not understand. Answer any questions your group receives.

Capstone

2. **e.** In the graph in the margin, the center line is the least squares regression line, $y = f(x)$, and the other lines represent $y = f(x) \pm$ RMS and $y = f(x) \pm 2(\text{RMS})$.

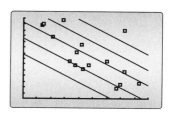

f. The only data point outside the range $y = f(x) \pm 2\text{RMS}$ is (72.9, 12), corresponding to Madagascar. The so-called RMS-plot in Part e and a control chart from "Patterns in Variation" are similar in that you begin with a benchmark, such as $\bar{x}$ or the regression line then you mark off zones, using standard deviations or RMSs; and then you look to see how the data points fall into those zones, with particular attention to those that are in zones more than 2 standard deviations or 2 RMSs from the benchmark. These faraway points can be indicators of out-of-control situations or outliers.

g. Removing the outlier (72.9, 12), corresponding to Madagascar, gives the scatterplot, least squares regression line, and correlation coefficient displayed in the margin. The fit is considerably better now that the outlier is removed. This outlier is an example of what was called an *influential point* in Course 2, Unit 3, "Patterns of Association."

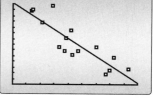

$$y = 14.33 - 0.1556x$$
$$r = -0.8685$$

h. You cannot conclude on the basis of correlation coefficients and regression lines that there is a cause-and-effect relationship. This is an important point for students to understand. Association does not necessarily mean cause-and-effect. There are arguments for and against a claim of cause-and-effect.

It does seem reasonable that if the women in a country are educated then they are better able to care for their infant children. So the mortality rate should go down. This argues for a claim that high literacy rates result in low mortality rates. However, literacy does not necessarily account for health-care education, which would seem to be the most relevant type of education. Women might be well educated about health care and yet not be literate. So a country could have a low literacy rate and also have a low infant mortality rate.

At the other extreme, consider a country like Madagascar, where the literacy rate is relatively high and the mortality rate is surprisingly high as well. This could be due to other variables influencing mortality rate, such as environmental factors. It is important for students to be aware of the potential effect of "hidden" factors.

In situations with high correlation and yet no cause-and-effect relationship, it is often the case that there are hidden factors that influence both of the variables being studied. In the situation here, the correlation is quite high, especially with outliers removed, but it may be that a variable like per capita income contributes to both high literacy rates and low mortality rates. Thus, both variables of interest here could be influenced by other lurking variables and not really have much influence directly on each other. One could test this idea by controlling for hypothesized hidden variables.

i. The 1970 data have a slightly better correlation (higher correlation coefficient), but the 1990 data have a slightly better RMS (smaller RMS). Given these mixed results, and in particular considering the higher correlation in 1970, there does not seem to be good evidence here to suggest that the association is any stronger in 1990 than in 1970.

3. This activity is an important part of each investigation. It provides a mechanism for students to talk to each other about what they have done, to compare answers, to make revisions, and to reflect more deeply upon their work. It also gives you the opportunity to monitor each group's progress and give feedback on any changes or additions that may need to be considered before the group gives its report.

NOTE: See Course 2, pages 197–200, for more on causation and hidden variables.

Capstone

▶On Your Own

Such data might be found through the World Resources Institute (www.wri.org).

INVESTIGATION ▶5 The Best Concert

In this investigation, students use and review the following topics: voting, surveys, confidence intervals, linear programming, and quadratic functions.

In this investigation students are expected to:
- apply and analyze different voting methods;
- design a good survey, including a sampling technique;
- use 90% box plot charts to find confidence intervals and margin of error, and then interpret the results;
- write a system of inequalities and equations that models an optimization situation;
- solve a linear programming problem; and
- solve a quadratic equation and find the maximum value of a quadratic function.

1. **a.** Two possibilities are a survey or voting.

   b. Different voting methods yield different results. There is no majority winner. The plurality winner is Classical. A runoff would be between Classical and Jazz, with Jazz winning. The pairwise-comparison winner is Country that is, Country beats all 4 others in a head-to-head two-way contest. Rock would be chosen as the second choice using the pairwise-comparison winner because Rock wins 3 pairwise contests. Using the points-for-preferences method, with a point distribution of 5-4-3-2-1, Country wins, and Rock comes in second. Using the sequential-elimination method, Jazz is the winner with Classical second. Although plurality and runoff may be the most commonly used methods in real elections, pairwise-comparison and points-for-preferences generally give fairer results. Since Country and Rock are the two winners under both pairwise-comparison and points-for-preferences, those are the most sensible choices for the two music types that will be used in the survey. Students may use software in this activity, but they should nevertheless explain how the voting method they decide to use works.

On Your Own

Find recent data on the annual number of births in Bangladesh.

- Do the projections given in Activity 1 match the actual recent data?

- Find a good model for this actual recent data. Make new projections based on your model and compare to the original projections. Explain.

INVESTIGATION 5 ▶ The Best Concert

Suppose your class is planning to put on a benefit concert to raise money for recent flood victims. You want the concert to be the best possible. In this situation, there are many factors to optimize.

1. What is the best type of music to feature at the concert? There are lots of choices, including rock, country, blues, alternative, folk, R & B, classical, hip-hop, jazz, and easy listening. You want to appeal to as many people as possible, including yourselves!

   a. What are some mathematical methods you could use to determine the optimal choice of music for the concert?

   b. Suppose you decide to carry out a two-step procedure. First, you vote within your class to narrow the options down to just two choices; then you do a sample survey within the community to decide which of the two to choose. Suppose your class vote is summarized in the following preference table.

   Musical Preferences

	Rankings			
Classical	1	1	5	5
Country	3	2	1	2
Jazz	4	5	3	1
Hip-hop	5	4	4	4
Rock	2	3	2	3
Number of Voters	5	7	8	9

   What are the top two music choices? Explain which vote-analysis method you used, how the method works, and why you used it.

MAKING THE BEST OF IT: OPTIMAL FORMS AND STRATEGIES   **565**

Capstone

2. Now you have two choices for the type of music to play at the concert. Suppose that you next conduct a sample survey of 40 people within the community to decide whether Choice 1 or Choice 2 should be played at the concert.

a. Describe a good way to select the sample of 40 people. Then give an example of a poor sampling plan and explain why the plan is poor.

b. Write a good survey question. Then give an example of a poorly worded question and explain why it is poor.

c. Suppose 26 out of the 40 people in the sample prefer Choice 1. Construct a 90% confidence interval for the actual population percent. Write the interval using the margin of error.

d. Think about how you would explain the results of the survey and its limitations. Which of the two types of music will you announce as the winner? Can you claim that, without doubt, a majority of people in the community prefer the winning choice? List several other key points you should include in your explanation.

3. Now that you've decided on the best music, it's time to advertise the concert. As usual, you want to optimize your strategy. In addition to placing posters around town, you will advertise on local television and radio. Donations from community businesses to pay for air time total $10,500. You  want to maximize your air time, whether from TV or radio, but you have to take into account the following facts and assumptions.

- A 15-second radio ad costs $50.
- A 30-second TV ad costs $750.
- You want to have at least 8 TV ads, but you will take as many TV ads as you can get.
- You have no minimum on radio ads, but you don't want more than 30 of them.

a. Since you want as many TV ads as possible, suppose you spend all your money on TV ads. How many TV ads can you buy? What is your total air time using this strategy?

b. Return to the original plan, maximizing air time from radio ads, TV ads, or both. Set up a linear programming problem that models this situation. How many radio and TV ads should you buy in order to maximize your total air time within the given constraints?

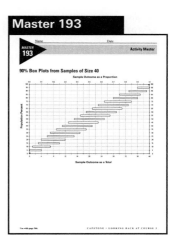

2. a. There is a variety of factors that should be considered when selecting the sample, such as, the population from which the sample is to be drawn. A reasonable population in this activity might be all community residents aged 15 and older. A good way to select the sample is to select a simple random sample, possibly by random telephone calls. A poor sampling plan would be, for example, to use the first 40 people who call into a radio program, as this sample is unlikely to represent the population. Bias due to the sampling process should be avoided.

b. Bias due to the measurement tool should also be avoided. In particular, the survey question should be carefully worded. An example of a good question is, "A benefit concert will be held to raise money to help victims of the recent flood. Which of the following two types of music would you prefer to have played at the concert?" An example of a poorly worded question is the following: "A benefit concert will be held to raise money to help victims of the recent flood. Although Rock concerts tend to get loud and riotous, we could have either Rock or Country music played at the concert. Which would you prefer?" This is a poor question because it steers people away from choosing Rock.

c. **See Teaching Master 193.**

The 90% confidence interval is 55%–75%. This can be written as 65% ± 10%, where 10% is the margin of error.

d. Choice 1 should be declared the winner since the confidence interval is entirely above 50%. However, it would not be correct to say that, without doubt, a majority of people prefers Choice 1 over Choice 2, since it is possible that the true population percent is not in the confidence interval. In particular, the true population percent could be less than 50%. To explain the meaning of the 90% confidence interval, you might say: "Suppose, theoretically, that the survey was carried out many, many times and each time a confidence interval was constructed based on the survey results. Then, about 90% of those confidence intervals would contain the actual population percent." Some other points to put in the explanation include the following.

- Description of the issue being studied
- Survey sponsor
- Description of the population
- Confidence interval
- Sample size
- Confidence level
- Method of sample selection
- Margin of error
- Survey question asked

3. a. If all money is spent on TV ads, then the number of ads you can buy is $10,500 \div 750$ or 14 ads. At 30 seconds per ad, the total air time is 420 seconds.

See additional Teaching Notes on page T568E.

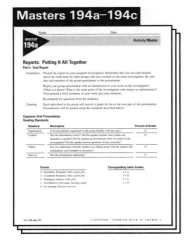
4. For this activity, students can use graphs, tables, or equations.

$$I(x) = 2,000x - 50x^2 = (50x)(40 - x)$$

The graph of $I(x)$ is shown below. The x-intercepts are at $x = 0$ and $x = 40$. The vertex is at $x = 20$, when $I(x) = 20,000$.

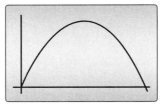

a. To find the ticket price for income of \$15,000, we must solve $I(x) = 15,000$. Thus, $2,000x - 50x^2 = 15,000$. Solve this by factoring, using the quadratic formula, using the solve function on a calculator or computer software, graphing, or using a table. There are two prices that will yield \$15,000 of income: $x = 10$ and $x = 30$. So, charging \$10 or charging \$30 will yield \$15,000 of income.

b. The most you could charge for a ticket and still make money is \$39 (assuming whole number prices), because the higher x-intercept is $x = 40$.

c. In order to maximize income, we need to find the vertex of the parabola, which is (20, 20,000). Thus, the optimum ticket price is \$20, which yields a maximum income of \$20,000.

5. **This activity is an important part of each investigation. It provides a mechanism for students to talk to each other about what they have done, to compare answers, to make revisions, and to reflect more deeply upon their work. It also gives you the opportunity to monitor each group's progress and give feedback on any changes or additions that may need to be considered before the group gives its report.**

SYNTHESIZE share and summarize

REPORTS: Putting It All Together

See Teaching Masters 194a–194c.

These reports take some time but are a valuable part of the unit.

If enough time has been available for students to have examined the work of other groups for the investigation they have selected for their oral report, they may wish to make amendments. This kind of collaborative effort mirrors a learning community in which insights are shared, developed, and maximized. Students are encouraged to see the whole course as such a learning community, not just a long exercise in finding predetermined answers. The quality of the oral reports will improve if this time for sharing is available. Encourage groups to give each other credit for ideas that are unique or to say on what and how they disagree.

You may want to give specific roles to the listening groups. For example, if two groups, A and B, each selected the same investigation and only group A will do an oral report on that investigation, then encourage group B to think of questions that will force group A to be clear. Why did you choose to... ? Did your answer make sense? We found a particular activity difficult. Did you? Why or why not? and so on.

Teaching Masters 194a–194c provide guidelines for possible methods of assessing the oral and written reports.

4. Of course, the most important factor to optimize regarding this benefit concert is profit. Since everyone is donating time and the school is providing facilities and equipment, there are no expenses and all income from ticket sales will be profit. Although the community has not had much experience with benefit concerts, there have been many community concerts in the past. Based on data from these past concerts, the chamber of commerce estimates that income from ticket sales $I(x)$ is a function of the price x, in dollars charged per ticket, according to the following rule: $I(x) = 2,000x - 50x^2$.

  a. According to this rule, what price would you have to charge per ticket in order to make \$15,000?

  b. What is the most you could charge per ticket and still make money?

  c. What price should you charge per ticket in order to maximize income? What is the maximum income?

5. Make a neat copy of your work on this investigation and file it at the location designated by your teacher. Examine the work filed by other groups and compare their work to what you did. Write a question to at least one group asking its members to explain something about their work that you found interesting or that you did not understand. Answer any questions your group receives.

REPORTS: Putting It All Together

Finish this Capstone by preparing two reports, one group oral report and one individual written report as described below.

1. Your group should prepare a brief oral report that meets the following guidelines:

- Choose one investigation from this Capstone. Confirm your choice with your teacher before beginning to prepare your report.

- Examine the work that other groups have filed on your investigation. Compare your work to theirs, discuss any differences with the other groups, and modify your solutions, if you think you should.

- Begin your presentation with a brief summary of your work in the investigation. Then explain your solutions to the various activities.

- Be prepared to discuss alternative solutions, particularly those proposed by other groups that worked on the same investigation.

- Be prepared to answer any questions.

2. Individually, write a two-page report summarizing how the mathematics you have learned can be used to model and solve optimization problems.

Checkpoint

In this course, you have learned important mathematical concepts and methods, and you have gained valuable experience in thinking mathematically. Look back over the investigations you completed in this Capstone and consider some of the mathematical thinking you have done. For each of the following habits of mind, describe, if possible, an example where you found the habit to be helpful.

a Search for patterns

b Formulate or find a mathematical model

c Collect, analyze, and interpret data

d Make and check conjectures

e Describe and use an algorithm

f Visualize

g Simulate a situation

h Predict

i Experiment

j Prove

k Make connections—between mathematics and the real world and within mathematics itself

l Use a variety of representations—like tables, graphs, equations, words, and physical models

Be prepared to share your examples and thinking with the entire class.

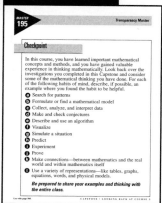

Master 195

See Teaching Master 195.

Responses may vary. Examples are given.

a Students looked for patterns to fit regression lines in Investigation 4. They also looked for patterns to determine which polygons would tile a plane in Investigation 1.

b Students found mathematical models for the measure of one angle of a polygon, the sum of the distances from the oil rigs to the refinery, and the number of births in Bangladesh, as well as in solving the linear programming problem in Investigation 5.

c Students did not really collect data, but they analyzed and interpreted data in Investigations 4 and 5.

d Students made conjectures about where to locate the oil refinery and about what shape would enclose maximum area with a fixed perimeter.

e Students described and used an algorithm to find RMS and to analyze the class voting results.

f Students used their visualization skills throughout Investigations 1, 2, and 3.

g Students may have simulated situations using geometry drawing programs.

h Students who did Investigation 5, "On Your Own," predicted (projected) annual number of births in Bangladesh and compared it to recent data.

i Students experimented with the areas of nonrectangular shapes and with the Isoperimetric Quotient in Investigation 2.

j Students proved that only regular polygons with 3, 4, or 6 sides will tile a plane, that the two statements of the Isoperimetric Theorem are equivalent, and that the Isoperimetric Quotients for similar figures are equal. They also proved the Triangle Inequality Theorem.

k Throughout the investigations, students made connections to the real world and between mathematical topics.

l Students probably used all these representations at different points during their work on the Capstone. When they used each one depends on the methods they chose to use.

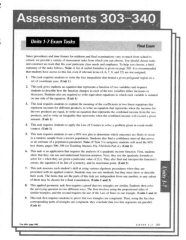

Assessments 303–340

CONSTRUCTING A MATH TOOLKIT: Students may wish to include their responses to this Checkpoint in their Math Toolkit to remind them of the valuable thinking skills that they are cultivating. Students should retain their Math Toolkits from Courses 1–3 as resources for following courses. This will allow them to access the mathematical tools they have learned thus far in the curriculum. You may wish to store students' Math Toolkits over the summer break to help prevent them from being misplaced.

NOTE: In addition to the Capstone, if you wish to administer a written, individual final exam, you may select items from the **Assessment Resources, pages 303–340**, that are appropriate for your students.

Capstone

Teaching Notes continued

**Notes continued
from page T551** ▶

Note that this Capstone is meant to provide a review and synthesis across Courses 1–3, although the emphasis is on Course 3. Also, not all of the mathematical content is previously studied material, so students are expected to apply their mathematical thinking skills in the context of some new mathematical content. Hence, this Capstone gives students the opportunity to synthesize and apply both the mathematical content they have learned and the mathematical thinking skills they have acquired.

▶Approximate Time Line

- ■ 1 day   Introduction and Investigation 1
- ■ 4 days   2 days for each of the two investigations that groups choose
- ■ 3 days   Preparing and presenting reports and discussing the final Checkpoint

With two weeks to spend on the Capstone, groups can complete two investigations. There will be time to read each other's reports. Oral reports will become more elaborate and more thorough because students have seen the work of others on the same subject. There will be time for students to choose an additional "On Your Own" task. Given two weeks, Investigation 8 becomes a viable group option.

▶Materials Needed

To facilitate students' work, their Math Toolkits or notebook should be available. It might also be helpful to have the texts from Courses 1 and 2 available as references. Graph paper will be helpful in Investigations 2, 4, and 5, although for Investigations 4 and 5 it may be more efficient if students have a way to print or display graphs from their calculators or computers. Teaching Masters 189 through 195 will also be helpful.

▶Assessment

One way to assess group presentations and written reports is provided in Teaching Masters 181a–181c. You may wish to have each student evaluate other groups' presenations. You may wish to have each group submit one written report or have each student write an individual report as suggested in the student text. The written report may be included in student portfolios. This comprehensive assessment may replace a final exam or be used along with selected tasks from the bank of assessment items for a final evaluation. See the Course 3 Final Exam assessment masters.

Capstone

Teaching Notes *continued*

Notes continued
from page T556

2. c. Suppose Figures B and C are similar with scale factor k. Then $P_B = kP_C$ and $A_B = k^2A_C$, where P_X is the perimeter of Figure X and A_X is the area. Thus, $IQ_B = \frac{4\pi A_B}{(P_B)^2} = \frac{4\pi k^2 A_C}{(k^2 P_C)^2} = \frac{4\pi k^2 A_C}{k^2(P_C)^2} = \frac{4\pi A_C}{(P_C)^2} = IQ_C$. Thus, similar figures will have equal IQs.

d. Students might choose to find the IQ for a specific square or for an arbitrary square. If they use a specific square, be sure they know why their result will be the IQ for any square. The computation for a square with side length s is

$$IQ = \frac{4\pi s^2}{(4s)^2} = \frac{4\pi s^2}{16s^2} = \frac{\pi}{4} \approx 0.785.$$

e. Similar figures have the same IQ, so all regular hexagons are similar to each other and all regular octagons are similar to each other. Thus, as in Part d, students may choose to use a specific side length rather than s.

Regular Hexagon: Each triangle in the diagram at the right is equilateral with side length s. Thus, the area of each triangle is $0.5(s)\left(\frac{s\sqrt{3}}{2}\right)$, or (using trigonometric ratios) $0.5s^2 \sin 60°$. So the area of the hexagon is $3s^2 \sin 60°$.

$$IQ = \frac{4\pi(3s^2 \sin 60°)}{(6s)^2} = \frac{12\pi \sin 60°}{36} = \frac{\pi \sin 60°}{3} \approx 0.907$$

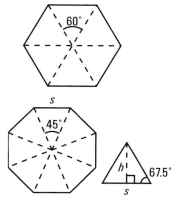

Regular Octagon:

$$\tan 67.5° = \frac{h}{\frac{s}{2}} = \frac{2h}{s}; \quad \frac{s \tan 67.5°}{2} = h$$

The area of one of the eight triangles is $0.5(s)\left(\frac{s \tan 67.5°}{2}\right)$.

Thus, the area of the octagon is $\frac{8(0.5)(\tan 67.5°)s^2}{2}$ or approximately $4.828s^2$.

$$IQ = \frac{4\pi(4.828s^2)}{(8s)^2} = \frac{4\pi(4.828s^2)}{64s^2} \approx 0.948$$

f. Isoperimetric Quotients

Figure	IQ
Equilateral triangle	0.605
Square	0.785
Regular pentagon	0.865
Regular hexagon	0.907
Regular octagon	0.948
Circle	1.0

Students may notice the following patterns in their tables: For all figures, $IQ \leq 1$. For all figures except circles, $IQ < 1$. As the number of sides gets larger, the IQ gets larger. This corresponds to the visual pattern of the regular polygon becoming a better approximation of the circle as n increases.

3. In this activity, students will verify that their results from the previous activities match the statements of the Isoperimetric Theorem. If the results do not match, then students should go back and examine their work in those activities.

a. Students should compare the Isoperimetric Theorem to their work in Activity 1.

b. It is true that, using a fixed amount of wax, one cylinder would hold more than a hexagonal prism. However, cylinders do not tessellate and are therefore not as efficient when there are many cells in a honeycomb. One wall of each hexagonal prism will be a side of two cells in the honeycomb. This would not be possible if each cell were a cylinder.

c. This statement should agree with the IQ data from Activity 2.

Capstone

Notes continued from page T557 ▶

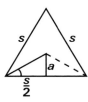

Optional instructional sequence for learning about and using the apothem: Consider the diagrams in the margin of 3-, 4-, 5-, and 6-sided regular polygons. An apothem is found by finding the intersection point of all the angle bisectors and dropping a perpendicular to a side. An apothem is shown in each figure below. First find the size of the marked angles, then find the length of the marked apothems, and then find the areas. Do the same for a general, regular *n*-gon.

The marked angles are $\frac{60°}{2}$, $\frac{90°}{2}$, $\frac{108°}{2}$, and $\frac{120°}{2}$. In general, an angle of a regular *n*-gon measures $\frac{(n-2)180°}{n}$ so half the measure of the angle is $\frac{(n-2)180°}{2n}$. The lengths a are $\frac{s}{2}\tan 30°$, $\frac{s}{2}\tan 45°$, $\frac{s}{2}\tan 54°$, and $\frac{s}{2}\tan 60°$; in general, this is $\frac{s}{2}\tan\frac{(n-2)180°}{2n}$. So the areas are $3\left(\frac{1}{2}\cdot s\cdot\frac{s}{2}\tan 30°\right)$, $4\left(\frac{1}{2}\cdot s\cdot\frac{s}{2}\tan 45°\right)$, $5\left(\frac{1}{2}\cdot s\cdot\frac{s}{2}\tan 54°\right)$, and $6\left(\frac{1}{2}\cdot s\cdot\frac{s}{2}\tan 60°\right)$; this is $n\left(\frac{1}{2}\cdot s\cdot\frac{s}{2}\tan\frac{(n-2)180°}{2n}\right)$.

b. The Isoperimetric Theorem stated at the beginning of Activity 3 says that for a fixed perimeter, the shape with maximum area is a circle. To prove this is equivalent to the statement given in Part c, we must prove each statement using the other statement.

First, prove the statement at the beginning of Activity 3 using the statement given in Part c. Let P be the perimeter of a shape. We want to prove that the shape that will have maximum area is a circle. From the theorem in Part c, we know that if the shape is not a circle, then $\frac{4\pi A}{P^2} < 1$ or $A < \frac{P^2}{4\pi}$. If the shape is a circle, then $\frac{4\pi A}{P^2} = 1$ or $A = \frac{P^2}{4\pi}$. Thus, if the shape is not a circle, it will have smaller area than the circle with the same perimeter, so for a fixed perimeter, the shape with maximum area is a circle.

Now, we must use the fact that for a fixed perimeter, the shape with maximum area is a circle, to prove the statement given in Part c. There are two statements that must be proved.

We are assuming that for perimeter P, the shape with maximum area is a circle. Since the area A is in the numerator of $\frac{4\pi A}{P^2}$, this quantity is also maximum if the shape is a circle. We proved in Activity 2 Part b that $\frac{4\pi A}{P^2} = 1$ for a circle. Hence, $\frac{4\pi A}{P^2} \leq 1$ for every region in the plane with area A and perimeter P.

We know from Activity 2 Part b that if a region is circular, then $\frac{4\pi A}{P^2} = 1$. Now we need only prove that the converse is true as well. We have already shown that $\frac{4\pi A}{P^2} \leq 1$, so $A \leq \frac{P^2}{4\pi}$. If $\frac{4\pi A}{P^2} = 1$, then $A = \frac{P^2}{4\pi}$, which is the maximum area, so (by the statement at the beginning of Activity 3) the region must be circular.

c. By 1998, the following was known about the Double-Bubble Conjecture: The two-dimensional problem has been solved. That is, the minimum perimeter required to enclose and separate two given areas in the plane is given by the standard double bubble, consisting of three circular arcs meeting at two points at equal 120° angles. This result was proven by a group of undergraduate students in 1990. In 1995, the Double-Bubble Conjecture for equal volumes was proven. That is, the standard double bubble uses the least possible area to enclose and separate two equal volumes of air. As of 1998, the problem with two unequal volumes was still unsolved, although most researchers believe that the solution is indeed a standard double bubble. Two good sources are *What's Happening in the Mathematical Sciences*, Volume 2, published by the American Mathematical Society (1994, pp. 33–36), and *FOCUS*, the newsletter of the Mathematical Association of America, December, 1995, pp. 6–7.

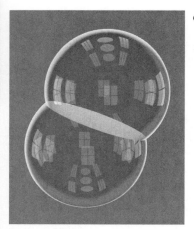

Double bubble by John Sullivan

Teaching Notes *continued*

Notes continued from page T559

1. **e.** ■ An equation for the line representing the shore is $y = 6 - 0.5x$. The point representing the reflected Oil Rig B has coordinates $(6, 0.5)$. An equation for the line between the reflected Oil Rig B and Oil Rig A is $y = -\frac{11}{7}x + \frac{139}{14}$. Solving the system of two linear equations yields the point of intersection $\left(\frac{11}{3}, \frac{25}{6}\right)$, which is the optimum location for the refinery.

■ The minimum total distance to the two oil rigs is the distance between the points $(2.5, 6)$ and $(6, 0.5)$. This distance is $\sqrt{(6 - 2.5)^2 + (0.5 - 6)^2}$ or approximately 6.52 units.

2. **a.** $a^2 = b^2 + c^2 - 2bc \cos A$ Law of Cosines

$\quad\quad < b^2 + c^2 - 2bc(-1)$ $\cos A \geq -1$. Moreover, A is strictly less than $180°$ since we have a triangle. So, $\cos A$ is strictly greater than -1. Thus, substituting -1 for $\cos A$ makes the last term ($2bc \cos A$) smaller. Subtracting a smaller number makes the whole expression larger; thus, $b^2 + c^2 - 2bc(-1)$ is larger than $b^2 + c^2 - 2bc \cos A$. Therefore, the expression on the right is strictly greater than a^2.

$\quad\quad = b^2 + c^2 + 2bc$

$\quad\quad = (b + c)^2$

So we have $a^2 < (b + c)^2$. Now, a, b, and c are all positive (since they are lengths), so taking the square root of both sides yields $a < b + c$.

Notes continued from page T563

2. **d.** ■ The formulas for standard deviation and RMS are very similar. Both are like average error, or average distance, taken over all data. The RMS is like average distance from the regression line, while the standard deviation is like average distance from the mean.

NOTE: The word *average* is used in the descriptions above in a nontechnical way. It is not a technical average like mean, median, or mode. However, it is useful to think intuitively of "average" because you are "adding up and dividing by n," and in a very loose sense the square root compensates for the squaring.

■ RMS = 2.754

One method to compute RMS, using a calculator, is the following. Put the percent adult female literacy in list L_1 and the percent infant mortality in list L_2. Enter the equation for the regression line as Y_1. Let list $L_3 = Y_1(L_1)$, so L_3 has the predicted y values, that is, the predicted infant mortality rates. Let $L_4 = (L_2 - L_3)^2$, so L_4 has the squared errors. Sum L_4, divide by n, and take the square root. The result is the RMS.

Capstone

Teaching Notes *continued*

**Notes continued
from page T566**

3. b. Use the following variables.

r = number of radio ads

t = number of TV ads

A = total number of seconds of air time

C = total cost of the ads

$A = 15r + 30t$

$C = 50r + 750t$

We want to maximize A, and we have only $10,500 to spend. The algebraic inequalities that give constraints on the variables are as follows:

$50r + 750t \leq 10,500$

$0 \leq r \leq 30$

$8 \leq t \leq 14$

The objective function is $A = 15r + 30t$.

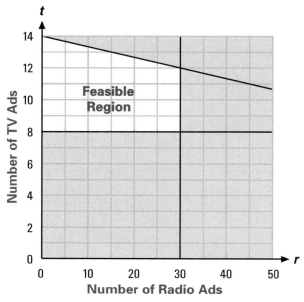

If you graph the constraints in the *rt*-plane and make a composite graph of the feasible region, you find the vertices of the feasible region to be (0, 14), (0, 8), (30, 12), and (30, 8). If you evaluate the objective function at each of these points, you find that the largest possible value of A is 810, which occurs when $(r, t) = (30, 12)$. Thus, the optimal strategy is to buy 30 radio ads and 12 TV ads. This strategy will yield the maximum air time of 810 seconds.

Capstone

Index of Mathematical Topics

Index of Contexts

Photo Credits for the Pupil Edition

Cover PhotoDisc; **T345** Krones, Inc.; **T346** courtesy The Boeing Company; **T349** Jack Demuth; **T350** Karen Engstrom/*Chicago Tribune;* **T355** David Poller/AP/ Wide World Photos; **T357** Meghan Scussel; **T360** Victah Sailor ©Photo Run, 1997 Worldwide Copyrights; **T361** Michael Newman/PhotoEdit; **T362** courtesy Lightning Calculator, Troy MI; **T366** Kelly MacLean; **T368** AP/Wide World Photos; **T369** Michael Newman/PhotoEdit; **T370** David Young-Wolff/Tony Stone Images; **T371** Educational Testing Service; **T372** Myrleen Ferguson/PhotoEdit; **T375** Chris Walker/*ChicagoTribune;* **T379** Paul Conklin/PhotoEdit; **T380** AP/Wide World Photos; **T381** Bill Perry/UPI; **T382** Tony Freeman/PhotoEdit; **T385** Steven Kagan/*New York Times* Permissions; **T394** Jim Prisching/*Chicago Tribune;* **T395** Steve Wanke/West Stock; **T396** Robertshaw Controls Co.; **T397** John Austad/*Chicago Tribune;* **T398** Mark Richards/PhotoEdit; **T401** Doug Pizac/AP/ Wide World Photos; **T403** Richard T. Nowitz/National Geographic Society Image Collection; **T406** Mary Kate Denny/PhotoEdit; **T407** Feleicai Martinez/PhotoEdit; **T408** Kelly MacLean; **T410** Jack Demuth/MONOPOLY® is a trademark of Hasbro, Inc. ©1997 Hasbro, Inc. All Rights Reserved. Used with permission; **T414** AP/Wide World Photos; **T416** Jack Demuth; **T417** Val Mazzenga/*Chicago Tribune;* **T421** NASA; **T422** Tony Craddock/Photo Researchers; **T423** Dwayne E. Newton/PhotoEdit; **T424** Duke Energy Corp.; **T425** George Mobley/National Geographic Society Image Collection; **T428** Phil Schermeister/National Geographic Society Image Collection; **T430** Gay Bumgarner/Tony Stone Images; **T434** Sergio Ortiz/West Stock; **T435** UPI/Bettmann/CORBIS; **T439** Jack Demuth; **T441** Rebecca Walker; **T446** Jack Demuth; **T447** Tim Zielenbach/*Chicago Tribune;* **T449** Aaron Haupt; **T450** Texas Instruments Inc., Dallas TX; **T451** UPI; **T453** Sensaphone® Remote Monitoring System ©Phonetic, Inc.; **T454** Kathryn Wright; **T456** Kelly MacLean; **T459** (left)Texas Instruments Inc., Dallas TX, (right)Robert Brenner/PhotoEdit; **T461** AP/Wide World Photos; **T462** NASA; **T467** Cathlyn Melloan/Tony Stone Images; **T468** Haeger Potteries, Dundee IL, est. 1871; **T481** Jerry Lodriguss; **T482** NASA; **T487** *Chicago Tribune;* **T488** Hung T. Vu/*Chicago Tribune;* **T490** AP/Wide World Photos; **T491** Kathryn Wright; **T492** Kelly MacLean; **T494** United States Census Bureau Public Information Office; **T495** Flip Nicklin/Minden Pictures; **T496** City of Kalamazoo Recreation, Leisure and Cultural Services; **T499** Texas Instruments Inc., Dallas TX; **T501** Mark Perlstein/*Chicago Tribune;* **T502** University Games Corp, Burlingame CA; **T503** Bob Fila/*Chicago Tribune;* **T504** Texas Instruments Inc., Dallas TX; **T505** Pat Rogers/UPI; **T507** AMI Air Card; **T508** Steve Winter/National Geographic Society Image Collection; **T511** Steve Fitchett/Getty Images; **T513** Larry Wolf; **T514** Kathryn Wright; **T515** AP/Wide World Photos; **T519** Western Michigan University; **T521** Bob Fila/*Chicago Tribune;* **T526** UPI; **T527** Thomas Nebbia/National Geographic Society Image Collection; **T538** National Fishery Education Center; **T540** Eric Karnowski; **T541** Jack Demuth; **T543** Texas Instruments Inc., Dallas TX; **T547** John R. MacGregor/Peter Arnold, Inc.; **T551** John Sullivan; **T553** Bianca Lavies/National Geographic Society Image Collection; **T555** Jack Demuth; **T557** Chuck Berman/*Chicago Tribune;* **T558** *Chicago Tribune;* **T559** Texas Instruments Inc., Dallas TX; **T561** Abdus Shahed/Reuters Archives Photo; **T563** AP/Wide World Photos; **T565** Candice C. Cusic/*Chicago Tribune;* **T566** WGN/*Chicago Tribune.*